INTRODUCTION TO SET THEORY AND TOPOLOGY

ADIWES INTERNATIONAL SERIES

IN MATHEMATICS

A. J. Lohwater, Consulting Editor

INTRODUCTION TO SET THEORY AND TOPOLOGY

by

KAZIMIERZ KURATOWSKI

Professor of Mathematics, The University of Warsaw
Vice-President of the Polish Academy of Sciences

TRANSLATED FROM THE REVISED POLISH EDITION

by

LEO F. BORON

Department of Mathematics
The Pennsylvania State University

PERGAMON PRESS LTD.
Oxford · London · Paris · Frankfurt

ADDISON-WESLEY PUBLISHING COMPANY INC.
Reading, Massachusetts, U.S.A.
1962

First published in English 1961

U.S.A. Edition distributed by
Addison-Wesley Publishing Company, Inc.
Reading, Massachusetts, U.S.A.

PERGAMON PRESS
International Series of Monographs in
PURE AND APPLIED MATHEMATICS
Volume 13

Library of Congress Card Number 59-14873

Printed in the United States of America

CONTENTS

IV. THE FUNCTION CONCEPT. INFINITE OPERATIONS

V. THE CONCEPT OF THE POWER OF A SET. COUNTABLE SETS

VI. OPERATIONS ON CARDINAL NUMBERS. THE NUMBERS $\mathfrak{a}$ AND $\mathfrak{c}$

VII. ORDERING RELATIONS

VIII. WELL ORDERING

Part II
Topology

XIII. SEPARABLE SPACES

XIV. COMPLETE SPACES

XV. COMPACT SPACES

XVI. CONNECTED SPACES

XVII. CONTINUA

XVIII. LOCALLY CONNECTED SPACES

XIX. THE CONCEPT OF DIMENSION

XX. SIMPLEXES AND THEIR PROPERTIES

XXI. COMPLEXES, CHAINS, HOMOLOGIES

XXII. CUTTINGS OF THE PLANE

FOREWORD TO THE ENGLISH EDITION

The ideas and methods of set theory and topology permeate modern mathematics. It is no wonder then that the elements of these two mathematical disciplines are now an indispensable part of basic mathematical training. Concepts such as the union and intersection of sets, countability, closed set, metric space, and homeomorphic mapping are now classical notions in the whole framework of mathematics.

The purpose of the present volume is to give an accessible presentation of the fundamental concepts of set theory and topology; special emphasis being placed on presenting the material from the viewpoint of its applicability to analysis, geometry, and other branches of mathematics such as probability theory and algebra. Consequently, results important for set theory and topology but not having close connections with other branches of mathematics, are given a minor role or are omitted entirely. Such topics are, for instance, axiomatic investigations, the theory of alephs, and the theory of curves.

The main body of the book is an introduction to set theory and topology, intended for the beginner. Sections marked with an asterisk cover either more complicated topics or points which are frequently omitted in a first course; this holds also for some exercises which allow the reader to get acquainted with many applications and some important results which could not be included in the text without unduly expanding it. Many new exercises not contained in the Polish edition have been included here.

I take great pleasure in thanking Professor J. Jaworowski and Dr. A. Granas for their cooperation in preparing the

Polish edition and to thank also Professors A. Mostowski and R. Sikorski, Dr. S. Mrówka, Mr. R. Engelking and Dr. A. Schinzel for numerous comments which helped me to improve the original manuscript. Also, my thanks go to Mr. Leo F. Boron and to Mr. A. H. Robinson for preparing the present text for English speaking students of mathematics.

KAZIMIERZ KURATOWSKI

Warsaw
September 1960

Part I

SET THEORY

INTRODUCTION TO PART I

The concept of a set is one of the most fundamental and most frequently used mathematical concepts. In every domain of mathematics we have to deal with sets such as the set of positive integers, the set of complex numbers, the set of points on a circle, the set of continuous functions, the set of integrable functions, and so forth.

The object of set theory is to investigate the properties of sets from the most general point of view; generality is an essential aspect of the theory of sets. In geometry we consider sets whose elements are points, in arithmetic we consider sets whose elements are numbers, in the calculus of variations we deal with sets of functions or curves; on the other hand, in the theory of sets we are concerned with the general properties of sets independently of the nature of the elements which comprise these sets. This will made clear by several examples which we shall give here and by a brief overall view of the contents of the first part of this volume.

In Chapter II we shall consider operations on sets which are analogous to arithmetic operations: for every pair of sets A and B we shall form their *union* $A \cup B$, understanding by this the set composed of all elements of the set A and all elements of the set B; we shall also form the *intersection* $A \cap B$ of the sets A and B, and we shall understand by this the set of all elements common to the sets A and B. These operations have, in a certain sense, an algebraic character, e. g. they have the properties of commutativity, associativity and distributivity. It is clear that these properties do not depend on whether these sets consist of numbers, points or other mathematical objects; they are general properties of sets and therefore the investigation of these properties belongs to the realm of set theory.

In Chapter III we consider another type of operation, called *cartesian multiplication*. For two given sets X and Y we denote by $X \times Y$ the set of all pairs of elements $\langle x, y \rangle$ in which the first belongs to the set X and the second to the set Y. Thus, e. g. if X and Y denote the set of real numbers then $X \times Y$ is the plane (whence the name "cartesian" product in honor of the great French mathematician Descartes (1596-1650), who, treating the plane as a set of pairs of real numbers, initiated a new branch of mathematics, called analytic geometry). The computational properties of cartesian multiplication in connection with the operations on sets mentioned above are given in Chapter III.

The concept of cartesian product allows us to define the concept of a *function* in a completely general way. We shall concern ourselves with the concept of function in Chapter IV. An especially important role in the theory of sets is played by the one-to-one functions. These are functions which map the set X onto the set Y so that to every two distinct elements of the set X there correspond two distinct elements of the set Y (and then the inverse function with respect to the given function, which maps the set Y onto the set X, is also one-to-one). If there exists such a one-to-one mapping of the set X onto the set Y we say that these sets are *of equal power*. The equality of powers is the generalization of the idea of equal number of elements; the significance of this generalization depends first of all on the fact that it can be applied to infinite as well as to finite sets. For example, it is easy to see that the set of all even numbers has the same power as the set of all odd numbers; on the other hand, the set of all real numbers does not have the same power as the set of all natural numbers—a fact which is not immediately obvious. Hence, we can—in some sense—classify infinite sets with respect to their power. We can also, thanks to this, extend the sequence of natural numbers, introducing numbers which characterize the power of infinite sets (called the *cardinal numbers*); in particular, to sets having the same power as the set of all natural numbers (or the countably infinite sets) we assign the cardinal number $\mathfrak{a}$, to the set of all real numbers we assign the number $\mathfrak{c}$ (the power of the continuum). It turns out that there is an infinite number of infinite cardinal numbers. However, in the applications of set theory to other branches of mathematics an essential role is played by only two of them: $\mathfrak{a}$ and $\mathfrak{c}$. So we also limit ourselves above all to the investigation of these two numbers. This forms the content of Chapter V and VI.

Chapter VII is devoted to *ordered sets* such as the set of all natural numbers, the set of all rational numbers, the set of all real numbers. For each of these sets the "less than" relation determines the ordering; here the order types of these three sets differ in an essential manner: in the first of them there exist elements which are immediately adjacent to one another (n and $n+1$), in the second there are no such elements (so we say, the ordering is dense), however, there exist gaps (in the Dedekind sense), but in the set of all real numbers there are no gaps.

An especially important kind of ordered sets are the *well ordered* sets, i. e. those whose every non-empty subset has a least element. An example of a well ordered set is the set of all natural numbers (but the set of all integers is not well ordered since this set does not have a least element). Also well ordered—although of a different order type—is the set consisting of numbers of the form $1-1/n$ and numbers of the form $2-1/n$, $n = 1, 2, 3, \ldots$ In Chapter VIII we give the most important theorems concerning well ordering. Among other things, we prove that of two distinct order types of well ordered sets one is always an extension of the other (in a sense which we shall make more precise). From this follows the important corollary that of two different well ordered sets one is of power equal to that of a subset of the other; in the terminology of cardinal numbers this means that for two distinct cardinal numbers corresponding to well ordered sets, one is always smaller than the other. In connection with this theorem, there arises the fundamental conjecture: does there exist a relation for any set which establishes its well ordering? We shall prove that this is in fact so, if we assume the axiom of choice. This theorem is the final theorem of the first part of this book.

The discussion of set theory given here is based on a system of *axioms*. Even though in the introductory part of set theory, e. g. in the algebra of sets, the concept of set, with which we have to deal in mathematics (and hence the concept of a set of numbers, points or curves, and so on) is such that it does not touch upon logical difficulties, a subsequent construction of set theory which is not based on a system of axioms turns out to be impossible; for there exist questions to which the so-called "naive" intuitive idea of a set does not give a unique answer. The lack of the necessary foundations of set theory in its initial period of development led to the so-called antinomies, i. e. contradictions, which one did not know how to interpret on the basis of the "naive" intuitive idea of set. Only the axiomatic concept of the theory of sets allowed the removal of these antinomies (cf. Chapter VI, § 2, Remark 2).

In the present book we do not analyze more closely the axiomatics of set theory or the logical foundation of the subject. Although these subjects form at the present time an important part of mathematics and are being actively developed, the discussion of them in this book lies outside the principal goal of the book which is: the presentation of the most important branches of set theory and topology from the point of view of their applications to other branches of mathematics.

In the first part of this book the reader will find a certain amount of information on *mathematical logic*. The notation of mathematical logic is an indispensable tool of set theory and can be applied with great profit far beyond set theory. In Chapters I and III we have given the main facts from this subject concerning the calculus of propositions, propositional functions and quantifiers. The notation of mathematical logic is not devoid of general didactical values; by examples for concepts such as uniform convergence or uniform continuity it is possible to observe how much the definition of these concepts gains in precision and lucidity, when they are written in the symbolism of mathematical logic.

In the first period of its existence, set theory was practically exclusively the creation of one scholar, G. Cantor (1845-1918). In the period preceding the appearance of the works of Cantor, there were published works containing concepts which are now included in the theory of sets (by authors such as Dedekind, Du Bois-Reymond, Bolzano), but nonetheless the systematic investigation of the general properties of sets, the establishment of fundamental definitions and theorems and the creation on their foundation of a new mathematical discipline is the work of G. Cantor (during the years 1871-1883).

The stimulus to the investigations from which the theory of sets grew, was given by problems of analysis, the establishing of the foundations of the theory of irrational numbers, the theory of trigonometric series, etc. However, the further development of set theory went initially in an abstract direction, little connected with other branches of mathematics. This fact, together with a certain strangeness of the methods of set theory which were entirely different from those applied up to that time, caused many mathematicians to regard this new branch of mathematics initially with a certain degree of distrust and reluctance. In the course of years, however, when set theory showed its usefulness in many branches of mathematics such as the theory of analytic functions or theory of measure, and when it became an indispensable basis for new mathematical disciplines (such as topology, the theory of functions of a real variable, the foundations of mathematics), it became an especially important branch and tool of modern mathematics.

Among the books which may be of aid in the study of set theory we mention the following (also the books on Topology mentioned in Part II, Introduction, contain the basic notions of Set Theory):

P. Bernays, *Axiomatic Set Theory,* N.-Holland Publ. Comp., Amsterdam 1958.

N. Bourbaki, *Théorie des Ensembles*, Paris, Hermann, NN° 1141, 1212, 1258.

J. Breuer, *Introduction to the Theory of Sets,* Prentice-Hall, Inc., Englewood Cliffs, N. J., 1958.

A. Fraenkel, *Abstract Set Theory*, N.-Holland Publ. Comp., Amsterdam 1953.

P. Halmos, *Naive Set Theory,* Van Nostrand Comp., Princeton, N. J., 1960.

F. Hausdorff, *Set Theory*, Chelsea, New York 1957.

D. Hilbert and P. Bernays, *Grundlagen der Mathematik*, 2 vol., Berlin 1934-1939.

E. Kamke, *Theory of Sets*, Dover Publications, New York 1950.

I. P. Natanson, *Theory of Functions of a Real Variable*, Ungar, New York 1955, Chapters I and II.

W. Sierpiński, *Algèbre des Ensembles*, Monografie Matematyczne, Warszawa-Wrocław 1951.

W. Sierpiński, *Cardinal and ordinal numbers*, Monografie Matematyczne, Warszawa-Wrocław 1958.

P. Suppes, *Axiomatic Set Theory,* Van Nostrand Comp., Princeton, N. J., 1960.

A. Tarski, *Cardinal Algebras*, Oxford Univ. Press, New York 1949.

CHAPTER I

PROPOSITIONAL CALCULUS

We apply the propositional calculus to propositions each of which has one of two logical values, 0 and 1, where we assign the value 0 to a false proposition and the value 1 to a true proposition (in particular, all the propositions in mathematics are of this type, i. e. they take values either 0 or 1).

§ 1. The disjunction and conjunction of propositions

If α and β are two propositions, then we write "α or β" in the form of the *disjunction* $\alpha \vee \beta$, and we write the proposition "α and β" in the form of the *conjunction* $\alpha \wedge \beta$.

Clearly, the proposition $\alpha \vee \beta$ is true if at least one of the components is a true proposition and the proposition $\alpha \wedge \beta$ is true if both factors are true propositions. The above can be put in the form of the following table:

$$(1) \quad 0 \vee 0 \equiv 0, \quad 0 \vee 1 \equiv 1, \quad 1 \vee 0 \equiv 1, \quad 1 \vee 1 \equiv 1,$$

$$(2) \quad 0 \wedge 0 \equiv 0, \quad 0 \wedge 1 \equiv 0, \quad 1 \wedge 0 \equiv 0, \quad 1 \wedge 1 \equiv 1.$$

The equivalence sign used in the above formulas occurs between propositions; namely, the equivalence $\alpha \equiv \beta$ holds if and only if α and β have the same logical value.

The disjunction and conjunction of propositions (called also logical sum $\alpha + \beta$ and logical product $\alpha \cdot \beta$) are commutative and associative, i. e.

$$(3) \quad \begin{aligned} \alpha \vee \beta \equiv \beta \vee \alpha, &\quad \alpha \wedge \beta \equiv \beta \wedge \alpha, \\ \alpha \vee (\beta \vee \gamma) \equiv (\alpha \vee \beta) \vee \gamma, &\quad \alpha \wedge (\beta \wedge \gamma) \equiv (\alpha \wedge \beta) \wedge \gamma. \end{aligned}$$

The distributive law

$$(4) \quad \alpha \wedge (\beta \wedge \gamma) \equiv (\alpha \wedge \beta) \vee (\alpha \wedge \gamma)$$

also holds and more generally we have

$$(5) \qquad (\alpha\vee\beta)\wedge(\gamma\vee\delta)\equiv(\alpha\wedge\gamma)\vee(\beta\wedge\gamma)\vee(\alpha\wedge\delta)\vee(\beta\wedge\delta)\,.$$

We can verify the above laws—as well as all laws of the propositional calculus—by substituting the values 0 or 1 for the variables and then applying formulas (1) and (2).

§ 2. Negation

Next we introduce the operation of *negation* of a proposition α which we shall denote by α' (or by $\sim\alpha$). The negation of a true proposition is a false proposition and, conversely, the negation of a false proposition is a true proposition. We therefore have the following table:

$$(6) \qquad 1'\equiv 0\,,\qquad 0'\equiv 1\,.$$

From this we obtain the so-called *law of double negation*,

$$(7) \qquad \alpha''\equiv\alpha\,.$$

Two fundamental theorems of Aristotelian logic (which follow easily from formulas (1), (2) and (6)) hold:

$$(8) \qquad \alpha\vee\alpha'\equiv 1\,,\qquad \alpha\wedge\alpha'\equiv 0\,;$$

they are the law of the excluded middle *(principium tertii exclusi)* and the law of contradiction (these are formulated in classical logic in the following manner: from two contradictory propositions, one is true; no proposition can be true simultaneously with its negation).

Further, the important *de Morgan laws* hold:

$$(9) \qquad (\alpha\vee\beta)'\equiv(\alpha'\wedge\beta')\,,$$

$$(10) \qquad (\alpha\wedge\beta)'\equiv(\alpha'\vee\beta')\,.$$

The first of these laws asserts that if it is not true that one of the propositions α and β is true then both of these propositions are false (and conversely); i. e. the negation of the first as well as the negation of the second are true propositions.

Similarly, if it is not true that both propositions α and β are true, then this means that the negation of one of them is a true proposition, and conversely.

Taking the negation of both members of identity (10) we obtain, by virtue of formula (7), the identity

(11) $$\alpha \wedge \beta \equiv (\alpha' \vee \beta')' .$$

From this it is clear that conjunction can be defined with the aid of disjunction and negation (after all, in a manner similar to the way one could define disjunction with the aid of conjunction and negation). This allows the reduction of the number of fundamental operations to two; however, from the computational-technical viewpoint it is more convenient to make use of three operations: disjunction, conjunction and negation.

§ 3. Implication

We write $\alpha \Rightarrow \beta$ if the proposition $\alpha' \vee \beta$ is true, i. e.

(12) $$(\alpha \Rightarrow \beta) \equiv (\alpha' \vee \beta) ;$$

$\alpha \Rightarrow \beta$ is read: the proposition α *implies* the proposition β, or: *if* α *then* β.

Tables (1) and (6) yield the following table:

(13) $$(0 \Rightarrow 0) \equiv 1, \quad (0 \Rightarrow 1) \equiv 1, \quad (1 \Rightarrow 0) \equiv 0, \quad (1 \Rightarrow 1) \equiv 1.$$

We also deduce from this that

(14) *if* $\alpha \Rightarrow \beta$ *and* $\beta \Rightarrow \alpha$ *then* $\alpha \equiv \beta$.

Clearly, implication has properties analogous to deduction. However, the current meaning of the expression "deduction" is different from the expression "implication". To say that a proposition β is deducible from a proposition α (e. g. from a given theorem) usually means the possibility of proving proposition β on the basis of proposition α; but the implication $\alpha \Rightarrow \beta$ always holds, provided that the proposition β is true (even if the proposition α were false).

Let us note further two easily proved laws: the *syllogism law* (or the law of transitivity of implication) and the *law of contraposition* (on which the proof by "reductio ad absurdum" or, the indirect method of proof, depends),

(15) $$\textit{if } \alpha \Rightarrow \beta \textit{ and } \beta \Rightarrow \gamma \textit{ then } \alpha \Rightarrow \gamma,$$

(16) $$\textit{if } \beta' \Rightarrow \alpha' \textit{ then } \alpha \Rightarrow \beta.$$

Exercises

1. Prove that, if α is a true proposition, then $\beta \Rightarrow \alpha$ is also a true proposition. [*Hint*: In this and the following exercises apply the "zero-unit" tables (1), (2), (6), (13)].

2. If $\alpha' \Rightarrow \beta$ for each β, then α is a true proposition. *Law of Clausius.*

3. If α is a false proposition, then $\alpha \Rightarrow \beta$. *Law of Duns Scotus.*

4. Prove that $\alpha \wedge \beta \Rightarrow \alpha \Rightarrow \alpha \vee \beta$.

5. If $\alpha \Rightarrow \beta$ and $\gamma \Rightarrow \delta$, then $\alpha \wedge \gamma \Rightarrow \beta \wedge \delta$ and $\alpha \vee \gamma \Rightarrow \beta \vee \delta$.

6. If $\alpha \Rightarrow \beta$, then $\alpha \wedge \beta \equiv \alpha$ and $\alpha \vee \beta \equiv \beta$.

7. Prove that $\alpha \vee (\alpha \wedge \beta) \equiv \alpha \equiv \alpha \wedge (\alpha \vee \beta)$. *Law of absorption.*

8. Let $(\alpha \dot{-} \beta) \equiv [(\alpha \wedge \beta') \vee (\alpha' \wedge \beta)]$. Prove that $(\alpha \vee \beta) \equiv [(\alpha \dot{-} \beta) \dot{-} (\alpha \wedge \beta)]$. We call $\alpha \dot{-} \beta$ the *symmetric difference* of the propositions α and β; what is its logical meaning?

CHAPTER II

ALGEBRA OF SETS. FINITE OPERATIONS

§ 1. Operations on sets

The *union* (or the set-theoretic sum) of two sets A and B is understood to be the set whose elements are all the elements of the set A and all the elements of the set B and which does not contain any other elements. We denote the union of the sets A and B by the symbol $A \cup B$ (or by $A+B$).

The *intersection* (or the set-theoretic product) of two sets A and B is understood to be the common part of these sets, i. e. the set containing those and only those elements which belong simultaneously to A and to B. We denote the intersection of the sets A and B by the symbol $A \cap B$ (or by $A \cdot B$).

Finally, the *difference* of two sets A and B, i. e. the set $A-B$, is the set consisting of those and only those elements which belong to A but which do not belong to B (instead of $A-B$ the symbols $A \backslash B$ and $A \sim B$ are also used).

The following examples illustrate the operations on sets: the union of the set of rational numbers and the set of irrational numbers is the set of all real numbers; the intersection of the set of numbers which are divisible by 2 and the set of numbers divisible by 3 is the set of numbers which are divisible by 6; the difference of the set of natural numbers and the set of even natural numbers is the set of odd natural numbers.

Other examples are given in Figs. 1-3, where the sets A and B are circular disks. From Fig. 2 we see that there exists no point which belongs to both the sets A and B; but despite this fact, we can consider forming the intersection to be possible in all cases by adopting the following definition.

The *null set* (or the *empty set* or the *void set*) is the set which contains no elements; we denote it by the symbol $\emptyset$.

Thus, in Fig. 2 we have $A \cap B = \emptyset$ and in Fig. 3 we have $B - A = \emptyset$.

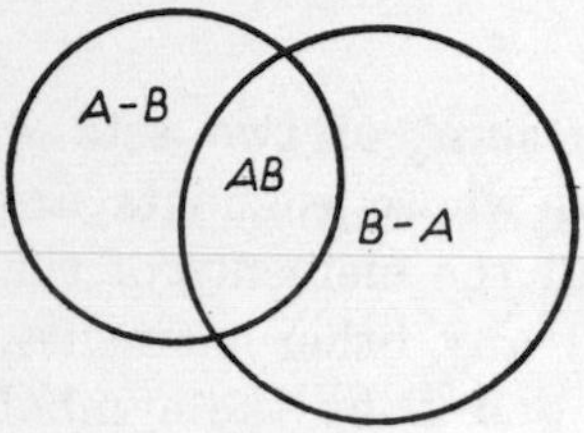

FIG. 1

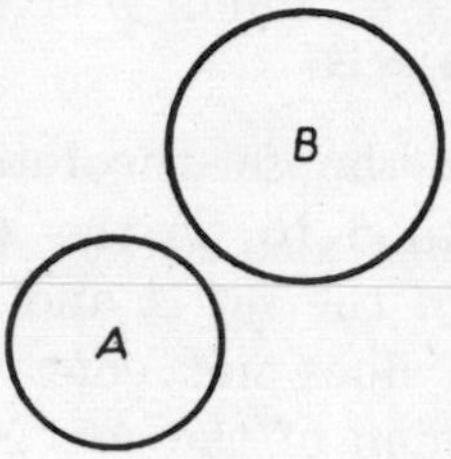

FIG. 2

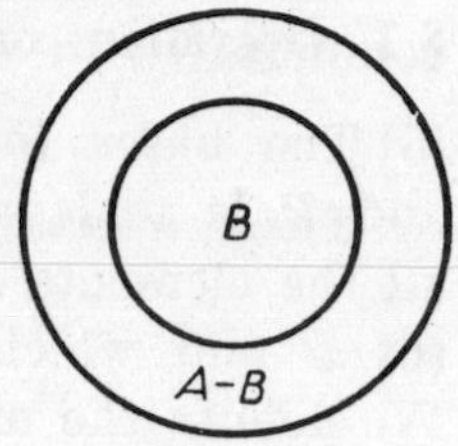

FIG. 3

The equality $A \cap B = \emptyset$ therefore denotes that the sets A and B do not have common elements. We then say that these sets are *disjoint*.

The role of the null set in set theory is analogous to the role of the number 0 in arithmetic; these concepts are necessary in order that it be possible to carry out all operations with no exception.

§ 2. Inter-relationship with the propositional calculus

Operations on sets are closely related to operations on propositions. Let us write $x \in A$ to denote that x is an element of the set A (as a rule we shall denote elements with lower case letters and sets with upper case letters); then we have the following equivalences (which hold for all x):

$$[x \in (A \cup B)] \equiv (x \in A) \vee (x \in B)\,, \tag{1}$$

$$[x \in (A \cap B)] \equiv (x \in A) \wedge (x \in B)\,, \tag{2}$$

$$[x \in (A - B)] \equiv (x \in A) \wedge (x \in B)'\,. \tag{3}$$

By virtue of formulas (1)-(3), we can easily deduce theorems on the calculus of sets from analogous theorems in propositional calculus.

In this connection, let us note that

(4) *if the equivalence* $x \epsilon A \equiv x \epsilon B$ *holds for all* x, *then* $A = B$;

and therefore the proof of the equality $A = B$ reduces to showing that x belongs to A if and only if it belongs to B.

The operations of union and intersection of sets are commutative, i. e.

(5) $$A \cup B = B \cup A, \quad A \cap B = B \cap A.$$

These operations also satisfy the associative law:

(6) $$A \cup (B \cup C) = (A \cup B) \cup C,$$
$$A \cap (B \cap C) = (A \cap B) \cap C.$$

The distributive law

(7) $$A \cap (B \cup C) = (A \cap B) \cup (A \cap C)$$

also holds, as can easily be verified.

It follows from this that

(8) $$(A \cup B) \cap (C \cup D)$$
$$= (A \cap C) \cup (B \cap C) \cup (A \cap D) \cup (B \cap D),$$

for, by virtue of formula (7), we have

$$(A \cup B) \cap (C \cup D) = [(A \cup B) \cap C] \cup [(A \cup B) \cap D]$$
$$= (A \cap C) \cup (B \cap C) \cup (A \cap D) \cup (B \cap D).$$

Therefore, in general, as in arithmetic, in order to expand the intersection of two unions one must take the intersection of each term of the first union with each term of the second union and then form the union of the intersections obtained in this manner.

The analogy between arithmetic and the theory of sets is not, however, complete. For example, the following obvious rules hold in set theory:

(9) $$A \cup A = A,$$

(10) $$A \cap A = A,$$

which point out that, in contrast to arithmetic, neither multiples nor exponents arise in set theory.

§ 3. Inclusion

We shall now introduce the important relation of *inclusion* between sets. We shall say that the set A is a *subset* of the set B (or also that the set A is *contained* in B) if every element of the set A is an element of the set B. We then write $A \subset B$ (or $B \supset A$).

We therefore have the following equivalence:

$$(11) \qquad (A \subset B) \equiv [\textit{the implication } (x \in A) \Rightarrow (x \in B) \textit{ holds for all } x].$$

In particular, it follows from this that

$$(12) \qquad A \subset A,$$

i. e. that every set is a subset of itself. Because of this inclusion, we also use the term *proper* subset for subsets of a given set which are different from the given set.

Obviously

$$(13) \qquad \textit{if } A \subset B \textit{ and } B \subset A, \textit{ then } A = B,$$

for the sets A and B consist of the same elements in this case.

Hence, in order to prove that $A = B$ it suffices to prove that $A \subset B$ and $B \subset A$; in other words, instead of the equivalence

$$(x \in A) \equiv (x \in B)$$

we prove the two implications

$$x \in A \Rightarrow x \in B \quad \text{and} \quad x \in B \Rightarrow x \in A$$

(cf. Chapter I, § 3, (14)).

It can easily be proved that

$$(14) \qquad \textit{if } A \subset B \textit{ and } B \subset C, \textit{ then } A \subset C,$$

$$(15) \qquad (A \cap B) \subset A \subset (A \cup B), \qquad A - B \subset A,$$

$$(16) \qquad \textit{if } A \subset B \textit{ and } C \subset D, \textit{ then } (A \cup C) \subset (B \cup D) \textit{ and } (A \cap C) \subset (B \cap D).$$

The following equivalences hold:

$$(17)\qquad (A \subset B) \equiv (A \cup B = B) \equiv (A \cap B = A).$$

For, let $A \subset B$. Combining this inclusion with the inclusion $B \subset B$ (cf. (12)), we obtain, by virtue of (16) and (9)

$$(A \cup B) \subset (B \cup B) = B,$$

but since (cf. (15)) $B \subset (A \cup B)$, we have $A \cup B = B$ (cf. (13)).

Conversely, it follows from the relation $A \cup B = B$ that $A \subset B$ (by virtue of (15)); hence these relations are equivalent.

Similarly, combining the inclusion $A \subset B$ with the inclusion $A \subset A$ we obtain $A \subset (A \cap B)$, whence $A = A \cap B$, because $A \cap B \subset A$ by virtue of (15).

Conversely, from the relation $A \cap B = A$ we obtain the relation $A \subset B$ because $(A \cap B) \subset B$.

From this we deduce the following formula which is important in applications:

$$(18)\qquad (A \cup B) \cap (A \cup C) = A \cup (B \cap C).$$

In fact, by virtue of (8) and (10) we have

$$(A \cup B) \cap (A \cup C) = (A \cap A) \cup (B \cap A) \cup (A \cap C) \cup (B \cap C)$$
$$= A \cup (B \cap A) \cup (A \cap C) \cup (B \cap C),$$

which yields $(B \cap A) \subset A$ by (15), and hence by virtue of (17) that $A \cup (B \cap A) = A$ and similarly that $A \cup (A \cap C) = A$. Formula (18) follows from this.

Let us note further the following formulas, the proof of which does not present any difficulties:

$$(19)\qquad A \cap B = A - (A - B),$$

$$(20)\qquad A \cup (B - A) = A \cup B,$$

$$(21)\qquad A - (A \cap B) = A - B,$$

$$(22)\qquad A \cap (B - C) = (A \cap B) - C.$$

§ 4. Space. Complement of a set

In the applications of the theory of sets, we assume, as a rule, that all the sets under consideration are subsets of some fixed set, called the *space*. For example, in analysis, the set of real numbers or the set of complex numbers forms a space, and in geometry we have to deal with the Euclidean space.

Under this assumption, the theorems of the algebra of sets assume a still simpler form which is closer to the calculus of propositional functions.

Hence, let 1 denote a given space (this notation is expedient from the calculational point of view). We therefore have $A \subset 1$ for each of the sets A considered. We denote by A^c (or by $\sim A$) the set of elements of the space which do not belong to A, i. e.

$$A^c = 1 - A .$$

A^c is called the *complement* of the set A (with respect to the given space 1). We therefore have

$$x \in A^c \equiv (x \in A)' \tag{23}$$

or, if we write $x \notin A$ instead of $(x \in A)'$, also

$$x \in A^c \equiv x \notin A .$$

Formulas (6)-(8) (Chapter I, § 2) yield immediately the (almost obvious) formulas:

$$1^c = \emptyset , \quad \emptyset^c = 1 , \tag{24}$$

$$A^{cc} = A , \tag{25}$$

$$A \cup A^c = 1 , \quad A \cap A^c = \emptyset . \tag{26}$$

Formulas (3), (23) and (2) imply the formula

$$A - B = A \cap B^c , \tag{27}$$

which allows us to define subtraction in terms of intersection and complementation.

In fact,

$$(x \in A - B) \equiv (x \in A) \wedge (x \in B)'$$
$$\equiv (x \in A) \wedge (x \in B^c) \equiv (x \in A \cap B^c).$$

Formula (16) (Chapter I, § 3) implies that:

(28) *if* $B^c \subset A^c$, *then* $A \subset B$.

Finally, formulas (9) and (10) (Chapter I, § 2) yield the de Morgan laws for sets:

(29) $$(A \cup B)^c = A^c \cap B^c,$$

(30) $$(A \cap B)^c = A^c \cup B^c.$$

For, we have

$$x \in (A \cup B)^c \equiv [x \in (A \cup B)]' \equiv [(x \in A) \vee (x \in B)]'$$
$$\equiv (x \in A^c) \wedge (x \in B^c) \equiv x \in (A^c \cap B^c).$$

The proof of formula (30) is analogous.

The obvious formula

(31) $$A \cap 1 = A$$

yields by (26), that

(32) $$A = (A \cap B) \cup (A \cap B^c),$$

inasmuch as

$$A = A \cap 1 = A \cap (B \cup B^c) = (A \cap B) \cup (A \cap B^c).$$

Formula (17) can be supplemented by the following equivalence which is frequently applied in practice:

(33) $$(A \subset B) \equiv (A \cap B^c = \emptyset).$$

For, forming the intersection of both sides of the inclusion $A \subset B$ with B^c we obtain $(A \cap B^c) \subset (B \cap B^c) = \emptyset$ (by virtue of (26)). But from formula (32) we deduce, assuming the equality $A \cap B^c = \emptyset$, that $A = A \cap B$, whence, by (17) it follows that $A \subset B$.

§ 5. The axiomatics of the algebra of sets

In the considerations up to this point we used only some properties of sets. The properties can be taken as a system of axioms, from which all the theorems of set theory, given above, follow.

We take, namely, as *primitive concepts* the concept of set and the relation of an element belonging to a set, i. e. the relation $x \in A$. We assume the following four axioms:—

I. UNIQUENESS AXIOM. *If the sets A and B have the same elements then A and B are identical.*

II. UNION AXIOM. *For arbitrary sets A and B there exists a set whose elements are all the elements of the set A and all the elements of the set B, and which does not contain any other elements.*

III. DIFFERENCE AXIOM. *For arbitrary sets A and B there exists a set whose elements are those and only those elements of the set A which are not elements of the set B.*

IV. EXISTENCE AXIOM. *There exists at least one set.*

It is not necessary to assume an axiom on the existence of an intersection because, as we saw (formula (19)), the intersection can be defined in terms of the difference. Likewise, the existence of the void set is a consequence of our system of axioms, for we can define the void set by means of the formula $\emptyset = A - A$, where A is an arbitrary set (the existence of at least one set is guaranteed by axiom IV).

An important consequence of axiom I is the uniqueness of the operations, i. e. for given sets A and B there exists only one set satisfying axiom II (which justifies the use of the symbol $A \cup B$ to denote this set); the same applies to the intersection and difference.

As we have already stated, it is possible from the above axioms to deduce all the theorems of the theory of sets considered till now, without referring back to the intuitive concept of set.

§ 6. Boolean algebra [G. Boole (1813-1864)]

We shall now give another method of the axiomatic concept of the algebra of sets.

Taking, namely, as primitive concepts the set $\emptyset$ and the operations $\cup$, $\cap$, $-$, we assume the following axioms:

(1°) $A \cup B = B \cup A$, (2°) $A \cap B = B \cap A$,

(3°) $$A \cup (B \cup C) = (A \cup B) \cup C,$$

(4°) $$A \cap (B \cap C) = (A \cap B) \cap C,$$

(5°) $$A \cup \emptyset = A,$$

(6°) $$A \cup (A \cap B) = A,$$

(7°) $$A \cap (B \cup C) = (A \cap B) \cup (A \cap C),$$

(8°) $$A \cap (A \cup B) = A,$$

(9°) $$(A - B) \cup B = A \cup B,$$

(10°) $$(A - B) \cap B = \emptyset.$$

From these axioms we are able to deduce all the theorems of the algebra of sets in which the relation ϵ does not appear. Also, if we desire to restrict the domain of the variables to subsets of a fixed set 1, we assume, in addition, the axiom

(11°) $$A \cap 1 = A.$$

We add that we define inclusion with the aid of the formula (cf. (17)):

$$(A \subset B) \equiv (A \cup B = B).$$

The theory based on the above axioms is called *Boolean algebra*. The applications of Boolean algebra extend far beyond the theory of sets; we need not interpret the variables $A, B, \ldots$ as sets. Interpreting them, e. g. as propositions we obtain the propositional calculus.

This explains the duality between the propositional calculus and the algebra of sets: to the disjunction (or sum) $\vee$

of propositions corresponds the union (or sum) $\cup$ of sets, to the conjuction (product) $\wedge$ of propositions—the intersection (product) $\cap$ of sets, to the negation a' of a proposition a—the complement A^c of a set A etc. (see also Chapter IV, § 3).

Other interpretations of Boolean algebra in recent times permit us to apply it in various branches of mathematics, and even outside mathematics (for example, in the theory of electrical networks).

Exercises

1. Prove the following formulas:

(a) $$A \cup (A \cap B) = A = A \cap (A \cup B),$$

(b) $$(A \cup B) - C = (A - C) \cup (B - C),$$

(c) $$A - (B - C) = (A - B) \cup (A \cap C),$$

(d) $$A - (B \cup C) = (A - B) - C.$$

2. The set

$$A \dot{-} B = (A - B) \cup (B - A)$$

is called the *symmetric difference* of the sets A and B.

Prove the following formulas:

(a) $$A \dot{-} (B \dot{-} C) = (A \dot{-} B) \dot{-} C \quad \text{(associativity)},$$

(b) $$A \cap (B \dot{-} C) = A \cap B \dot{-} A \cap C \quad \text{(distributivity)},$$

(c) $$A \cup B = A \dot{-} B \dot{-} A \cap B,$$

(d) $$A - B = A \dot{-} A \cap B.$$

3. We say that the operations $x + y$ and $x \cdot y$ form a *ring* if they satisfy the following conditions:

(i) $$x + y = y + x,$$

(ii) $$x + (y + z) = (x + y) + z,$$

(iii) there exists an element 0 such that $x + 0 = x$,

(iv) for every pair x, y there exists an element z $(z = x - y)$ such that $y + z = x$,

(v) $$x \cdot y = y \cdot x,$$

(vi) $$x \cdot (y \cdot z) = (x \cdot y) \cdot z,$$

(vii) $$x \cdot (y + z) = x \cdot y + x \cdot z.$$

Prove that sets form a ring with respect to the operations $A \dot{-} B$ and $A \cap B$, but that they do not form a ring with respect to the operations $A \cup B$ and $A \cap B$.

4. We define *division* by means of the formula $A : B = A \cup B^c$. Compute

$$A : (B \cap C), \; A : (B \cup C), \; A \cap (B : A).$$

5. Let $A_1, A_2, \ldots, A_n$ be fixed subsets of the space 1. Let us assume that $A_i^1 = 1 - A_i$, $A_i^0 = A_i$. Every intersection of the form

$$A_1^{i_1} \cap A_2^{i_2} \cap \ldots \cap A_n^{i_n}, \quad \text{where} \quad i_j = 0 \text{ or } 1,$$

is called a *constituant* of the space (with respect to the sets $A_1, A_2, \ldots, A_n$).

Prove that the constituants are disjoint and that their union is equal to 1 (therefore the decomposition into constituants effects a classification of the elements of the space with respect to their belonging to sets $A_1, A_2, \ldots, A_n$).

6. Represent the set $A - (B - C)$ as the union of constituants of the space with respect to the sets A, B and C.

7. Let us suppose that the set A has been obtained from the finite system of sets $A_1, \ldots, A_n$ by joining them in an arbitrary way with the aid of the symmetric difference. Prove that A is the set of elements belonging to an odd number of sets $A_1, \ldots, A_n$. (Thus the set A is not affected by changing order in which the operations are performed.)

CHAPTER III

PROPOSITIONAL FUNCTIONS. CARTESIAN PRODUCTS

Let a fixed set be given, which in the sequel we shall consider to be the space. Let $\varphi(x)$ be an expression which becomes a proposition when one substitutes for x an arbitrary value of x belonging to the considered space. We call this expression a *propositional function* (with bounded domain of the argument; we sometimes consider propositional functions for which the domain of variation of the variable x is not restricted to any set.)

For example, if the space is the set of all real numbers, then the expression "$x > 0$" is a propositional function; it becomes a true proposition if we substitute, say, 1 for x; it becomes a false proposition if we substitute -1 for x.

§ 1. The operation $\underset{}{E}$

The set of all those values of the variable x for which $\varphi(x)$ is a true proposition (or, as we say, the set of x's which satisfy the propositional function $\varphi(x)$) is denoted by the symbol

$$\underset{x}{E}\varphi(x),$$

or by $\{x : \varphi(x)\}$.

For example, in the space of real numbers $\underset{x}{E}(x > 0)$ is the set of all positive numbers, $\underset{x}{E}(x = x)$ is the set of all real numbers, and $\underset{x}{E}(x+1 = x)$ is the null set.

It follows from the definition of the operation E that a necessary and sufficient condition, that the element a should belong to the set $\underset{x}{E}\varphi(x)$, is that the proposition $\varphi(a)$ be true. Hence, the following equivalence holds:

(1) *for every* a: $[a \in \underset{x}{E}\varphi(x)] \equiv \varphi(a)$.

The following four formulas hold:

(2) $$E_x[\varphi(x) \vee \psi(x)] = E_x\varphi(x) \cup E_x\psi(x),$$

(3) $$E_x[\varphi(x) \wedge \psi(x)] = E_x\varphi(x) \cap E_x\psi(x),$$

(4) $$E_x[\varphi(x) \wedge \{\psi(x)\}'] = E_x\varphi(x) - E_x\psi(x),$$

(5) $$E_x[\varphi(x)]' = [E_x\varphi(x)]^c.$$

We obtain the proof of the formula (2) from the formula (1) above and formula (1) of Chapter II, § 2:

$$a \in E_x[\varphi(x) \vee \psi(x)] \equiv [\varphi(a) \vee \psi(a)]$$

$$\equiv [a \in E_x\varphi(x)] \vee [a \in E_x\psi(x)] \equiv a \in [E_x\varphi(x) \cup E_x\psi(x)],$$

whence equality (2) follows (cf. Chapter II, § 2, (4)).

Formulas (3)-(5) are proved similarly.

§ 2. Quantifiers

Let us now consider the following two operations on propositional functions:

$$\bigvee_x \varphi(x) \quad \text{and} \quad \bigwedge_x \varphi(x).$$

We read the formula $\bigvee_x \varphi(x)$ as follows: there exists *some* x which satisfies the function $\varphi(x)$; $\bigwedge_x \varphi(x)$ denotes that *every* x satisfies this function. (The symbols $\exists_x$, Σ_x and $\forall_x$, Π_x, respectively, are used in the same sense.)

Clearly, the above operations transform propositional functions into propositions. The symbols of these operations $\bigvee$ and $\bigwedge$ are called the *existential* and the *universal quantifiers*, respectively.

For example, in the space of real numbers the proposition $\bigvee_x (x > 0)$ is true but the proposition $\bigwedge_x (x > 0)$ is false.

The variable x which appears as the *free* variable in the propositional function $\varphi(x)$ becomes a *bound* variable in the proposition $\bigvee_x \varphi(x)$ (like x in $\int_0^1 f(x)dx$). It may be noted that

$$\bigvee_x \varphi(x) \equiv \bigvee_y \varphi(y).$$

Analogous remarks can be made about the universal quantifier.

The operations $\bigvee$ and $\bigwedge$ may be considered as generalizations of the operations of disjunction and conjunction. For, if the domain of variation of x is finite, consisting of the elements $a_1, a_2, \ldots, a_n$, then

$$(6)\qquad \begin{aligned} \bigvee_x \varphi(x) &\equiv [\varphi(a_1) \vee \varphi(a_2) \vee \ldots \vee \varphi(a_n)]\,,\\ \bigwedge_x \varphi(x) &\equiv [\varphi(a_1) \wedge \varphi(a_2) \wedge \ldots \wedge \varphi(a_n)]\,. \end{aligned}$$

We now set down the following easily proved formulas:

(7) *for every* x_0 *we have* $[\bigwedge_x \varphi(x)] \Rightarrow \varphi(x_0) \Rightarrow [\bigvee_x \varphi(x)]$,

$$(8)\qquad [\bigvee_x \varphi(x) \vee \bigvee_x \psi(x)] \equiv \bigvee_x [\varphi(x) \vee \psi(x)]\,,$$

$$(9)\qquad \bigvee_x [\varphi(x) \wedge \psi(x)] \Rightarrow \bigvee_x \varphi(x) \wedge \bigvee_x \psi(x)\,.$$

Let us note that in formula (9) we cannot replace the implication sign by the equivalence sign; in other words, implication in the opposite direction may not hold. For example, both of the propositions

$\bigvee_x$ (x is a positive number)

and $\bigvee_x$ (x is a negative number)

are true, and hence a true proposition appears in the right member of formula (9); but on the left side there appears, in this example, a false proposition (inasmuch as there is no number which is simultaneously positive and negative).

The duals of formulas (8) and (9) are the following formulas:

$$(10)\qquad [\bigwedge_x \varphi(x) \wedge \bigwedge_x \psi(x)] \equiv \bigwedge_x [\varphi(x) \wedge \psi(x)]\,,$$

$$(11)\qquad [\bigwedge_x \varphi(x) \vee \bigwedge_x \psi(x)] \Rightarrow \bigwedge_x [\varphi(x) \vee \psi(x)]\,.$$

This duality is expressed by the *generalized de Morgan formulas* (which appear very frequently in applications):

$$(12)\qquad [\bigwedge_x \varphi(x)]' \equiv \bigvee_x \varphi'(x)\,,$$

$$(13)\qquad [\bigvee_x \varphi(x)]' \equiv \bigwedge_x \varphi'(x)\,.$$

As in the case of finite operations, the de Morgan formulas permit the definition of the universal quantifier in terms of the existential quantifier and negation (and the existential quantifier in terms of the universal quantifier and negation):

(14) $\bigwedge_x \varphi(x) \equiv \big(\bigvee_x \varphi'(x)\big)', \quad \bigvee_x \varphi(x) \equiv \big(\bigwedge_x \varphi'(x)\big)'.$

Remark. Instead of the symbols $\bigvee_x$ and $\bigwedge_x$ we often use the more complicated symbols $\bigvee_{\psi(x)}$ and $\bigwedge_{\psi(x)}$ where $\psi(x)$ is a given propositional function. We assume that

$$\bigvee_{\psi(x)} \varphi(x) \equiv \bigvee_x [\psi(x) \wedge \varphi(x)],$$

$$\bigwedge_{\psi(x)} \varphi(x) \equiv \bigwedge_x [\psi(x) \Rightarrow \varphi(x)].$$

Similarly, we assume that

$$E_{\psi(x)}\varphi(x) = E_x[\psi(x) \wedge \varphi(x)].$$

§ 3. Ordered pairs

We denote a set consisting of only one element a by the symbol $\{a\}$ (let us note that $\{a\} \neq a$). We denote the set consisting of the two elements a and b by $\{a, b\}$; similarly, $\{a, b, c\}$ denotes the set consisting of the elements a, b and c.

Obviously the symbols $\{a, b\}$ and $\{b, a\}$ denote the same set. In the sequel we shall need the concept of an *ordered pair* with antecedent a and successor b which we shall denote by the symbol $\langle a, b\rangle$. We consider the pair $\langle a, b\rangle$ as distinct from the pair $\langle b, a\rangle$ (unless $a = b$); more generally, the pairs $\langle a, b\rangle$ and $\langle c, d\rangle$ are equal only when $a = c$ and $b = d$, i. e. when they have identical antecedents and identical successors:

(15) $[\langle a, b\rangle = \langle c, d\rangle] \Rightarrow (a = c) \wedge (b = d).$

The concept of ordered pair can be defined in various ways; we can, for instance, adopt the following definition:

(16) $\langle a, b\rangle = \{\{a\}, \{a, b\}\}.$

It is easy to verify that condition (15) is satisfied by this definition.

§ 4. Cartesian product

The *cartesian product* of the sets X and Y is the set of all ordered pairs $\langle x, y\rangle$ where $x \in X$ and $y \in Y$. We denote this set by $X \times Y$ and therefore

$$(17) \qquad [\langle x, y\rangle \in (X \times Y)] \equiv (x \in X) \wedge (y \in Y).$$

Cartesian products appear very frequently in mathematics. For example, the complex number plane is $\mathcal{E} \times \mathcal{E}$, where $\mathcal{E}$ is the set of all real numbers (since a complex number is an ordered pair made up of two real numbers). A cylinder can be considered as the cartesian product of the circumference of a circle (base) by a closed interval (height); the surface of a torus can be treated as the cartesian product of two circles.

Let us set down several easily proved formulas concerning the distributivity of cartesian multiplication with respect to the operations of the algebra of sets:

$$(18) \qquad (X_1 \cup X_2) \times Y = X_1 \times Y \cup X_2 \times Y,$$

whence

$$(19) \qquad (X_1 \cup X_2) \times (Y_1 \cup Y_2) = X_1 \times Y_1 \cup X_1 \times Y_2 \cup X_2 \times Y_1 \cup X_2 \times Y_2,$$

$$(20) \qquad (X_1 - X_2) \times Y = X_1 \times Y - X_2 \times Y,$$

$$(21) \qquad (X_1 \cap X_2) \times (Y_1 \cap Y_2) = (X_1 \times Y_1) \cap (X_2 \times Y_2).$$

If the sets X_1, X_2, Y_1 and Y_2 are nonvoid then

$$(22) \qquad [(X_1 \times Y_1) = (X_2 \times Y_2)] \Rightarrow (X_1 = X_2) \wedge (Y_1 = Y_2).$$

All the above formulas can easily be interpreted geometrically, if we assume that $X \times Y$ is the plane with axes X and Y and that $X_1 \subset X$, $X_2 \subset X$, $Y_1 \subset Y$, $Y_2 \subset Y$.

Similarly, the following two formulas have a clear geometric interpretation:

$$(23) \qquad A \times B = (A \times Y) \cap (X \times B),$$

$$(24) \qquad (A \times B)^c = (A^c \times Y) \cup (X \times B^c),$$

where $A \subset X$, $B \subset Y$, A^c and B^c denote the complements with respect to X and Y, respectively, and $(A \times B)^c$ denotes the complement with respect to $X \times Y$.

Formula (23) follows from (21), and (24) follows from (23) by virtue of the de Morgan rules since

$$(A \times Y) \cap (X \times B) = (A \cap X) \times (Y \cap B) = A \times B\,,$$

$$(A \times Y)^c = (A^c \times Y) \quad \text{and} \quad (X \times B)^c = (X \times B^c)\,.$$

§ 5. Propositional functions of two variables

Let the cartesian product $Z = X \times Y$ be given. Let $\varphi(z)$ be a propositional function of the variable z which ranges over the set Z. Since $z = \langle x, y\rangle$, the propositional function $\varphi(z)$ can be considered as *a function of two variables x and y*; we write $\varphi(x, y)$ instead of $\varphi(\langle x, y\rangle)$. We also call a propositional function of two variables a *relation* (in the sense of logic).

A propositional function of two variables ranging over the spaces X and Y is the same as a propositional function of one variable ranging over the cartesian product of these spaces.

Instead of $\underset{z}{E}\varphi(z)$ we also write $\underset{x,y}{E}\varphi(x, y)$. For example, $\underset{x,y}{E}(x < y)$ is the half-plane situated above the line $x = y$, and $\underset{x,y}{E}(y = x^2)$ is the parabola which is determined by the equation $y = x^2$.

Let $\varphi(x, y)$ be a given propositional function of two variables. Hence $\bigvee_y \varphi(x, y)$ and $\bigwedge_y \varphi(x, y)$ are propositional functions of one variable, namely of the variable x.

We set down the following easily proved formulas:

$$(25) \qquad \bigvee_x \bigvee_y \varphi(x, y) \equiv \bigvee_y \bigvee_x \varphi(x, y)\,,$$

$$(26) \qquad \bigwedge_x \bigwedge_y \varphi(x, y) \equiv \bigwedge_y \bigwedge_x \varphi(x, y)\,.$$

In both of these formulas we may alternatively write $\bigvee_{x,y} \varphi(x, y)$ or $\bigvee_z \varphi(z)$, and $\bigwedge_{x,y} \varphi(x, y)$ or $\bigwedge_z \varphi(z)$.

These formulas express the commutativity of the operation $\bigvee$ with respect to $\bigvee$ and similarly of the operation $\bigwedge$ with respect to $\bigwedge$. On the other hand, the sequence of the quantifiers $\bigvee$ and $\bigwedge$ is significant. The following important formula holds:

$$(27) \qquad \bigvee_x \bigwedge_y \varphi(x, y) \Rightarrow \bigwedge_y \bigvee_x \varphi(x, y).$$

The left hand member denotes that there exists an x_0 such that, for every value of the variable y, $\varphi(x_0, y)$ is true; and therefore to every y we can assign an x (namely, $x = x_0$) such that $\varphi(x, y)$ is true; and this is exactly what the right hand member states.

On the other hand, the implication in the opposite direction does not hold (compare formula (9)). For example, in the domain of real numbers it is true that

$$\bigwedge_y \bigvee_x (y < x),$$

but it is not true that

$$\bigvee_x \bigwedge_y (y < x).$$

Another example is: the assumption that the real valued function f is bounded can be written in the following form:

$$\bigvee_y \bigwedge_x \big(|f(x)| < y\big).$$

On the other hand, the proposition $\bigwedge_x \bigvee_y (|f(x)| < y)$ is true in general (for all real valued functions), for it suffices to set $y = |f(x)| + 1$.

The obvious formula

$$(28) \qquad \bigwedge_x \varphi(x) \Rightarrow \bigvee_x \varphi(x)$$

(under the assumption that $X \neq \emptyset$) can be replaced, for functions of two variables, with the additional assumption that $X = Y$, by the more general formula

$$(29) \quad \bigwedge_{x,y} \varphi(x,y) \Rightarrow \bigwedge_x \varphi(x, x) \Rightarrow \bigvee_x \varphi(x, x) \Rightarrow \bigvee_{x,y} \varphi(x, y).$$

With this same assumption we can replace formula (9) by the following formula

$$(30) \quad \bigvee_x [\varphi(x) \wedge \psi(x)] \Rightarrow \bigvee_{x,y} [\varphi(x) \wedge \psi(y)]$$
$$\equiv \bigvee_x \varphi(x) \wedge \bigvee_y \psi(y) \equiv \bigvee_x \varphi(x) \wedge \bigvee_x \psi(x).$$

Analogously, (11) can be replaced by the formula

$$(31)\qquad \bigwedge_x \varphi(x) \vee \bigwedge_x \psi(x) \equiv \bigwedge_{x,y} [\varphi(x) \vee \psi(y)] \Rightarrow \bigwedge_x [\varphi(x) \vee \psi(x)]\,.$$

§ 6. Propositional functions of n variables

The above reasoning can easily be generalized to a larger number of variables than two. For example, Euclidean three-dimensional space is the set of ordered triples of real numbers, i. e. $\mathcal{E}\times\mathcal{E}\times\mathcal{E}$, which we write more briefly as $\mathcal{E}^3$. More generally, $\mathcal{E}^n$ denotes n-dimensional Euclidean space; denoting by $\mathcal{J}$ the closed interval $0 \leqslant t \leqslant 1$ we denote the n-dimensional unit cube by $\mathcal{J}^n$.

Similarly, we may speak about a propositional function of n variables which run over the same or distinct spaces. The following examples illustrate the role of the quantifiers and the meaning of some formulas which are related to them:

1. The continuity of a function f at a given point x_0 is expressed by the following condition (in the Cauchy formulation):

$$(32)\qquad \bigwedge_\varepsilon \bigvee_\delta \bigwedge_h (|h| < \delta) \Rightarrow \big(|f(x_0+h) - f(x_0)| < \varepsilon\big)\,,$$

where the domain of variation of the variables ε and δ is the set of positive real numbers.

Therefore the continuity of a function in the interval under consideration $a < x < b$ is expressed by prefacing formula (32) with the quantifier $\bigwedge_x$ and replacing the constant x_0 by the variable x. Since we can interchange the order of the quantifiers $\bigwedge_x$ and $\bigwedge_\varepsilon$, this condition takes on the following form:

$$(33)\qquad \bigwedge_\varepsilon \bigwedge_x \bigvee_\delta \bigwedge_h (|h|) < \delta) \Rightarrow \big(|f(x+h) - f(x)| < \varepsilon\big)\,.$$

If we interchange the order of the quantifiers $\bigwedge_x$ and $\bigvee_\delta$, we obtain a *stronger* condition, namely the condition for *uniform* continuity. Since, after this interchange, the quantifier $\bigvee_\delta$ follows $\bigwedge_\varepsilon$, but is still before $\bigwedge_x$, it is immediately clear that δ depends on ε but that it does not depend on x (which is exactly what "uniform" continuity means).

2. The condition that the sequence $a_1, a_2, \ldots$ be convergent to the limit b can be written in the form

$$(34) \qquad \bigvee_{\varepsilon} \bigvee_{m} \bigwedge_{n} |a_{m+n} - b| < \varepsilon .$$

Therefore the condition that the sequence of functions $f_1, f_2, \ldots$ be convergent to the limit f is

$$(35) \qquad \bigwedge_{x} \bigwedge_{\varepsilon} \bigvee_{m} \bigwedge_{n} |f_{m+n}(x) - f(x)| < \varepsilon .$$

By interchanging the order of $\bigwedge_x$ and $\bigwedge_\varepsilon$, we obtain an equivalent condition. Let us now interchange $\bigwedge_x$ and $\bigvee_m$. We then obtain the stronger condition from which condition (35) follows, namely

$$(36) \qquad \bigwedge_{\varepsilon} \bigvee_{m} \bigwedge_{x} \bigwedge_{n} |f_{m+n}(x) - f(x)| < \varepsilon .$$

This is the condition for *uniform* convergence.

§ 7. Remarks on the axiomatics

The four axioms given in Chapter II, § 5, are not sufficient for the discussions of Chapter III. Adding three further axioms, we obtain a system of axioms which expresses all those properties of the set concept with which we shall deal in this volume, and which—generally speaking—suffice for the applications of the theory of sets to other branches of mathematics. These are the new axioms.

V. *For every propositional function $\varphi(x)$ and for every set A there exists a set consisting of those and only those elements of the set A which satisfy this propositional function.*

As is known (see § 1), we denote this set by the symbol

$$E_x \varphi(x) \wedge (x \in A)\,, \text{ or, more briefly, by } E_x \varphi(x)\,,$$

where the domain of variation of x is restricted to A.

We had examples of the applications of axiom V in § 3. The existence of the sets $\{a\}$, $\{a, b\}$, and so on (where $a \in A$, $b \in A$) follows from axiom V, since

$$\{a\} = \underset{x}{E}(x = a) \wedge (x \in A),$$
$$\{a, b\} = \underset{x}{E}[(x = a) \vee (x = b)] \wedge (x \in A).$$

On the other hand, the existence of an ordered pair requires the use of a further axiom.

VI. *For every set A there exists a set whose elements are all the subsets of the set A.*

VII. AXIOM OF CHOICE. *For every family* **R** *of non-empty disjoint sets there exists a set which has one and only one element in common with each of the sets of the family* **R**.

(We shall use the expression "family" to denote the set whose elements are sets. We shall then write **R** instead of R.)

We have not applied the axiom of choice yet but we shall use it in the later chapters.

We point out that if we complete the system of axioms I-IV by means of the axioms V-VII we can at the same time omit some of the earlier axioms. In particular, axiom III follows from the rest, for the set

$$A - B = \underset{x}{E}(x \in A) \wedge (x \in B)',$$

exists by virtue of axiom V.

Similarly, we can do without axiom II in the formation of the union of the sets A and B provided that we assume that both A and B are subsets of a fixed "space" C (which is usually the case). For the existence of the set

$$A \cup B = \underset{x}{E}[(x \in A) \vee (x \in B)] \wedge (x \in C)$$

follows from axiom V.

Axiom IV is also superfluous in applications; for in its place appears the axiom which asserts that the space under consideration is a set.

Exercises

1. Prove that none of the implications in formula (29) can be replaced by an equivalence.

2. Prove that

$$\bigvee_x \varphi(x) \vee \bigwedge_x \psi(x) \equiv \bigvee_x \bigwedge_y [\varphi(x) \vee \psi(y)] \equiv \bigwedge_y \bigvee_x [\varphi(x) \vee \psi(y)],$$

$$\bigvee_x \varphi(x) \wedge \bigwedge_x \psi(x) \equiv \bigvee_x \bigwedge_y [\varphi(x) \wedge \psi(y)] \equiv \bigwedge_y \bigvee_x [\varphi(x) \wedge \psi(y)].$$

3. Prove the following equivalences:

$$\bigwedge_x \{[\bigwedge^y \varphi(x, y)] \Rightarrow \psi(x)\} \equiv \bigwedge_x \bigvee_y [\varphi(x, y) \Rightarrow \psi(x)],$$

$$\bigwedge_x \{[\bigvee_y \varphi(x, y)] \Rightarrow \psi(x)\} \equiv \bigwedge_{x,y} [\varphi(x, y) \Rightarrow \psi(x)].$$

4. Write down the definition of the uniform convergence of the improper integral $\int_a^\infty f(x, y)\,dy$ making use of quantifiers.

CHAPTER IV

THE FUNCTION CONCEPT. INFINITE OPERATIONS

§ 1. The function concept

We usually say in analysis that we are dealing with a real valued function f of a real variable if to each real number there is assigned one and only one real number. It is also known that, from the geometric point of view, a function can be identified with its graph (in the same sense that a real number can be identified with a point on the real line, or a complex number with a point in the plane). On the basis of the theory of sets we can define the general concept of function as follows.

Definition. Let X and Y be two given sets. By a *function* whose *arguments* run over the set X (domain) and whose *values* belong to the set Y (range) we understand the subset f of the cartesian product $X \times Y$ with the property that for every $x \in X$ there exists one and only one y such that $\langle x, y \rangle \in f$. The set of all these functions f is denoted by Y^X.

We usually write $y = f(x)$ instead of $\langle x, y \rangle \in f$.

We, therefore, have

$$f = E_{x,y}[y = f(x)] .$$

Clearly, in the case where X and Y denote sets of real numbers the right member of this formula denotes the graph of the function in the usual sense of the word. An analogous remark applies to a function of two real variables (or a function of a complex variable).

We do not assume that the values of the function f fill the entire set Y. But if this condition is fulfilled, then we say that the function f is a *mapping* of the set X *onto* the set Y.

If X is the set of natural numbers then we call the function f an *infinite sequence.* Instead of $f(n)$ we then write f_n (or more frequently: a_n) and we call the values of the function the *terms* of the sequence.

Remark. The concept of function is a particular case of the concept of *relation* in the set-theoretic sense. Namely by a relation in this sense we mean an arbitrary subset R of the cartesian product $X \times Y$. Instead of writing $\langle x, y\rangle \in R$ we usually write xRy (which is read "x is in the relation R to y").

Every propositional function $\varphi(x, y)$ of the variables x and y, having the sets X and Y as domains of variation respectively (i. e. a relation in the sense of logic), determines a set $R \subset X \times Y$, namely

$$R = E_{x,y}\varphi(x, y) .$$

§ 2. Generalized operations

We shall now consider the case where the values of the function are sets. Thus, let F be a function whose arguments run over the non-empty set T and whose values are subsets of some fixed set X (i. e. they are elements of the family $\boldsymbol{R}$ of all subsets of the set X). We shall write F_t instead of $F(t)$.

We introduce the following two operations on functions, called *generalized union* and *generalized intersection* (which are analogues of the quantifiers $\bigvee_t$ and $\bigwedge_t$).

$\bigcup_t F_t$ is the set to which x belongs if and only if it belongs to at least one of the sets F_t (it is also denoted by $\Sigma_t F_t$).

$\bigcap_t F_t$ is the set to which x belongs if and only if it belongs to all the sets F_t (it is also denoted by $\Pi_t F_t$).

In the notation of logic this means that

$$(1) \qquad (x \in \bigcup_t F_t) \equiv \bigvee_t (x \in F_t) ,$$

$$(2) \qquad (x \in \bigcap_t F_t) \equiv \bigwedge_t (x \in F_t) .$$

These operations are indeed generalizations of known operations of union and intersection of sets (see Chapter II, § 1). For if the set T is the set consisting of the numbers $1, 2, \ldots, n$, then

$$\bigcup_t F_t = F_1 \cup F_2 \cup \ldots \cup F_n, \qquad \bigcap_t F_t = F_1 \cap F_2 \cap \ldots \cap F_n.$$

Let us add that in the case where F is an infinite sequence of sets, i. e. if T is the set of natural numbers, we then use the notation

$$\bigcup_{n=1}^{\infty} F_n \text{ instead of } \bigcup_t F_t, \qquad \bigcap_{n=1}^{\infty} F_n \text{ instead of } \bigcap_t F_t.$$

We now set down several formulas which can easily be proved ((4) is the generalized de Morgan formula):

(3) $$\bigcap_t F_t \subset F_t \subset \bigcup_t F_t,$$

(4) $$\Big(\bigcup_t F_t\Big)^c = \bigcap_t F_t^c, \qquad \Big(\bigcap_t F_t\Big)^c = \bigcup_t F_t^c,$$

(5) *if* $F_t \subset A$ *for every* t, *then* $\bigcup_t F_t \subset A$,

(6) *if* $A \subset F_t$ *for every* t, *then* $A \subset \bigcap_t F_t$.

As an example, we shall prove formula (5). Hence, let $x \in \bigcup_t F_t$. By virtue of (1) there exists a t_0 such that $x \in F_{t_0}$; but by assumption $F_{t_0} \subset A$. Therefore $x \in A$. This means that $\bigcup_t F_t \subset A$.

Remark. As in Chapter II (cf. Remark, § 2) we also make use of the operations $\bigvee_{\psi(t)} F_t$ and $\bigwedge_{\psi(t)} F_t$, where $\psi(t)$ is a given propositional function. The meaning of these operations is defined by formulas (1) and (2), replacing $\bigvee_t$ by $\bigvee_{\psi(t)}$ and $\bigwedge_t$ by $\bigwedge_{\psi(t)}$ in them.

§ 3. The function $F_x = E_y \varphi(x, y)$

Let $\varphi(x, y)$ be a given propositional function of two variables. For fixed x_0, $E_y \varphi(x_0, y)$ is some subset of the space Y. Hence, if we put

(7) $$F_x = E_y \varphi(x, y),$$

we define a function F which assigns to every element $x \in X$ a subset of the space Y. Let us apply the operations

$\bigvee_x$ and $\bigwedge_x$ to this function. We obtain the following formulas which display the duality between generalized disjunction and conjunction, and quantifiers (compare Chapter III, § 1, (2) and (3)):

(8) $$\bigcup_x E_y \varphi(x, y) = E_y \bigvee_x \varphi(x, y),$$

(9) $$\bigcap_x E_y \varphi(x, y) = E_y \bigwedge_x \varphi(x, y).$$

In fact, by formulas (1), § 2, and (1), Chapter III, § 1, we have

$$y_0 \in \bigcup_x E_y \varphi(x, y) \equiv \bigvee_x [y_0 \in E_y \varphi(x, y)]$$
$$\equiv \bigvee_x \varphi(x, y_0) \equiv y_0 \in E_y \bigvee_x \varphi(x, y).$$

Formula (9) is proved analogously.

The set $E_y \bigvee_x \varphi(x, y)$ has the following interesting geometric interpretation.

Noting the analogy to analytic geometry, we shall say that the element $\langle x, y\rangle$ of the cartesian product $X \times Y$ has the *abscissa* x and the *ordinate* y, and that X is the axis of abscissae and Y is the axis of ordinates of the space $X \times Y$. Similarly, if $A \subset X \times Y$, then the set of abscissas of the elements of the set A will be called the *X-projection* of the set A and the set of ordinates will be called the *Y-projection* of A. Now:

(10) *the set* $E_y \bigvee_x \varphi(x, y)$ *is the* Y*-projection of the set* $E_{x,y} \varphi(x, y)$.

In fact, y_0 is an element of the Y-projection of the set $A = E_{x,y}(x, y)$ if and only if there exists an x_0 such that $\langle x_0, y_0\rangle \in A$, i. e. if $\varphi(x_0, y_0)$ holds; in other words, if $\bigvee_x \varphi(x, y_0)$, i. e. if $y_0 \in E_y \bigvee_x \varphi(x, y)$.

The universal quantifier does not lead to such a simple geometric interpretation.

EXAMPLE. By the parametric definition of the circle S with center $\langle 0, 0\rangle$ and radius r the point $\langle x, y\rangle$ belongs to this circle if there exists a t such that

(11) $$x = r \cos t, \quad y = r \sin t,$$

that is

$$S = E_{x,y} \bigvee_t (x = r\cos t) \wedge (y = r\sin t)\,.$$

This means that the formulas (11) which give the parametric definition of the circle S define this circle as the projection onto a subset of the plane $X \times Y$ (i. e. the XY-projection) of the helix lying in the three-dimensional space $X \times Y \times T$ and defined (in an explicit manner) by this same system of equations (11).

§ 4. Images and inverse images determined by a function

Let f be a function with arguments running over the space X and with values belonging to the space Y. Suppose $A \subset X$. We denote the *image* of the set A with respect to the function f by $f(A)$, i. e. $f(A)$ is the set of values which the function f assumes when the argument x runs over the set A; in other words,

(12) $$[y \in f(A)] \equiv \bigvee_x (x \in A) \wedge \big(y = f(x)\big)\,,$$

i. e.

$$f(A) = E_y \bigvee_x (x \in A) \wedge \big(y = f(x)\big)\,.$$

We can also formulate this definition in the following way: Let us denote by $f|A$ the function which we obtain from the function f by restricting its arguments to the set A (that is, $f|A$ is a *partial* or *restricted* function). Then $f(A)$ is the projection of the function $f|A$ onto a subset of the Y-axis.

The *inverse image* of the set B contained in Y is the set $f^{-1}(B)$ consisting of all x such that $f(x) \in B$; thus

(13) $$[x \in f^{-1}(B)] \equiv [f(x) \in B]\,, \quad \text{i. e.} \quad f^{-1}(B) = E_x f(x) \in B.$$

(Note: in order to avoid misunderstanding we assume that $A \notin X$ and $B \notin Y$.)

For example, for the function given by the equation $y = x^2$, the set $f^{-1}(\{1\})$ consists of two numbers: 1 and -1.

Let us note the following formulas:

(14) $$f(A_1 \cup A_2) = f(A_1) \cup f(A_2)$$

and more generally $f(\bigcup_t F_t) = \bigcup_t f(F_t)$,

(15) $f(A_1 \cap A_2) \subset f_1(A) \cap f(A_2)$

and more generally $f(\bigcap_t F_t) \subset \bigcap_t f(F_t)$,

(16) $$f^{-1}(B_1 \cup B_2) = f^{-1}(B_1) \cup f^{-1}(B_2), \quad f^{-1}(\bigcup_t G_t) = \bigcup_t f^{-1}(G_t),$$

(17) $$f^{-1}(B_1 \cap B_2) = f^{-1}(B_1) \cap f^{-1}(B_2), \quad f^{-1}(\bigcap_t G_t) = \bigcap_t f^{-1}(G_t),$$

(17 a) $$f^{-1}(B_1 - B_2) = f^{-1}(B_1) - f^{-1}(B_2),$$

(18) $$ff^{-1}(B) = B \quad \text{if} \quad B \subset f(X),$$

(19) $$A \subset f^{-1}f(A).$$

We shall prove, say, formula (15). Since $(\bigcap_t F_t) \subset F_t$, we have $f(\bigcap_t F_t) \subset f(F_t)$ and (15) follows by (6).

§ 5. The operations $S(\boldsymbol{R})$ and $P(\boldsymbol{R})$

Besides the operations $\bigcup$ and $\bigcap$ on functions we consider the operations $S(\boldsymbol{R})$ and $P(\boldsymbol{R})$ on families of sets. Namely assuming that $\boldsymbol{R}$ is a non-empty family of subsets of some fixed set A, we denote by $S(\boldsymbol{R})$ the union and by $P(\boldsymbol{R})$ the intersection of all the sets belonging to the family $\boldsymbol{R}$, that is

(20) $$x \in S(\boldsymbol{R}) \equiv \bigvee_X (x \in X \in \boldsymbol{R}),$$

(21) $$x \in P(\boldsymbol{R}) \equiv \bigwedge_X [(X \in \boldsymbol{R}) \Rightarrow (x \in X)].$$

We use the same terminology ("union" and "intersection") here as in the case where $\boldsymbol{R}$ is a family consisting of a finite number of sets: $\boldsymbol{R} = \{A_1, \ldots, A_n\}$; for

$$S(\boldsymbol{R}) = A_1 \cup A_2 \cup \ldots \cup A_n,$$
$$P(\boldsymbol{R}) = A_1 \cap A_2 \cap \ldots \cap A_n.$$

§ 6. Additive and multiplicative families of sets

We say that the family $\boldsymbol{R}$ of sets is *additive* if

(22) $$(X \in \boldsymbol{R}, Y \in \boldsymbol{R}) \Rightarrow (X \cup Y \in \boldsymbol{R}),$$

multiplicative if

(23) $$(X \in \boldsymbol{R}, Y \in \boldsymbol{R}) \Rightarrow (X \cap Y \in \boldsymbol{R}),$$

subtractive if

(24) $$(X \in \boldsymbol{R}, Y \in \boldsymbol{R}) \Rightarrow (X - Y \in \boldsymbol{R}).$$

An additive and subtractive family of sets is multiplicative since $X \cap Y = X - (X - Y)$. Clearly, the operations of union, intersection and subtraction performed on sets belonging to that family do not take us outside it.

EXAMPLES. The family of finite subsets of a fixed set A satisfies (22)-(24). Sets which are the unions of a finite number of closed intervals form an additive family, but they do not form a subtractive family.

THEOREM. *For every family* $\boldsymbol{Z}$ *of subsets of a set* A *there exists*

1. *a smallest additive family* $\boldsymbol{R}_s$ *such that* $\boldsymbol{Z} \subset \boldsymbol{R}_s$,

2. *a smallest multiplicative family* $\boldsymbol{R}_p$ *such that* $\boldsymbol{Z} \subset \boldsymbol{R}_p$, *and*

3. *a smallest additive and subtractive family of sets* $\boldsymbol{R}_c$ *such that* $\boldsymbol{Z} \subset \boldsymbol{R}_c$.

Proof. Let us denote by $\mathcal{M}$ the totality of all additive families $\boldsymbol{R}$ which satisfy the condition $\boldsymbol{Z} \subset \boldsymbol{R}$ (consisting of subsets of the set A). Obviously $\mathcal{M} \neq \emptyset$, for the family of all subsets of the set A is an element of the totality $\mathcal{M}$. Let us take

(25) $$\boldsymbol{R}_s = P(\mathcal{M}).$$

We shall show that the family $\boldsymbol{R}_s$ is additive and that $\boldsymbol{Z} \subset \boldsymbol{R}_s$.

Let $X \in \boldsymbol{R}_s$ and let $Y \in \boldsymbol{R}_s$. Therefore (cf. (21)) $X \in \boldsymbol{R}$ and $Y \in \boldsymbol{R}$ for every $\boldsymbol{R} \in \mathcal{M}$. Since the families $\boldsymbol{R}$ belonging to $\mathcal{M}$ are additive, we therefore have $X \cup Y \in \boldsymbol{R}$; but since this last formula holds for every $\boldsymbol{R} \in \mathcal{M}$, hence (cf. (21)) $X \cup Y \in \boldsymbol{R}_s$.

We shall next prove that $\boldsymbol{Z} \subset \boldsymbol{R}_s$. By assumption we have $\boldsymbol{Z} \subset \boldsymbol{R}$ for every $\boldsymbol{R} \in \mathcal{M}$. In other words, if $X \in \boldsymbol{Z}$, then $X \in \boldsymbol{R}$; and therefore $X \in \boldsymbol{R}_s$. This means that $X \in \boldsymbol{Z} \Rightarrow X \in \boldsymbol{R}_s$, or that $\boldsymbol{Z} \subset \boldsymbol{R}_s$.

Finally, the family $\boldsymbol{R}_s$ is the smallest additive family containing the family $\boldsymbol{R}$, being the intersection of all the families with this property.

In order to define the family $\boldsymbol{R}_p$, we denote by $\mathcal{N}$ the totality of all multiplicative families $\boldsymbol{R}$ which satisfy the condition $\boldsymbol{Z} \subset \boldsymbol{R}$ and we set

$$\boldsymbol{R}_p = P(\mathcal{N}) . \tag{26}$$

The proof of the fact that the family $\boldsymbol{R}_p$ satisfies condition 2. is entirely analogous to the preceding proof.

We define the family $\boldsymbol{R}_c$ in a similar manner.

Remark. Denoting by $\boldsymbol{Z}$ the family of all the one-element subsets of the set A, we obtain as the family $\boldsymbol{R}_s$ the family of all finite subsets of the set A.

From this it follows that a necessary and sufficient condition that the set A be finite is that the family of all its non-empty subsets be identical with $\boldsymbol{R}_s$. This equivalence can serve as the definition of a finite set (which does not refer to the concept of natural number).

§ 7. Borel families

We say that the family $\boldsymbol{R}$ of sets is *countably additive* or *countably multiplicative* if the conditions $X_n \in \boldsymbol{R}$ for $n = 1, 2, \ldots$ imply that

$$\bigcup_{n=1}^{\infty} X_n \in \boldsymbol{R} , \quad \text{or} \quad \bigcap_{n=1}^{\infty} X_n \in \boldsymbol{R} , \text{ respectively.} \tag{27}$$

(These concepts play an important role in the theory of probability.)

We shall encounter a rather large number of examples of families of this sort in the second part of this book; e. g. the family of closed subsets of the space of real numbers is countably multiplicative (a closed set is a set which contains all its accumulation points); the family of its complements is countably additive. Note that the family of closed sets is not only countably multiplicative, it is *absolutely* multiplicative, i. e. the intersection of an arbitrary family of closed sets is closed (see Part II, Chapter XI, § 2).

A family of sets is said to be a *Borel family* if it is simultaneously countably additive and countably multiplicative.

The operations $\bigcup_{n=1}^{\infty}$ and $\bigcap_{n=1}^{\infty}$ therefore do not take us outside the Borel family.

The following theorem, analogous to the theorem of § 6, holds:

THEOREM. *To every family* $\boldsymbol{Z}$ *of subsets of the set* A *there exists*

1. *a smallest countably additive family* $\boldsymbol{R}_\sigma$ *such that* $\boldsymbol{Z} \subset \boldsymbol{R}_\sigma$,

2. *a smallest countably multiplicative family* $\boldsymbol{R}_\delta$ *such that* $\boldsymbol{Z} \subset \boldsymbol{R}_\delta$,

3. *a smallest Borel family* $\boldsymbol{R}_\beta$ *such that* $\boldsymbol{Z} \subset \boldsymbol{R}_\beta$.

In order to prove 1. let us consider the totality $\mathfrak{A}$ of all countably additive families $\boldsymbol{R}$ which satisfy the condition $\boldsymbol{Z} \subset \boldsymbol{R}$ (and consisting of subsets of the set A) and let us set $\boldsymbol{R}_\sigma = P(\mathfrak{A})$. In exactly the same way that we proved the theorem of § 6, we show that the family $\boldsymbol{R}_\sigma$ satisfies condition 1.

The families $\boldsymbol{R}_\delta$ and $\boldsymbol{R}_\beta$ are defined analogously.

Remarks. We also say that the family $\boldsymbol{R}_\beta$ is the Borel family *generated* by the family $\boldsymbol{Z}$. If $\boldsymbol{Z}$ is the family of all closed intervals then the sets belonging to $\boldsymbol{R}_\beta$ are called briefly the Borel subsets of the space of real numbers. It is worthy remarking that all the sets (contained in the space of real numbers) with which we have to deal in practice are Borel sets (cf. also Chapter XI, § 6).

§ 8. Generalized cartesian products

Let $A_1, A_2, \ldots, A_n, \ldots$ be a given infinite sequence of sets. By the *cartesian product* of these sets we understand the set of all infinite sequences of the form

$$(28) \quad a_1, a_2, \ldots, a_n, \ldots, \qquad \text{where} \quad a_n \in A_n \text{ for every } n.$$

We denote this set by the symbol

$$P_{n=1}^{\infty} A_n. \tag{29}$$

The product (29) when $A_n = \mathcal{E}$, i. e. when A_n is the set of real numbers for all n, is especially important in applications. We denote this product by the symbol $\mathcal{E}^{a}$; this is the natural extension of the concept of n-dimensional Euclidean space to an infinite number of dimensions.

Similarly, if $\mathcal{J}$ denotes the interval $0 \leqslant t \leqslant 1$, then $\mathcal{J}^{a}$, called the infinite dimensional cube, is the set of all infinite sequences with terms belonging to the interval $\mathcal{J}$.

We obtain further generalizations of the concept of cartesian product by considering, instead of sequences, sets of arbitrary functions whose values are sets. Let F be a function whose arguments run over the set $T(\neq \emptyset)$ and whose values are subsets of a fixed set X. Then the cartesian product

$$P_t F_t \tag{30}$$

is the set of all functions f such that $f(t) \in F_t$ (where $t \in T$). Thus we have

$$(f \in P_t F_t) \equiv \bigwedge_t [f(t) \in F_t].$$

As can be seen, when T is the set of all natural numbers, then the sets (30) and (29) are identical. It can also be easily shown that if $F_t = X$ for each $t \in T$, then $P_t F_t = X^T$.

Exercises

1. Prove the following formulas:

(a) $\bigcap_t (F_t \cap G_t) = \bigcap_t F_t \cap \bigcap_t G_t, \quad \bigcup_t (F_t \cup G_t) = \bigcup_t F_t \cup \bigcup_t G_t,$

(b) $\bigcap_t F_t \cup \bigcap_t G_t = \bigcap_{t,s} (F_t \cup G_s) \subset \bigcap_t (F_t \cup G_t),$

(c) $\bigcup_t (F_t \cap G_t) \subset \bigcup_{t,s} (F_t \cap G_s) = \bigcup_t F_t \cap \bigcup_t G_t,$

(d) $\bigcup_t (A \cup F_t) = A \cup \bigcap_t F_t, \quad \bigcup_t (A \cap F_t) = A \cap \bigcup_t F_t.$

Prove that the inclusion sign cannot be replaced by the equality sign in formulas (b) and (c).

2. Prove that if

$$A_1 \supset A_2 \supset \dots \supset A_n \supset \dots \quad \text{and} \quad B_1 \supset B_2 \supset \dots \supset B_n \supset \dots$$

then

$$\bigcap_{n=1}^{\infty} (A_n \cup B_n) = \bigcap_{n=1}^{\infty} A_n \cup \bigcap_{n=1}^{\infty} B_n .$$

3. Prove that

$$(\bigcup_t F_t) \times (\bigcup_t G_t) = \bigcup_{t,s} (F_t \times G_s),$$

$$(\bigcap_t F_t) \times (\bigcap_t G_t) = \bigcap_{t,s} (F_t \times G_s).$$

4. If $F_n \subset F_0$ for $n = 1, 2, \dots$, then

$$F_0 = (F_0 - F_1) \cup (F_1 - F_2) \cup (F_2 - F_3) \cup \dots \cup \bigcap_{n=0}^{\infty} F_n .$$

If $F_0 \supset F_1 \supset F_2 \supset \dots$, then

$$(F_1 - F_2) \cup (F_3 - F_4) \cup \dots \cup \bigcap_{n=0}^{\infty} F_n = F_0 - [(F_0 - F_1) \cup (F_2 - F_3) \cup \dots].$$

5. If $\bigcap_{n=1}^{\infty} A_n \cap \bigcap_{n=1}^{\infty} B_n = \emptyset$ and $B_0 = 1$, then

$$\bigcap_{n=1}^{\infty} A_n \subset \bigcup_{n=1}^{\infty} A_n \cap (B_{n-1} - B_n).$$

6. We define the *least upper bound* and the *greatest lower bound* of an infinite sequence of sets $F_1, F_2, \dots, F_n, \dots$ as follows:

$$\operatorname{Lim\,sup} F_n = \bigcap_{n=0}^{\infty} \bigcup_{k=0}^{\infty} F_{n+k}, \qquad \operatorname{Lim\,inf} F_n = \bigcup_{n=0}^{\infty} \bigcap_{k=0}^{\infty} F_{n+k}.$$

Prove the following formulas:

(a) $\operatorname{Lim\,inf} A_n^c = (\operatorname{Lim\,sup} A_n)^c$,

(b) $\operatorname{Lim\,inf} (A_n \cap B_n) = \operatorname{Lim\,inf} A_n \cap \operatorname{Lim\,inf} B_n$,

(c) $\operatorname{Lim\,sup} (A_n \cup B_n) = \operatorname{Lim\,sup} A_n \cup \operatorname{Lim\,sup} B_n$,

(d) $\bigcap_{n=1}^{\infty} A_n \subset \operatorname{Lim\,inf} A_n \subset \operatorname{Lim\,sup} A_n \subset \bigcup_{n=1}^{\infty} A_n$,

(e) $\operatorname{Lim\,inf} A_n \cup \operatorname{Lim\,inf} B_n \subset \operatorname{Lim\,inf} (A_n \cup B_n)$,

(f) $\operatorname{Lim\,sup} (A_n \cap B_n) \subset \operatorname{Lim\,sup} A_n \cap \operatorname{Lim\,sup} B_n$,

(g) $A \dot{-} \operatorname{Lim\,inf} A_n \subset \operatorname{Lim\,sup} (A \dot{-} A_n)$,

(h) $A \dot{-} \operatorname{Lim\,sup} A_n \subset \operatorname{Lim\,sup} (A \dot{-} A_n)$.

Show that the inclusion sign cannot be replaced by equality in the above formulas.

7. If $\operatorname{Lim\,sup} F_n = \operatorname{Lim\,inf} F_n$, then we say that the sequence $F_1, F_2, \dots$ *converges* to the limit

$$\operatorname{Lim} F_n = \operatorname{Lim\,sup} F_n = \operatorname{Lim\,inf} F_n .$$

Prove that

(a) if $F_1 \subset F_2 \subset \dots$, then $\bigcup_{n=1}^{\infty} F_n = \operatorname{Lim} F_n$,

(b) if $F_1 \supset F_2 \supset \dots$, then $\bigcap_{n=1}^{\infty} F_n = \operatorname{Lim} F_n$.

8. Define the *characteristic function* f_A of the set A by the conditions

$$f_A(x) = \begin{cases} 1 & \text{if} \quad x \in A, \\ 0 & \text{if} \quad x \in A^c, \end{cases}$$

and prove the equivalence

$$(F = \mathrm{Lim}F_n) \equiv \big(f_F(x) = \lim f_{F_n}(x)\big) .$$

9. Prove the formulas:

(a) $f(A_1) - f(A_2) \subset f(A_1 - A_2)$,
(b) $f[A \cap f^{-1}(B)] = f(A) \cap B$,
(c) if $A_1 \subset A_2$, then $f(A_1) \subset f(A_2)$,
(d) if $B_1 \subset B_2$, then $f^{-1}(B_1) \subset f^{-1}(B_2)$.

10. Let $g = f|A$ (cf. Chapter IV, § 4). Prove that

$$g^{-1}(B) = A \cap f^{-1}(B) .$$

11. Use the axiom of choice to prove that

(a) $\bigwedge_x \bigvee_y \varphi(x, y) \equiv \bigvee_f \bigwedge_x \varphi(x, f(x))$,
(b) $\bigcup_y \bigcap_x F_{x,y} \subset \bigcap_x \bigcup_y F_{x,y}$,
(c) if the conditions $x \neq x_1$ and $y \neq y_1$ imply that

$$F_{x,y} \cap F_{x_1,y_1} = \emptyset ,$$

then

$$\bigcup_y \bigcap_x F_{x,y} = \bigcap_x \bigcup_y F_{x,y} .$$

12. $\boldsymbol{R}$ being a family of sets, we denote by $\boldsymbol{R}_\varrho$ the family of all sets of the form $Z = X - Y$, where $X, Y \in \boldsymbol{R}$. Prove that $\boldsymbol{R}_\varrho \subset \boldsymbol{R}_{\varrho\varrho}$, and show by an example that the reverse inclusion can be false.

13. Prove that

$$S(\boldsymbol{R}_1 \cup \boldsymbol{R}_2) = S(\boldsymbol{R}_1) \cup S(\boldsymbol{R}_2), \qquad S(\boldsymbol{R}_1 \cap \boldsymbol{R}_2) \subset S(\boldsymbol{R}_1) \cap S(\boldsymbol{R}_2) .$$

Prove that if the elements of $\boldsymbol{R}_1 \cup \boldsymbol{R}_2$ are disjoint sets, then

$$S(\boldsymbol{R}_1 \cap \boldsymbol{R}_2) = S(\boldsymbol{R}_1) \cap S(\boldsymbol{R}_2) .$$

14. Prove that if $\boldsymbol{R}_1 \cap \boldsymbol{R}_2 \neq \emptyset$, then

$$P(\boldsymbol{R}_1) \cap P(\boldsymbol{R}_2) \subset P(\boldsymbol{R}_1 \cap \boldsymbol{R}_2) .$$

CHAPTER V

THE CONCEPT OF THE POWER OF A SET. COUNTABLE SETS

§ 1. One-to-one functions

A function f is said to be *one-to-one* if to distinct values of the argument there correspond distinct values of the function, i. e. if

$$(1) \qquad (x_1 \neq x_2) \Rightarrow [f(x_1) \neq f(x_2)]$$

or, equivalently, if

$$(2) \qquad [f(x_1) = f(x_2)] \Rightarrow (x_1 = x_2) .$$

For example, the function x^3 is one-to-one (in the domain of reals) but the function x^2 is not one-to-one.

Let X be the set of arguments of the function f and let Y be the set of its values. Then the function f is one-to-one if it forms a set of pairs $\langle x, y\rangle$ such that every element $x \in X$ is the predecessor and every $y \in Y$ is the successor of one and only one of these pairs.

Still another way of stating this is: the function f is one-to-one if for every $y \in f(X)$ the set $f^{-1}(y)$ reduces to one element x (such that $y = f(x)$). In this case we usually use the symbol $f^{-1}(y)$ to denote x (and not the set $\{x\}$) and we call the function f^{-1} of the variable y the *inverse function* of the given function f; Y is the set of its arguments and X is its set of values (or range).

Obviously

$$(3) \qquad [y = f(x)] \equiv [x = f^{-1}(y)] .$$

THEOREM 1. *The inverse of a one-to-one function is a one-to-one function.*

For

$$(4) \qquad (f^{-1})^{-1} = f .$$

Geometrically, the transition to the inverse function can be interpreted (in the case where X and Y each denote the set of real numbers) as the reflection of the graph of the function with respect to the line $y = x$.

THEOREM 2. *The composition of two one-to-one functions is a one-to-one function.*

In other words, if f is a one-to-one mapping of the set X onto the set Y and g is a one-to-one mapping of the set Y onto the set Z, then the function h defined by the condition $h(x) = g(f(x))$ is one-to-one also.

For, if $h(x_1) = h(x_2)$, then $g(f(x_1)) = g(f(x_2))$, whence it follows that $f(x_1) = f(x_2)$, and consequently $x_1 = x_2$.

Under the assumption that the function f is one-to-one, formulas (15) and (19) (Chapter IV, § 4) may be simplified: we can replace them namely by the formulas

(5) $$f(A_1 \cap A_2) = f(A_1) \cap f(A_2)$$

and more generally $$f(\bigcap_t F_t) = \bigcap_t f(F_t),$$

(6) $$A = f^{-1}f(A).$$

In the case where f is one-to-one, we have besides the equivalence (13) of Chapter IV, § 4, the symmetric equivalence

(7) $$[x \in A] \equiv [f(x) \in f(A)].$$

§ 2. Sets having the same power

Two sets X and Y are said *to have the same power* if there exists a one-to-one mapping of the set X onto Y.

If the set X is a finite set: $X = (a_1, \ldots, a_n)$, then the set Y has the same power as X if and only if it has the same number n of elements. The concept of sets having the same power therefore coincides, in the case of finite sets, with the elementary concept of having the same number of elements; this concept can however be applied also to infinite sets.

For example, the set of all odd natural numbers has the same power as the set of all even natural numbers; in fact, the function $f(n) = n+1$ establishes a one-to-one mapping of the set $(1, 3, 5, \ldots)$ onto the set $(2, 4, 6, \ldots)$.

Similarly, the set of all natural numbers is of the same power as the set of all even numbers (which shows that an infinite set can have the same power as a proper subset of itself!). Here the corresponding function is the function $f(n) = 2n$.

Two intervals $a < x < b$ and $c < x < d$ are of equal power, as is easily shown using a linear mapping. The open interval $-\pi/2 < x < +\pi/2$ has the same power as the set of all real numbers; the corresponding mapping is $y = \tan x$.

Next, we shall show that the set of all natural numbers has not the same power as the set of all real numbers; it will follow from this that, in the domain of infinite sets, there exist sets of different powers, and—as we shall show—there even exists an infinite number of infinite sets of which no two have the same power.

We write

$$\overline{\overline{X}} = \overline{\overline{Y}}$$

to express the fact that the sets X and Y have the same power.

This notation is based on the following theorem:

THEOREM 3. *The power relation is reflexive, symmetric and transitive*; *i. e.*

$$(8) \qquad \overline{\overline{X}} = \overline{\overline{X}},$$

$$(9) \qquad \textit{if } \overline{\overline{X}} = \overline{\overline{Y}}, \textit{ then } \overline{\overline{Y}} = \overline{\overline{X}},$$

$$(10) \qquad \textit{if } \overline{\overline{X}} = \overline{\overline{Y}} \textit{ and } \overline{\overline{Y}} = \overline{\overline{Z}}, \textit{ then } \overline{\overline{X}} = \overline{\overline{Z}}.$$

Proof. Formula (8) follows from the fact that the identity, i. e. the function $f(x) = x$, is a one-to-one mapping of the set X onto itself. Formulas (9) and (10) follow from Theorems 1 and 2, respectively.

Theorem 3 permits the classification of sets with

respect to their "power". This leads to the extension to infinite sets of the elementary concept of the number of elements in a set. Namely, to each set X we assign a *cardinal number*, or its power, which we denote by the symbol $\overline{\overline{X}}$, in such a way that the same cardinal number is assigned to two distinct sets if and only if these sets have the same power. (Cardinal numbers play an auxiliary role in the theory of sets, inasmuch as all the theorems of set theory can be formulated without using them. However, by making use of them many theorems gain in lucidity and we are able better to display the analogy with theorems of arithmetic.)

The cardinal number of a finite set is the number of its elements.

§ 3. Countable sets

A set A is said to be an *infinitely countable* set if it has the same power as the set of all natural numbers; in other words, if its elements can be arranged in an infinite sequence of distinct terms.

Finite sets are called countable sets as well.

Hence we can say that *a nonvoid set is countable if its elements can be arranged in an infinite sequence* (which may have repetitions). For, if the infinite sequence contains an infinite number of distinct terms, then there exists a subsequence which contains each of these terms precisely once.

As we saw above, the set of even natural numbers (and similarly the set of odd natural numbers) is countable.

THEOREM 1. *The set of all real numbers is noncountable.*

To prove this theorem it obviously suffices to show that for every sequence of real numbers $a_1, a_2, \ldots, a_n, \ldots$ we can define a real number c which does not belong to this sequence.

To this end, we define a sequence of closed intervals $p_1q_1, p_2q_2, \ldots, p_nq_n, \ldots$ which are such that

$$q_n - p_n = 1/3^n, \quad p_nq_n \subset p_{n-1}q_{n-1}, \quad a_n \notin p_nq_n.$$

Thus, in the closed interval $[0, 1]$ we determine the closed interval p_1q_1 which does not contain the point a_1 [this will be one of the three intervals $(0, 1/3)$ or $(1/3, 2/3)$ or $(2/3, 1)$]. Similarly, in the interval p_1q_1 we determine a closed interval p_2q_2 of length $1/9$ which does not contain the point a_2. In general, in the closed interval $p_{n-1}q_{n-1}$ we determine a closed interval p_nq_n of length $1/3^n$ which does not contain the point a_n.

Let c be the common point of all the closed intervals p_nq_n:

$$\{c\} = \bigcap_{n=1}^{\infty} p_nq_n\,, \quad \text{i. e.} \quad c = \lim_{n\to\infty} p_n = \lim_{n\to\infty} q_n\,.$$

Obviously, $c \neq a_n$ for every n since $a_n \notin p_nq_n$ whereas $c \in p_nq_n$.

We shall now list several important properties of countable sets.

THEOREM 2. *The union $A \cup B$ of the countable sets A and B is countable.*

In fact, under the assumption that the elements of the set A can be written in the form of an infinite sequence $a_1, a_2, \ldots, a_n, \ldots$, and the elements of the set B in the form of a sequence $b_1, b_2, \ldots, b_n, \ldots$, we consider the sequence

$$a_1, b_1, a_2, b_2, \ldots, a_n, b_n, \ldots \tag{11}$$

The terms of this sequence obviously form the set $A \cup B$.

It follows from this that *the set of all integers is countable.* For the set of all positive integers as well as the set of all nonpositive integers is countable.

THEOREM 3. *The cartesian product of two (or, more generally, of a finite number) of countable sets is a countable set.*

Proof. We shall prove that the set of pairs $\langle m, n\rangle$, where m and n are natural numbers, is countable. Hence we have to represent this set as a sequence. To this end, we adopt the following rule: of two pairs $\langle m, n\rangle$ and $\langle m', n'\rangle$ we consider that one to be the earlier whose sum of elements is smaller; but if $m+n = m'+n'$, then the earlier pair is the one with the smaller antecedent. And therefore this sequence can be represented as follows:

$$(12)\qquad \langle 1,1\rangle, \langle 1,2\rangle, \langle 2,1\rangle, \langle 1,3\rangle, \langle 2,2\rangle, \langle 3,1\rangle, \ldots$$

From this we already easily deduce, that having given two arbitrary infinite sequences $a_1, a_2, \ldots, a_m, \ldots$ and $b_1, b_2, \ldots, b_n, \ldots$, we can write the sequence of all pairs $\langle a_m, b_n\rangle$ in the form of an infinite sequence.

The generalization from two to an arbitrary finite number of countable sets presents no trouble.

If follows from Theorem 3 that *the set of all rational numbers is countable.*

For, every positive rational number can be represented as a pair of numbers p/q (in the irreducible form), i. e. the set of positive rational numbers can be represented as a subsequence of the sequence (12). The set of positive rational numbers is therefore countable. The same is true of the set of negative rational numbers together with the number zero. Therefore, according to Theorem 2, the set of all rational numbers is countable.

From Theorem 3 it also follows that every double sequence $\{a_{mn}\}$ can be transformed into a simple sequence, i. e. it is possible to write down the elements of the array

$$(13)\qquad \begin{array}{l} a_{11}, a_{12}, \ldots, a_{1n}, \ldots \\ a_{21}, a_{22}, \ldots, a_{2n}, \ldots \\ \ldots\ldots\ldots\ldots\ldots \\ a_{m1}, a_{m2}, \ldots, a_{mn}, \ldots \\ \ldots\ldots\ldots\ldots\ldots \end{array}$$

in the form of the infinite sequence

$$(14)\qquad a_{11}, a_{12}, a_{21}, a_{13}, \ldots$$

From this we deduce the following theorem:

THEOREM 4. *The union* $S = A_1 \cup A_2 \cup \ldots \cup A_m \cup \ldots$ *of a countable sequence of countable sets is countable.*

Proof. We write each of the sets A_m in the form of a sequence $a_{m1}, a_{m2}, \ldots, a_{mn}, \ldots$, and then we transform the double sequence $\{a_{mn}\}$ into the simple sequence (14) (perhaps with repetitions). [Here we apply the axiom of choice (Chapter III, § 7), for the set of sequences consisting of the elements of the set A_m contains more than one element (and none of them in general can be distinguished).]

THEOREM 5. *The set of all finite sequences with terms belonging to a given countable set is countable.*

For this set can be represented in the form of a union $A_1 \cup A_2 \cup \ldots \cup A_m \cup \ldots$, where A_m is the set of sequences with m elements. And the countability of the set A_m follows from Theorem 3.

From this we deduce that the *set of all polynomials with rational coefficients is countable.*

For every polynomial is determined by its coefficients, i. e. the polynomial $a_0 + a_1 x + \ldots + a_m x^m$ is determined by the sequence consisting of $m+1$ rational numbers $a_0, a_1, \ldots, a_m$.

COROLLARY. *The set of all algebraic numbers is countable.*

In fact, the set of all polynomials with rational coefficients is countable and hence we can write it in the form of an infinite sequence $w_1, w_2, \ldots, w_m, \ldots$ Let A_m denote the set of roots of the equation $w_m(x) = 0$; this set, as is known, is finite (the number of its elements does not exceed the degree of the polynomial w_m). By virtue of Theorem 4, the set $A_1 \cup A_2 \cup \ldots \cup A_m \cup \ldots$, i. e. the set of all algebraic numbers is therefore countable.

Remark. This last result together with Theorem 1 leads to the result that transcendental (i. e. nonalgebraic) numbers exist, and even that there is a noncountable number of them (for the union of two countable sets is countable). Making use of the methods given here, one could even define a transcendental number; namely, to this end we set down all real algebraic numbers in the form of an infinite sequence and then apply the method used in the proof of Theorem 1, which determines a real number not belonging to this sequence.

We recall that the numbers e and π are proved to be transcendental numbers—by entirely different means.

Exercises

1. Consider the transformation of the plane into itself given by the system of equations

$$x = au + bv\,, \qquad y = cu + dv\,.$$

Give the conditions on the coefficients a, b, c, d under which this transformation is one-to-one.

2. Is the homographic transformation of the Gaussian plane (i. e. the plane of complex numbers together with the point at infinity)

$$w = (az + b)/(cz + d)$$

one-to-one?

3. Suppose $u_1, u_2, \ldots, u_n, \ldots$ is a given sequence of real numbers. Let

$$u_n = c_{n0} \cdot c_{n1} c_{n2} c_{n3} \ldots$$

be the decimal expansion of the number u_n containing an infinite number of digits different from 9.

We define the number $l = 0 \cdot e_1 e_2 e_3 \ldots$ in the following way: $e_n = 0$ if $c_{nn} \neq 0$, $e_n = 1$ if $c_{nn} = 0$. Prove that the number l is not a term of the sequence $u_1, u_2, \ldots$, and deduce from this Theorem 1, § 3.

4. Prove that the set of all intervals (in the set of real numbers) with both endpoints rational is countable.

5. We say that a function f (with real arguments and values) has a proper maximum at the point a if there exists an interval bc containing the point a in its interior such that the conditions $b < x < c$ and $x \neq a$ imply the inequality $f(x) < f(a)$. Prove that the set of proper maxima of the function f is countable.

Hint: Give the points b and c rational values.

6. Prove that every family of disjoint intervals is countable.

Hint: Make use of the countability of the set of rational numbers.

7. Prove that the set of points of discontinuity of a monotonic function is countable.

Hint: A monotonic function has at every point a left and right limit (which are different at points of discontinuity). Then make use of Exercise 6.

8. Prove that the set of spheres (in 3-dimensional space) which have both rational radii and rational coordinates of the center is countable.

9. A relation $x\varrho y$ is called an *equivalence relation* if it is reflexive, symmetric and transitive, i. e. if

$$x\varrho x, \qquad (x\varrho y) \Rightarrow (y\varrho x), \qquad (x\varrho y) \wedge (y\varrho z) \Rightarrow (x\varrho z).$$

Let X be a given set and ϱ an equivalence relation whose variables range over X. Given an element x_0 of X, the set $E_x(x\varrho x_0)$ is called an *equivalence set*; the family of equivalence sets is called the *quotient* X/ϱ. Show that the elements of X/ϱ are disjoint and that X is their union.

CHAPTER VI

OPERATIONS ON CARDINAL NUMBERS. THE NUMBERS $\mathfrak{a}$ AND $\mathfrak{c}$

We denote the power of the set of natural numbers by $\mathfrak{a}$ and the power of the set of real numbers (the power of the „continuum") by $\mathfrak{c}$.

The numbers $\mathfrak{a}$ and $\mathfrak{c}$ are the most important of the infinite cardinal numbers which occur in analysis and geometry. So far, we know (Chapter V, § 3, Theorem 1) that

$$(1) \qquad \mathfrak{a} \neq \mathfrak{c}.$$

The operations on arbitrary cardinal numbers which we shall now define will interest us primarily in relation to the numbers $\mathfrak{a}$ and $\mathfrak{c}$.

§ 1. Addition and multiplication

The *sum* $\mathfrak{m}+\mathfrak{n}$ of two cardinal numbers $\mathfrak{m}, \mathfrak{n}$ is defined to be the power of the union of two disjoint sets which have the powers $\mathfrak{m}$ and $\mathfrak{n}$ respectively.

We therefore have

$$(2) \qquad \overline{\overline{X}}+\overline{\overline{Y}}=\overline{\overline{X \cup Y}}, \quad \text{if} \quad X \cap Y = \emptyset .$$

We note that for every pair of sets X and Y there exists a pair of disjoint sets X_1 and Y_1 such that $\overline{\overline{X_1}} = \overline{\overline{X}}$ and $\overline{\overline{Y_1}} = \overline{\overline{Y}}$. For, denoting any two distinct elements by a and b, it suffices to set $X_1 = \{a\} \times X$ and $Y_1 = \{b\} \times Y$.

Keeping this remark in mind, we can assert that for every two cardinal numbers their sum is defined uniquely (i. e. independently of the choice of the sets X and Y).

We define the *product* $\mathfrak{m} \cdot \mathfrak{n}$ of $\mathfrak{m}$ and $\mathfrak{n}$ to be the power of the cartesian product of two sets having powers $\mathfrak{m}$ and $\mathfrak{n}$ respectively, i. e.

$$(3) \qquad \overline{\overline{X}} \cdot \overline{\overline{Y}} = \overline{\overline{X \times Y}} .$$

Thus, the product of cardinal numbers is uniquely defined.

It can easily be verified that the above definitions, in the case where $\mathfrak{m}$ and $\mathfrak{n}$ denote natural numbers, are in agreement with the usual definitions of addition and multiplication in arithmetic. We deduce from Theorems 2 and 3 (Chapter V, § 3) that

$$(4) \qquad \mathfrak{a}+\mathfrak{a}=\mathfrak{a}, \quad \mathfrak{a}\cdot\mathfrak{a}=\mathfrak{a}, \quad \mathfrak{a}+n=\mathfrak{a}, \quad \mathfrak{a}\cdot n=\mathfrak{a},$$

where n is a natural number.

Multiplication and addition satisfy the associative and commutative laws. The distributive law is also satisfied:

$$(5) \qquad \mathfrak{m}\cdot(\mathfrak{n}+\mathfrak{p})=\mathfrak{m}\cdot\mathfrak{n}+\mathfrak{m}\cdot\mathfrak{p}.$$

For, let $\mathfrak{m}=\overline{\overline{X}}$, $\mathfrak{n}=\overline{\overline{Y}}$ and $\mathfrak{p}=\overline{\overline{Z}}$ where $Y\cap Z=\emptyset$. Then (cf. Chapter III, § 4 (18) and (21)):

$$X\times(Y\cup Z)=X\times Y\cup X\times Z,$$
$$(X\times Y)\cap(X\times Z)=X\times(Y\cap Z)=\emptyset,$$

and therefore $\overline{\overline{X\times(Y\cup Z)}}=\overline{\overline{X\times Y}}+\overline{\overline{X\times Z}}$, which was to be proved.

It follows from this (by induction) that

$$(6) \qquad \mathfrak{m}\cdot n=\mathfrak{m}+\mathfrak{m}+\ldots+\mathfrak{m},$$

where the right member has n terms.

For formula (6) is obvious for $n=1$, and by virtue of (5):

$$\mathfrak{m}\cdot(n+1)=\mathfrak{m}\cdot n+\mathfrak{m}\cdot 1=\mathfrak{m}\cdot n+\mathfrak{m}.$$

Equation (6) asserts that $\mathfrak{m}\cdot n$ is the power of the union of n disjoint sets each of which is of power $\mathfrak{m}$. This theorem can be generalized to the sum of an infinite number of terms as follows.

Let $\overline{\overline{T}}=\mathfrak{n}$ and let F be a function whose arguments run over the set T and whose values are disjoint sets of power $\mathfrak{m}$, that is,

$$(7) \qquad \overline{\overline{F_t}}=\mathfrak{m}, \quad F_t\cap F_{t'}=\emptyset \ \textit{for}\ t\neq t',$$

then

(8) $$\overline{\overline{\bigcup_t F_t}} = \mathfrak{m} \cdot \mathfrak{n}.$$

In fact, let t_0 be a fixed element of the set T and let g_t be a one-to-one mapping of F_{t_0} onto F_t (we apply the axiom of choice here). Let us set

(9) $$f(x, t) = g_t(x), \quad \text{where} \quad x \in F_{t_0} \text{ and } t \in T.$$

The function f is a one-to-one mapping of the cartesian product $F_{t_0} \times T$ onto the union $\bigcup_t F_t$. For let

(10) $$f(x, t) = f(x', t'), \quad \text{i. e.} \quad g_t(x) = g_{t'}(x').$$

If $t \neq t'$, then $g_t(x) \neq g_{t'}(x')$, since $g_t(x) \in F_t$, $g_{t'}(x') \in F_{t'}$, and $F_t \cap F_{t'} = \emptyset$.

Thus $t = t'$. If $x \neq x'$, then $g_t(x) \neq g_{t'}(x')$, because the function g_t is one-to-one.

Therefore, equality (10) implies that $t = t'$ and $x = x'$.

We have thus proved that the sets $F_{t_0} \times T$ and $\bigcup_t F_t$ have the same power. This means that formula (8) is satisfied.

§ 2. Exponentiation

Let $\overline{\overline{X}} = \mathfrak{m}$ and $\overline{\overline{Y}} = \mathfrak{n}$. The cardinal number $\mathfrak{n}^{\mathfrak{m}}$ is defined to be the power of the set, which we denoted by Y^X, of all functions whose arguments run over the set X and whose values belong to the set Y, i. e.

$$\overline{\overline{Y}}^{\overline{\overline{X}}} = \overline{\overline{Y^X}}.$$

The following formulas, known from the arithmetic of natural numbers, are valid:

(11) $$\mathfrak{n}^{\mathfrak{m}+\mathfrak{p}} = \mathfrak{n}^{\mathfrak{m}} \cdot \mathfrak{n}^{\mathfrak{p}},$$

(12) $$(\mathfrak{m}\mathfrak{n})^{\mathfrak{p}} = \mathfrak{m}^{\mathfrak{p}} \cdot \mathfrak{n}^{\mathfrak{p}},$$

(13) $$(\mathfrak{n}^{\mathfrak{m}})^{\mathfrak{p}} = \mathfrak{n}^{\mathfrak{m}\mathfrak{p}}.$$

In fact, let $\mathfrak{m} = \overline{\overline{X}}$, $\mathfrak{n} = \overline{\overline{Y}}$ and $\mathfrak{p} = \overline{\overline{T}}$.

In order to prove formula (11), we must prove that

(14) $$\overline{\overline{Y^{X \cup T}}} = \overline{\overline{Y^X \times Y^T}} \quad \text{provided} \quad X \cap T = \emptyset.$$

Hence, let $f \in Y^{X \cup T}$. Denoting by $f|X$ the restricted function which we obtain from f by restricting the variation of its argument to the set X and giving an analogous meaning to the symbol $f|T$ (cf. Chapter IV, § 4), we assign to the function f the pair of functions $\langle f|X, f|T\rangle$. This correspondence, as can easily be verified, establishes a one-to-one correspondence between the elements of the sets $Y^{X \cup T}$ and $Y^X \times Y^T$. Thus formula (14) is proved.

Formula (12) means that

$$(15) \qquad \overline{\overline{(X \times Y)^T}} = \overline{\overline{X^T \times Y^T}}.$$

Let $f \in (X \times Y)^T$. Hence the values of the function f are ordered pairs belonging to $X \times Y$; we can therefore write

$$f(t) = \langle g(t), h(t)\rangle, \quad \text{where} \quad g(t) \in X \text{ and } h(t) \in Y.$$

And therefore $g \in X^T$ and $h \in Y^T$. We have thus assigned to the function f a pair of functions $\langle g, h\rangle$, i. e. an element of the set $X^T \times Y^T$. It is easy to verify that this correspondence is one-to-one. This yields equality (15).

In order to prove (13) we have to show that

$$(16) \qquad \overline{\overline{(Y^X)^T}} = \overline{\overline{Y^{X \times T}}}.$$

Hence let $f \in Y^{X \times T}$. The function f is a function which assigns to every pair $\langle x, t\rangle$ the element $f(x, t)$ of the set Y. For a fixed t we obtain a function g_t of the variable x defined by means of the formula

$$g_t(x) = f(x, t),$$

i. e. $g_t \in Y^X$, for every value of the variable t. We have thus defined a function—let us denote it by g—which assigns to elements of the set T elements of the set Y^X, i. e. $g \in (Y^X)^T$.

To every function f belonging to the set $Y^{X \times T}$ we have therefore assigned some function g belonging to the set $(Y^X)^T$. It is easy to prove that this correspondence is one-to-one.

Let us now consider certain particular cases.

It is almost obvious that

$$\mathfrak{n}^1 = \mathfrak{n} \tag{17}$$

(in this case the set of arguments reduces to a single element).

Let m be a natural number. By (11) and (17) we have

$$\mathfrak{n}^{m+1} = \mathfrak{n}^m \cdot \mathfrak{n}^1 = \mathfrak{n}^m \cdot \mathfrak{n}\,.$$

And therefore (by induction)

$$\mathfrak{n}^m = \mathfrak{n} \cdot \mathfrak{n} \cdot \ldots \cdot \mathfrak{n}\,, \tag{18}$$

where the right hand member has m factors.

It also follows from this that the definition of exponentiation of cardinal numbers which we assumed coincides with the arithmetic definition when these numbers are finite ($\mathfrak{m} = m$, $\mathfrak{n} = n$).

Let us now assume that $\mathfrak{n} = 2$. Hence let $\overline{\overline{X}} = \mathfrak{m}$, and $Y = \{0, 1\}$ (i. e. Y is the set consisting of two numbers: 0 and 1). Hence the set Y^X is the set of functions defined on the set X and assuming only two values 0 and 1 (or only one of them). We call such functions *characteristic* functions (see Chapter IV, exercise 8); namely, a function satisfying the condition

$$f(x) = \begin{cases} 1 & \text{for} \quad x \in A\,, \\ 0 & \text{for} \quad x \in X - A \end{cases} \tag{19}$$

is the characteristic function of the set A.

The set $\{0, 1\}^X$ *and the set of all subsets of the set* X *are of equal power, namely of the power* $2^{\mathfrak{m}}$, *where* $\mathfrak{m} = \overline{\overline{X}}$.

Proof. Assign to the set $A \subset X$ its characteristic function f_A. This correspondence is one-to-one. For let $A \neq B$ and let $a \in A - B$. Hence we have $f_A(a) = 1$ but $f_B(a) = 0$ and therefore $f_A \neq f_B$. Here every characteristic function has been assigned to some subset of the set X.

We shall now prove the following theorem:

CANTOR THEOREM. $2^{\mathfrak{m}} \neq \mathfrak{m}$; in other words, *no set X has power equal to that of the family of all its subsets.*

Proof. It suffices to show that if F is a function whose arguments run over the set X and whose values are subsets of the set X, then there exists a set $Z \subset X$ which is not a value of this function. (This is the so-called *diagonal theorem.*) The Cantor theorem will follow from this because if the set X were of power equal to that of the family of all its subsets, then there would exist a (one-to-one) function F whose arguments would run over the set X and which would take on as values all the subsets of the set X.

Define the set Z as follows:

(20) $$Z = E_x[x \notin F(x)].$$

We have to show that $Z \neq F(x)$ for every $x \in X$. Let us assume on the contrary that $Z = F(x_0)$. Then by virtue of (20) the following equivalence holds:

$$(x \in Z) \equiv [x \notin F(x)].$$

Setting $x = x_0$ in this equivalence, we obtain

$$(x_0 \in Z) \equiv [x_0 \notin F(x_0)],$$

and therefore $Z \neq F(x_0)$. We have thus arrived at a contradiction.

Remarks. 1. The diagonal theorem can be illustrated geometrically as follows. Let X be the closed interval $0 \leqslant x \leqslant 1$. We place the set $F(x)$, which by assumption is a subset of this interval, on the vertical line passing through the point x. In this way we obtain a planar set $M = E_{x,y}[y \in F(x)]$ contained in the square $X \times X$. Let P denote the diagonal of this square. Thus, the set Z is the projection of the set $P - M$ onto the X-axis.

2*. The proof of the Cantor theorem given above permits us to verify easily that the family of all subsets of the set X is not of the same power as that of any of the subsets of this set.

It follows from this immediately that *there does not exist a set of all sets* (for the family of its subsets would itself be one of its subsets).

This same conclusion follows, after all, immediately from the theorem on the diagonal. For, if there existed a set X whose elements were all sets then the function F defined by the condition $F(x) = x$ (i. e. the identity) would obviously assume as values all subsets of the set X (since these subsets would be elements of the set X).

Let us add that from the (false) assumption that there exist the set of all sets follows the existence of

$$Z = \underset{x}{E}(x \notin x) .$$

However, the existence of the set Z leads immediately to a contradiction (so-called Russell antinomy) because $x \in Z \equiv x \notin x$, and therefore $Z \in Z \equiv Z \notin Z$.

The theorem on the non-existence of the set of all sets was deduced by us from the axioms given in Chapter III, § 7. The assumption, that for a given set A, the propositional function $\varphi(x)$ (with unbounded domain of variation for x) determines the set $\underset{x}{E}\varphi(x) \wedge (x \in A)$ plays an essential role in the formulation of axiom V. Omitting the expression $x \in A$ would lead to a contradiction. For, taking as $\varphi(x)$ the propositional function "x is a set", we should obtain as an immediate consequence the existence of the set of all sets which—as we saw—leads to a contradiction.

Let us note that in the period before the axiomatization of set theory, and hence in the period of "naive" set theory, it was common to assume as obvious the existence for every propositional function $\varphi(x)$ of the set $\underset{x}{E}\varphi(x)$. This has led to the contradictions which we already mentioned above (which were then called antinomies of set theory), and which have necessitated revising the foundations of set theory. Consequently there arose an axiomatic theory of sets (in 1904) which eliminated these antinomies.

§ 3. Inequalities for cardinal numbers

Let $\overline{\overline{X}} = \mathfrak{m}$ and $\overline{\overline{Y}} = \mathfrak{n}$. Let us assume that $\mathfrak{m} \leqslant \mathfrak{n}$ if the set X has the same power as some subset of the set Y. Therefore

$$(X \subset Y) \Rightarrow (\overline{\overline{X}} \leqslant \overline{\overline{Y}}).$$

If $\mathfrak{m} \leqslant \mathfrak{n}$ and $\mathfrak{m} \neq \mathfrak{n}$, then we write $\mathfrak{m} < \mathfrak{n}$.

By virtue of (1) we have

(21) $$\mathfrak{a} < \mathfrak{c}.$$

We can state the Cantor theorem (§ 2) in the form

(22) $$\mathfrak{m} < 2^{\mathfrak{m}}.$$

In fact, $\mathfrak{m} \neq 2^{\mathfrak{m}}$, and at the same time $\mathfrak{m} \leqslant 2^{\mathfrak{m}}$, since the set X has the same power as the family of all its one-element subsets.

It is easy to prove the following formulas:

(23) if $\mathfrak{m} \leqslant \mathfrak{n}$ and $\mathfrak{n} \leqslant \mathfrak{p}$ then $\mathfrak{m} \leqslant \mathfrak{p}$,

(24) if $\mathfrak{m} \leqslant \mathfrak{n}$ then $\mathfrak{m}+\mathfrak{p} \leqslant \mathfrak{n}+\mathfrak{p}$,

(25) if $\mathfrak{m} \leqslant \mathfrak{n}$ then $\mathfrak{m}\mathfrak{p} \leqslant \mathfrak{n}\mathfrak{p}$,

(26) if $\mathfrak{m} \leqslant \mathfrak{n}$ then $\mathfrak{m}^{\mathfrak{p}} \leqslant \mathfrak{n}^{\mathfrak{p}}$,

(27) if $\mathfrak{m} \leqslant \mathfrak{n}$ then $\mathfrak{p}^{\mathfrak{m}} \leqslant \mathfrak{p}^{\mathfrak{n}}$.

We shall now prove the fundamental *Cantor-Bernstein theorem*:

(28) *if* $\mathfrak{m} \leqslant \mathfrak{n}$ *and* $\mathfrak{n} \leqslant \mathfrak{m}$ *then* $\mathfrak{m} = \mathfrak{n}$.

Proof. (We shall make use of some simplifications which were recently given by M. Reichbach in this proof.) Let $\overline{\overline{X}} = \mathfrak{m}$. Since $\mathfrak{n} \leqslant \mathfrak{m}$, the set X contains a subset Y of power $\mathfrak{n}$. But since $\mathfrak{m} \leqslant \mathfrak{n}$, the set X is of power equal to that of some subset of the set Y; i. e. there exists a one-to-one function f defined on X and such that

(29) $$f(X) \subset Y \subset X.$$

We have to define a one-to-one mapping of X onto Y.

Let us set

(30) $$Z = Y - f(X), \qquad S = Z \cup f(Z) \cup ff(Z) \cup \ldots$$

(see Fig. 4 in which X is the largest rectangle, Y is the second in size, $f(X)$ is the third, and so on; $X-S$ is the shaded part).

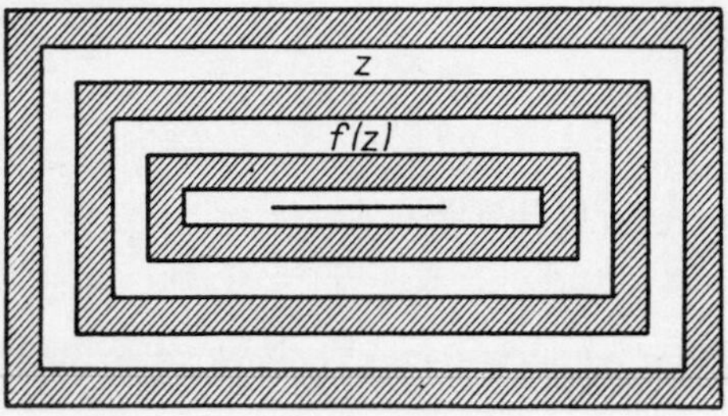

FIG. 4

We define the function g as follows:

$$g(x) = \begin{cases} x & \text{for} \quad x \in S, \\ f(x) & \text{for} \quad x \in X - S. \end{cases} \tag{31}$$

We shall first prove that the following equality holds:

$$g(X) = Y. \tag{32}$$

Since $S \subset X$,

$$X = S \cup (X-S). \tag{33}$$

And therefore

$$g(X) = g(S) \cup g(X-S) = S \cup f(X-S) \tag{34}$$

by virtue of (31). At the same time (because of (30) and Chapter IV, § 4 (14)):

$$f(S) = f(Z) \cup ff(Z) \cup fff(Z) \cup \ldots,$$

and hence applying to (30):

$$S = Z \cup f(S). \tag{35}$$

From this and (34) and (33), we obtain the equalities

$$g(X) = S \cup f(X-S) = Z \cup f(S) \cup f(X-S) = Z \cup f(X),$$

but taking (30) into consideration we have

$$Z \cup f(X) = [Y - f(X)] \cup f(X) = Y.$$

We have thus proved formula (32).

It remains to show that the function g is one-to-one. Since this function (according to (31)) is one-to-one on each of the sets S and $X-S$ individually, we ought to prove that

$$g(S) \cap g(X-S) = \emptyset . \tag{36}$$

Now by (31) we have

$$g(S) = S \quad \text{and} \quad g(X-S) = f(X-S) = f(X)-f(S); \tag{37}$$

at the same time, $f(X) = f(X)-Z$ because $f(X) \cap Z = \emptyset$, and hence

$$f(X)-f(S) = f(X)-[Z \cup f(S)] = f(X)-S$$

because of (35).

Hence, we have $S \cap [f(X)-f(S)] = \emptyset$, whence formula (36) follows by virtue of (37).

We have thus completed the proof of the Cantor-Bernstein theorem.

Another form of this theorem, which is frequently convenient for applications, is the following:

$$\text{if } A \subset B \subset C \quad \text{and} \quad \overline{\overline{A}} = \overline{\overline{C}}, \quad \text{then} \quad \overline{\overline{A}} = \overline{\overline{B}} = \overline{\overline{C}}. \tag{38}$$

The following theorem holds for arbitrary functions:

If X is the set of arguments of the function f, then

$$\overline{\overline{f(X)}} \leqslant \overline{\overline{X}} . \tag{39}$$

For, let $y \in f(X)$ and let $g(y)$ be an arbitrary element of the set $f^{-1}(y)$ [we make use of the axiom of choice (Chapter III, § 7) here]. Since the sets $f^{-1}(y)$ for various y's are disjoint, the function g determines a one-to-one mapping of the set $f(X)$ onto a subset of the set X. From this follows formula (39).

§ 4. Properties of the number $\mathfrak{c}$

We have defined the number $\mathfrak{c}$ as the power of the set $\mathcal{E}$ of all real numbers. Let us note that, as stated in Chapter V, § 2, *every open interval $a < x < b$ is of power $\mathfrak{c}$.*

The interval $a \leqslant x \leqslant b$ (where $a < b$) is also of power $\mathfrak{c}$. This follows immediately from formula (28) since

$$E_x(a < x < b) \subset E_x(a \leqslant x \leqslant b) \subset \mathcal{E},$$

and hence

$$\mathfrak{c} = \overline{\overline{E_x(a < x < b)}} \leqslant \overline{\overline{E_x(a \leqslant x \leqslant b)}} \leqslant \overline{\overline{\mathcal{E}}} = \mathfrak{c}.$$

Further, we also deduce from formula (28) that

(40) $\quad \mathfrak{c} = \mathfrak{c} + n = \mathfrak{c} + \mathfrak{a} = \mathfrak{c} + \mathfrak{c} = n \cdot \mathfrak{c}$

(n being a natural number);

for (cf. (24)) $\mathfrak{c} \leqslant \mathfrak{c} + n \leqslant \mathfrak{c} + \mathfrak{a} \leqslant \mathfrak{c} + \mathfrak{c}$ and $\mathfrak{c} + \mathfrak{c} \leqslant \mathfrak{c}$, $\mathfrak{c} + \mathfrak{c}$ being the power of the set

$$E_x(0 < x < 1) \cup E_x(1 < x < 2),$$

which is a subset of the set $\mathcal{E}$.

The generalization to n terms is obtained immediately by induction.

(41) $$2^{\mathfrak{a}} = \mathfrak{c}.$$

In fact, let A denote the set of all infinite sequences consisting of the numbers 0 and 1. Therefore $\overline{\overline{A}} = 2^{\mathfrak{a}}$. Let B denote the subset of the set A consisting of sequences with an infinite number of zeros. To the sequence $t = (t_1, t_2, \ldots)$ belonging to B we assign the number

$$f(t) = t_1/2 + t_2/4 + \ldots + t_n/2^n + \ldots, \quad \text{i. e.} \quad f(t) = (0 . t_1 t_2 \ldots)_2,$$

and if $t \in A - B$ we let

$$f(t) = 1 + t_1/2 + t_2/4 + \ldots + t_n/2^n + \ldots, \quad \text{i. e.} \quad f(t) = (1 . t_1 t_2 \ldots)_2$$

(in the binary system of calculation).

It is easy to verify that the function f is one-to-one. At the same time

$$E_x(0 < x < 1) \subset f(A) \subset \mathcal{E},$$

and therefore $\overline{\overline{A}} = \overline{\overline{f(A)}} = \mathfrak{c}$ by virtue of (38).

We deduce from this that

(42) $$\mathfrak{a}^{\mathfrak{a}} = \mathfrak{c} = \mathfrak{c}^{\mathfrak{a}},$$

because (cf. (26)) $2^{\mathfrak{a}} \leqslant \mathfrak{a}^{\mathfrak{a}} \leqslant \mathfrak{c}^{\mathfrak{a}} = (2^{\mathfrak{a}})^{\mathfrak{a}} = 2^{(\mathfrak{a}^2)} = 2^{\mathfrak{a}}$.

Similarly, we have

(43) $$\mathfrak{n}^{\mathfrak{a}} = \mathfrak{c} \quad \text{for} \quad n \geqslant 2 .$$

Formula $\mathfrak{a}^{\mathfrak{a}} = \mathfrak{c} = n^{\mathfrak{a}}$ asserts that the set of all infinite sequences whose terms are natural numbers (or whose terms are $1, 2, \ldots, n$) is of power $\mathfrak{c}$.

We shall now deduce from (42) that

(44) $$\mathfrak{c} = \mathfrak{c}\cdot\mathfrak{a} = \mathfrak{c}\cdot\mathfrak{c} = \mathfrak{c}^n = \mathfrak{c}^{\mathfrak{a}} \quad (n \text{ is a natural number } >1).$$

In fact

$$\mathfrak{c} \leqslant \mathfrak{c}\cdot\mathfrak{a} \leqslant \mathfrak{c}\cdot\mathfrak{c} \leqslant \mathfrak{c}^n \leqslant \mathfrak{c}^{\mathfrak{a}} = \mathfrak{c} .$$

Let us note that $\mathfrak{c}^2$ is the power of the plane, and more generally: $\mathfrak{c}^n$ is the power of n-dimensional Euclidean space $\mathcal{E}^n$. Formula (44) asserts that *the set of all infinite sequences whose terms are real numbers* (or the infinite cartesian product $\mathcal{E}\times\mathcal{E}\times\ldots$) *is also of power* $\mathfrak{c}$.

We now give the last formula dealing with the numbers $\mathfrak{a}$ and $\mathfrak{c}$:

(45) $$2^{\mathfrak{c}} = \mathfrak{a}^{\mathfrak{c}} = \mathfrak{c}^{\mathfrak{c}}.$$

In fact, $\mathfrak{c}^{\mathfrak{c}} = (2^{\mathfrak{a}})^{\mathfrak{c}} = 2^{\mathfrak{a}\mathfrak{c}} = 2^{\mathfrak{c}}$ for $\mathfrak{a}\mathfrak{c} = \mathfrak{c}$ by (44).

Let us set $2^{\mathfrak{c}} = \mathfrak{f}$. By virtue of (22), $2^{\mathfrak{c}} > \mathfrak{c}$; $\mathfrak{f}$ is therefore a cardinal number greater than $\mathfrak{a}$ and $\mathfrak{c}$. Formula (45) asserts that $\mathfrak{f}$ is the power of the family of all subsets of the real line (or more generally—of the family of all subsets of the space $\mathcal{E}^n$); it is at the same time the power of the set of all real valued functions of a real variable (as well as the power of the set of all functions of a real variable whose values are natural numbers).

Remark. We now give a more direct proof of the formula $\mathfrak{c}^2 = \mathfrak{c}$ because of its fundamental importance.

Let A be the square determined by the conditions $0 < x < 1$ and $0 < y < 1$. Since $\overline{\overline{A}} = \mathfrak{c}^2$, our problem depends on the definition of a one-to-one real valued function on the square A (it will follow from this that $\mathfrak{c}^2 \leqslant \mathfrak{c}$; the inequality $\mathfrak{c} \leqslant \mathfrak{c}^2$ is obvious).

Let us develop the numbers x and y in essentially infinite decimal expansions (i. e. containing an infinite number of nonzero digits):

$$x = 0\,.\,a_1 a_2 \dots, \qquad y = 0\,.\,b_1 b_2 \dots,$$

and let

$$f(x, y) = 0 \cdot a_1 b_1 a_2 b_2 \dots a_n b_n \dots \tag{46}$$

We must prove that if $f(x, y) = f(\bar{x}, \bar{y})$, then $x = \bar{x}$ and $y = \bar{y}$.

Now the development (46) contains an infinite number of digits which are different from zero; at the same time no number has two different essentially infinite developments, and therefore the equality

$$f(x, y) = 0\,.\,a_1 b_1 a_2 b_2 \dots = 0\,.\,\bar{a}_1 \bar{b}_1 \bar{a}_2 \bar{b}_2 \dots = f(\bar{x}, \bar{y})$$

implies that

$$a_1 = \bar{a}_1, \quad b_1 = \bar{b}_1, \quad a_2 = \bar{a}_2, \quad b_2 = \bar{b}_2, \quad \dots,$$

i. e. $x = \bar{x}$ and $y = \bar{y}$.

Exercises

1. Let $\boldsymbol{R}$ be a family of sets each of which has power $\mathfrak{c}$ and let $\overline{\overline{\boldsymbol{R}}} = \mathfrak{c}$. Prove that $\overline{\overline{S(\boldsymbol{R})}} = \mathfrak{c}$.

2. Let $\overline{\overline{A}}_n = \mathfrak{c}$ for $n = 1, 2, \dots$ Prove that

$$\overline{\overline{A_1 \times A_2 \times \dots}} = \mathfrak{c}.$$

3. Let $\overline{\overline{T}} = \mathfrak{n}$ and $\overline{\overline{F}}_t = \mathfrak{m}$ for every $t \in T$. Calculate $\overline{\overline{\boldsymbol{P}_t F_t}}$.

4. Prove that a necessary and sufficient condition that the set A be of power equal to that of one of its proper subsets (i. e. to some subset distinct from A) is that $\mathfrak{a} \leqslant \overline{\overline{A}}$.

Hint: In the proof of necessity take into consideration an element $a \in A - f(A)$, then $f(a)$, $ff(a)$, and so on. In the proof of sufficiency consider the sequence $a_1, a_2, \dots$ contained in A and the function f defined as follows:

$$f(x) = x \quad \text{for} \quad x \neq a_n \quad (n = 1, 2, \dots) \quad \text{and} \quad f(a_n) = a_{n+1}.$$

CHAPTER VII

ORDERING RELATIONS

§ 1. Ordering relations

Definition. Let there be given a set A and a relation amongst its elements, i. e. a propositional function $\varphi(x, y)$ of two variables, whose domain of variation is the set A. We say that this relation establishes an *ordering* (or a simple ordering) of the set A [and then instead of $\varphi(x, y)$ we write $x \prec y$ which is read: *x precedes y*], if the following conditions are satisfied:

1. if $a \prec b$, then the relation $b \prec a$ does not hold;
2. if $a \prec b$ and $b \prec c$, then $a \prec c$;
3. if $a \neq b$, then either $a \prec b$ or $b \prec a$.

For example, the "less than" relation $x < y$ (and similarly the relation $x > y$) establishes an ordering of the set of real numbers as well as of each of its subsets.

§ 2. Similarity. Order types

We say that the relation $\prec$ which orders the set A and the relation $\prec^*$ which orders the set A^* establish *similar* orderings if there exists a one-to-one mapping f (called a *similarity mapping*) of the set A^* onto the set A which satisfies the identity

$$(x \prec y) \equiv \big(f(x) \prec^* f(y)\big),$$

i. e. the element x precedes the element y in the set A if and only if the element $f(x)$ precedes the element $f(y)$ in the set A^*.

For example, the "less than" relation establishes a similarity ordering of the set of natural numbers and the set of numbers of the form $1-1/n$.

In an analogous way to the way in which cardinal numbers are assigned to sets, we assign *order types* to order relations or as we say, to ordered sets. In this connection, we assign the same order type to two ordered sets if and only if they are similar. We lean here on the reflexivity, symmetry and transitivity of the similarity relation, i. e.

a) every ordered set is similar to itself,

b) if the set A is similar to B, then the set B is similar to A,

c) if the set A is similar to B and the set B is similar to C, then the set A is similar to C.

We omit the simple proofs of these properties.

The following order types are particularly important: ω—the type of the set of natural numbers, ω^*—the type of the set of negative integers, η—the type of the set of rational numbers, and λ—the type of the set of all real numbers (all these sets are considered to be ordered by the relation "less than").

The type of a finite set, consisting of n elements, is denoted by n.

THEOREM. *Every countable ordered set A is similar to some subset of the set R of all rational numbers (ordered with respect to the relation "less than").*

Let us arrange the elements of the set A in a sequence $a_1, a_2, \ldots, a_n, \ldots$ consisting of distinct terms (we assume that A is infinite; for finite sets the theorem is obvious).

We define a similarity mapping f of A onto a subset of R, in the following way.

Let $f(a_1) = 0$; $f(a_2)$ is defined as an (arbitrary) rational number which is less than $f(a_1)$ if $a_2 \prec a_1$, but larger than $f(a_1)$ if $a_1 \prec a_2$. The inductive definition of the number $f(a_{n+1})$ is the following: if, in the set A, a_{n+1} precedes all the elements $a_1, a_2, \ldots, a_n$, then $f(a_{n+1})$ is a rational number less than all the numbers $f(a_1), f(a_2), \ldots, f(a_n)$; analogously if a_{n+1} follows all the elements $a_1, a_2, \ldots, a_n$, then the number $f(a_{n+1})$ is larger than all the numbers $f(a_1), f(a_2), \ldots, f(a_n)$; finally, if none of these cases holds, then let a_k be the last among those elements $a_1, a_2, \ldots, a_n$, which precede a_{n+1} and let a_m be the first among those which follow a_{n+1}; then let us set

$$f(a_{n+1}) = \{f(a_k) + f(a_m)\}/2 .$$

The function f defined in this way is obviously one-to-one. Moreover, for every n it is a similarity transformation of the set $\{a_1, a_2, \ldots, a_{n+1}\}$ onto the set $\{f(a_1), f(a_2), \ldots, f(a_{n+1})\}$. But from this it follows that the function f is a similarity mapping of the entire set A onto $f(A)$. For if $a_i \prec a_j$ then, denoting by $n+1$ the larger of the two numbers i and j, we deduce from the similarity of the sets $\{a_1, a_2, \ldots, a_{n+1}\}$ and $\{f(a_1), f(a_2), \ldots, f(a_{n+1})\}$ that $f(a_i) < f(a_j)$.

§ 3. Dense ordering

We say that an ordering of the set A is *dense* if an intermediate element can be found between every pair of its elements, i. e. whenever $a \prec b$ then there exists a c such that $a \prec c$ and $c \prec b$.

An example of a dense ordering is the ordering of the rational numbers (with respect to the "less than" relation). We add that every countable set with dense ordering, without a first and last element, is of type η. (For a proof, see Hausdorff, *Set Theory*, Chapter 3, § 11, Theorem IV.)

§ 4. Continuous ordering

In order to give a more lucid formulation of the definition of a continuous ordering we shall introduce the following auxiliary definitions.

A subset B of an ordered set A is said to be an *initial interval* of A if together with each of its elements $x \in B$ it contains all the elements of the set A which precede x, i. e. if

$$(y \prec x \in B) \Rightarrow (y \in B) .$$

Given a set $Z \subset A$, the earliest element a of the set A which satisfies the condition

$$(x \in Z) \Rightarrow (x \lesssim a)$$

(if it exists) is called the *least upper bound* ot Z.

Now, let us say that an ordering of the set A is *continuous* if it is dense, and if furthermore, for each of its initial intervals B which is nonvoid and distinct from A exists a least upper bound.

The set $\mathcal{E}$ of all real numbers is of continuous type. The verification of this fact involves only a different formulation of the known Dedekind axiom of continuity.

On the other hand, the ordering of the set of rational numbers is not continuous; in order to convince ourselves of this fact, it suffices to take as the set B the set of rational numbers less than $\sqrt{2}$. (We also say that $\sqrt{2}$ determines a "cut" possessing a "gap" in the set of rational numbers.)

Remark. The following theorem which we give here without proof contains the most essential part of the theory of irrational numbers due to Dedekind.

Let A denote the set of all rational numbers and let $\mathbf{K}$ *denote the family of all its initial intervals which are non-empty, distinct from A, and which do not possess a last element. Then the inclusion relation (with the exclusion of equality) establishes an ordering of the family* $\mathbf{K}$ *of type* λ.

Hence, real numbers can be defined as the initial intervals of the set R of all rational numbers which are non-empty, distinct from R, and which do not possess a last element.

Exercises

1. Let X and Y be two subsets of the ordered set A such that $X \cup Y = A$, $X \cap Y = \emptyset$ and $(x \in X) \wedge (y \in Y) \Rightarrow (x \lessdot y)$. We say that the pair X, Y is a *cut* of the set A.

Prove that if X_1, Y_1 and X_2, Y_2 are cuts of the set A, then either $X_1 \subset X_2$ or $X_2 \subset X_1$.

2. We say that a family of sets $\boldsymbol{R}$ is *monotonic* if for every pair of sets X and Y belonging to $\boldsymbol{R}$ it is true that either $X \subset Y$ or $Y \subset X$.

A natural ordering of this family is the ordering with respect to the relation $X \subset Y \neq X$.

Prove that every ordered set is similar to some monotonic family of subsets of this set.

3. Let $\boldsymbol{R}$ be a monotonic family of subsets of the set Z. Prove that the family of all sets $S(\boldsymbol{X})$ and $P(\boldsymbol{X})$, where $\boldsymbol{X} \subset \boldsymbol{R}$, is also monotonic.

4. Give an example of an ordered set which is not of type ω, but which despite this fact possesses a first element and which is such that to every element there exists an element immediately following and (except to the first) an element immediately preceding it.

5. A subset G of an ordered set A is said to be *dense with respect to A* if between every two elements x and y of the set A there lies an element z of the set G.

Prove that a set A of type λ contains a countable part which is dense with respect to A.

6. Let us establish an ordering of the set $\mathcal{E}^2$, of all complex numbers, by assuming that of two complex numbers with distinct imaginary parts that one is earlier whose imaginary part is smaller and of two numbers with equal imaginary parts that one is earlier which has the smaller real part.

Prove that in the set $\mathcal{E}^2$ there does not exist a countable part which is dense with respect to $\mathcal{E}^2$.

7. We say that a relation which satisfies conditions 1° and 2°, § 1, establishes a *partial ordering*.

Prove that:

(a) every family of sets is partially ordered with respect to the inclusion relation $X \subset Y \neq X$,

(b) the family of all infinite sequences with real terms can be partially ordered in the following way: we consider the sequence $a_1, a_2, \ldots$ to precede the sequence $b_1, b_2, \ldots$ if there exists a k such that $a_n < b_n$ for $n > k$,

(c) a family of real valued functions is partially ordered by the relation

$$(f \prec g) \equiv \bigwedge_x [f(x) \leqslant g(x)] \wedge (f \neq g).$$

8. A partially ordered set is said to be a *lattice* if the greatest lower bound and the least upper bound exist for every arbitrary pair of its elements (the definition of the least upper bound was given in § 4; the definition of the greatest lower bound is analogous).

Prove that

(a) the family of all subsets of a given set is a lattice with respect to the inclusion relation $X \subset Y \neq X$,

(b) the family of functions considered in Exercise 7 (c) is a lattice,

(c) the family of all linear subsets of the n-dimensional Euclidean space (i. e. of straight lines, planes, and generally, the spaces with dimension $k \leqslant n$ containing the origin of the coordinate system) is a lattice with respect to the inclusion relation; what is the geometric meaning of the least upper bound of two linear sets?

CHAPTER VIII

WELL ORDERING

§ 1. Well ordering

Definition. We say that an ordering of a set A is a *well ordering* if every non-empty subset of the set A has a first element.

We call the order types of well-ordered sets *ordinal numbers*.

EXAMPLES. The set of all natural numbers is a well ordered set (this follows directly from the principle of finite induction). Therefore ω is an ordinal number. On the other hand, none of the order types ω^*, η, λ is an ordinal number.

It follows from the definition of well ordering that every subset of a well ordered set is well ordered. It also follows that for every element a of a well ordered set (with the exception of the last element, provided the set contains a last element) there exists an element b which is its immediate successor. Namely, b is the first element of the set $\underset{x}{E}(a \prec x)$.

On the other hand, a well ordered set can contain an element (which is not its first element), for which there does not exist an element which is an immediate predecessor. For example, the set consisting of the numbers $1-1/n$ $(n = 1, 2, \ldots)$ together with the number 1 is well ordered, but there does not exist an element in this set which immediately precedes the number 1.

If the set A is well ordered, then for every initial interval B which is distinct from A there exists one and only one element b in A such that

$$B = \underset{x}{E}(x \prec b).$$

Namely, b is the first element of the set $A-B$. It is therefore the least upper bound of the interval B if B does not contain a last element; but if B contains a last element, then b is the element which immediately succeeds this element.

Let us set

$$P(a) = \underset{x}{E}(x \prec a) . \tag{1}$$

We have thus established a one-to-one correspondence between the elements of the set A and the family $\boldsymbol{R}$ of all initial intervals of the set A which are distinct from A.

This correspondence expresses the similarity of the set A and the family $\boldsymbol{R}$ (ordered with respect to the inclusion relation: $X \subset Y$, $X \neq Y$).

For if $a \prec b$, then $x \prec a \Rightarrow x \prec b$, i.e. $P(a) \subset P(b)$; at the same time $P(a) \neq P(b)$ for $a \in P(b)$ and $a \notin P(a)$.

§ 2. Theorem on transfinite induction

Let A be a well ordered set and let $\varphi(x)$ be a propositional function with argument running through the set A and satisfying the following condition for every x:

$$\text{if } \bigwedge_y[(y \prec x) \Rightarrow \varphi(y)] \text{ then } \varphi(x) . \tag{2}$$

Then every element of the set A satisfies the propositional function $\varphi(x)$, i. e. $\bigwedge_x \varphi(x)$.

Let us assume that this is not the case, i. e. that the set Z of elements of the set A which do not satisfy the propositional function $\varphi(x)$ is nonvoid. Let x_0 be the first element of the set Z. Therefore

$$\bigwedge_y [(y \prec x_0) \Rightarrow \varphi(y)] .$$

But it follows from this by virtue of (2) that the proposition $\varphi(x_0)$ is true. But then $x_0 \notin Z$.

Remark. The principle of finite induction known from arithmetic is a particular case of the preceding theorem; namely, the case where A is the set of natural numbers.

§ 3. Theorems on the comparison of ordinal numbers

Let α and β be ordinal numbers; let α be the order type of the set A and let β be that of the set B. We write

$\alpha < \beta$ if the set A is similar to some initial interval of the set B which is distinct from B.

We assume the above definition of the "less than" relation in connection with the following theorems.

THEOREM 1. *A well ordered set is not similar to any of its initial intervals which are distinct from the set itself, i. e.*

(3) $$\alpha \nless \alpha .$$

Let us assume the contrary. That is, let us assume that a function f establishes the similarity of the sets A and $P(a)$ for some $a \in A$. Since $f(a) \in P(a)$ we have $f(a) \prec a$. Therefore the set

$$Z = \underset{x}{E}[f(x) \prec x]$$

is not empty. Let x_0 be the first element in this set. Hence

(4) $$f(x_0) \prec x_0 ,$$

whence—taking into consideration the fact that the function f establishes the similarity of the sets A and $P(a)$—we deduce that

(5) $$f[f(x_0)] \prec f(x_0) ;$$

but then—comparing formula (5) with (4)—we see that x_0 is not the first element of the set Z.

THEOREM 2. *No two initial intervals of a well ordered set are similar.*

This follows directly from the preceding theorem, for of two distinct initial intervals $P(a)$ and $P(b)$ one is an initial interval of the other (depending on whether $a \prec b$ or $b \prec a$).

Theorem 2 can also be expressed in the following manner:

(6) *if* $\alpha < \beta$ *then* $\beta \nless \alpha$.

Since an initial interval of an initial interval of the set A is an initial interval of this set, we have:

(7) *if* $\alpha < \beta$ *and* $\beta < \gamma$ *then* $\alpha < \gamma$.

We shall now prove the following fundamental theorem:

THEOREM 3. *If* $\alpha \neq \beta$ *then* $\alpha < \beta$ *or* $\beta < \alpha$. In other words, *if the sets A and B are well ordered, then either the set A is similar to an initial interval of the set B or the set B is similar to an initial interval of the set A.*

Proof. We shall denote by $P_A(x)$ the initial intervals of the set A and by $P_B(y)$ the initial intervals of the set B. We shall write $M \simeq N$ if the sets M and N are similar.

We set

$$X = E_x \bigvee_y [P_A(x) \simeq P_B(y)]. \tag{8}$$

By Theorem 2, for every $x \in X$, there exists only one element y such that $P_A(x) \simeq P_B(y)$. Hence we can denote this y by $f(x)$. Therefore the equivalence

$$[y = f(x)] \equiv [P_A(x) \simeq P_B(y)] \tag{9}$$

holds for every $x \in X$.

We shall prove that the set X is an initial interval of the set A. Let $x' \precsim x \in X$. We must prove that $x' \in X$. Since $x \in X$, there exists (by virtue of (8)) a function which is a similarity mapping of the interval $P_A(x)$ into the interval $P_B[f(x)]$; but since $P_A(x')$ is an initial interval of the set $P_A(x)$, under this mapping the interval $P_A(x')$ goes over into an initial interval of $P_B[f(x)]$, and hence onto an initial interval of the set B. This means that $x' \in X$, i. e. that X is an initial interval of the set A.

Analogously, the set $f(X)$ is an initial interval of the set B. For by virtue of (9), and formula (12) of Chapter IV, § 4, we have

$$f(X) = E_y \bigvee_x [y = f(x)] = E_y \bigvee_x [P_B(y) \simeq P_A(x)]. \tag{10}$$

Moreover, as we have already proved, the condition $x' \precsim x$ implies that the interval $P_B[f(x')]$ is an initial interval of the interval $P_B[f(x)]$, and hence that $f(x') \precsim f(x)$. This means that

$$X \simeq f(X). \tag{11}$$

It remains to prove that either $X = A$ or $f(X) = B$. Let us assume the contrary, that $X \neq A$ and that $f(X) \neq B$. Since the sets X and $f(X)$ are initial intervals of the sets A and B, there exist therefore elements $a \in A$ and $b \in B$ such that

$$X = P_A(a) \quad \text{and} \quad f(X) = P_B(b).$$

By virtue of (11) we therefore have $P_A(a) \simeq P_B(b)$, whence it follows by virtue of (8) that $a \in X$, i. e. that $a \in P_A(a)$, hence $a \prec a$. We have thus arrived at a contradiction.

Theorem 3 implies the following corollary:

THEOREM 4. *If the sets A and B are well ordered then their powers satisfy the trichotomy condition, i. e.*

$$\textit{either } \overline{\overline{A}} = \overline{\overline{B}}, \textit{ or } \overline{\overline{A}} < \overline{\overline{B}}, \textit{ or } \overline{\overline{B}} < \overline{\overline{A}}.$$

A question of fundamental significance which arises here naturally is: can every set be well ordered?

We shall consider this question in § 7.

§ 4. Sets of ordinal numbers

We shall use the following notation:

$$\text{(12)} \qquad \Gamma(a) = \underset{\xi}{E}(\xi < a).$$

THEOREM 1. *The set $\Gamma(a)$ is well ordered (with respect to the "less than" relation) and the order type of this ordering is a.*

In fact, let A be a well ordered set of type a and let $\tau(x)$ for $x \in A$ be the order type of the interval $P(x)$.

The function τ establishes the similarity of A and $\Gamma(a)$. For if $x' \prec x$, then the set $P(x')$ is distinct from $P(x)$ and is an initial interval of $P(x)$, and hence (cf. Theorem 1, § 3) $\tau(x') < \tau(x)$. At the same time every element ξ of the set $\Gamma(a)$ is a value of the function τ. For let $\xi \in \Gamma(a)$, i. e. $\xi < a$; by virtue of the definition of the "less than" relation for ordinal numbers, a set of type ξ is similar to some initial interval $P(x')$ of the set A; and hence $\xi = \tau(x')$.

THEOREM 2. *Every set of ordinal numbers is well ordered (by the "less than" relation).*

It suffices to prove that every non-empty set Φ of ordinal numbers contains a least number. Let $\alpha \in \Phi$. If α is not the least number of the set Φ then the set $\Phi \cap \Gamma(\alpha)$ is nonvoid and therefore, being a subset of the well ordered set $\Gamma(\alpha)$, it contains a least number β. The number β is the least number of the set Φ. For if $\xi \in [\Phi - \Gamma(\alpha)]$ then $\xi \geqslant \alpha$ and hence $\xi > \beta$.

THEOREM 3. *For every set Φ of ordinal numbers there exists an ordinal number which is greater than every number of this set.*

Namely, such a number is $\alpha+1$, where α is the order type of the set

$$\Psi = \bigcup_\xi \Gamma(\xi) \quad \text{where} \quad \xi \in \Phi,$$

and $\alpha+1$ denotes the type of the set $\Psi \cup \{\alpha\}$ (cf. § 6).

In fact, for every ξ the set $\Gamma(\xi)$ is an initial interval of the set Ψ. If $\Gamma(\xi) = \Psi$, then $\xi = \alpha$ (by virtue of Theorem 1); and in the contrary case $\xi < \alpha$. Therefore for every ξ we have $\xi < \alpha+1$.

THEOREM 4. *There does not exist the set of all ordinal numbers.*

§ 5. The number Ω

Definition. Let us denote by Ξ the set of all order types of countable well ordered sets and by Ω the order type of the set Ξ.

By Theorem 2 of § 4, Ω is an ordinal number.

We shall prove that

$$\Xi = \Gamma(\Omega). \tag{13}$$

By virtue of Theorem 3 there exists an ordinal number α greater than every number of the set Ξ. Therefore $\Xi \subset \Gamma(\alpha)$. At the same time Ξ is an initial interval of the set $\Gamma(\alpha)$. For let $\xi' < \xi \in \Xi$; ξ' is therefore an order type of some subset of a countable well ordered set (of type ξ); this subset is obviously countable and hence $\xi' \epsilon \Xi$.

Since Ξ is an initial interval of $\Gamma(\alpha)$, there exists (cf. (1)) a number $\gamma \leqslant \alpha$ such that $\Xi = \Gamma(\gamma)$. In order to prove formula (13) it remains to show that $\gamma = \Omega$. But this follows immediately from the definition of the number Ω and from Theorem 1, § 4, by virtue of which the set $\Gamma(\gamma)$ has the type γ.

The set $\Gamma(\Omega)$ *is noncountable*, i. e.

$$(14) \qquad \overline{\overline{\Gamma(\Omega)}} > \mathfrak{a} .$$

In fact, if the set $\Gamma(\Omega)$ were countable, then its order type would belong to Ξ, i. e. $\Omega \epsilon \Xi$, whence by (13) we should have $\Omega \epsilon \Gamma(\Omega)$, i. e. $\Omega < \Omega$ which is impossible.

Remarks. The cardinal number $\overline{\overline{\Gamma(\Omega)}}$ is denoted by the symbol $\aleph_1$ ("aleph" 1). Hence we have $\aleph_1 > \mathfrak{a}$, as well as $\mathfrak{c} > \mathfrak{a}$ (Chapter VI, § 3 (21)). However, as is clear, we arrive at the number $\aleph_1$ by entirely different reasoning than that used to arrive at the number $\mathfrak{c}$. Are these numbers equal? This is a problem which has not yet been resolved. The hypothesis asserting that

$$(15) \qquad \aleph_1 = \mathfrak{c}$$

is called the *continuum hypothesis*.

Let us note that $\aleph_1$ *is the number immediately following the number* $\mathfrak{a}$, i. e. if $\mathfrak{m} < \aleph_1$ then $\mathfrak{m} \leqslant \mathfrak{a}$.

In fact, let $\overline{\overline{A}} = \mathfrak{m}$. According to our assumption, A is of power equal to that of some subset B of the set Ξ. Let β denote the order type of the set B. Therefore the sets B and $\Gamma(\beta)$ are similar and hence of equal power, i. e. $\overline{\overline{\Gamma(\beta)}} = \mathfrak{m}$. It follows from this that $\beta < \Omega$, for in the contrary case we should have $\Omega \leqslant \beta$, whence $\Gamma(\Omega) \subset \Gamma(\beta)$, and therefore $\aleph_1 = \overline{\overline{\Gamma(\Omega)}} \leqslant \overline{\overline{\Gamma(\beta)}} = \mathfrak{m}$ contrary to assumption. It follows from the inequality $\beta < \Omega$, by the definition of Ω, that the set B is countable, i. e. $\mathfrak{m} \leqslant \mathfrak{a}$.

§ 6. The arithmetic of ordinal numbers

Let α and β be two ordinal numbers (or more generally, two order types). Let A and B be two sets with order types α and β, respectively; let us assume also that $A \cap B = \emptyset$ (see Chapter VI, § 1, concerning the possibility of making such an assumption). Let us establish an ordering of the set $A \cup B$ by assuming that every element of the set A precedes every element of the set B and that in the domain of each of the sets A and B individually the ordering does not change.

We denote *the order type of the set* $A \cup B$ *by* $\alpha+\beta$.

We shall prove that, *under the assumption that* α *and* β *are ordinal numbers,* $\alpha+\beta$ *is also an ordinal number.*

We have to prove that the set $A \cup B$ with the above-established ordering of its elements is well ordered. Hence, let $\emptyset \neq X \subset A \cup B$. If $X \cap A \neq \emptyset$, then—since the set A is well ordered—the set $X \cap A$ contains an earliest element; this element is the earliest element of the entire set $X = (X \cap A) \cup (X \cap B)$, inasmuch as it precedes, by the definition of the ordering of the set $A \cup B$, each of the elements of the set $X \cap B$.

Now, if $X \cap A = \emptyset$, then $X \subset B$ and therefore there exists an earliest element in the set X.

EXAMPLES. $\alpha+1 > \alpha$ whereby $\alpha+1$ follows immediately after α. The number $\omega+\omega$ is the type of the set of numbers of the form $1-1/n$ together with the numbers of the form $2-1/n$ where $n = 1, 2, \ldots$ Let us note that $1+\omega = \omega$; and hence addition is not commutative.

We denote *by* $\alpha \cdot \beta$ *the order type of the cartesian product* $A \times B$ *ordered as follows:*

$$[\langle x, y\rangle \precsim \langle u, v\rangle] \equiv \big[(y \precsim v) \vee \big((y = v) \wedge (x \precsim u)\big)\big].$$

Under the assumption that α *and* β *are ordinal numbers,* $\alpha \cdot \beta$ *is also an ordinal number.*

For, let $\emptyset \neq Z \subset A \times B$. Let Y denote the projection of the set Z onto the B-axis. Hence we have $\emptyset \neq Y \subset B$. Let b be the earliest element of the set B and let

$X = E_x[\langle x, b\rangle \in Z]$. Finally let a be the first element of the set X. It is easy to verify that $\langle a, b\rangle$ is the first element of the set Z.

EXAMPLES. $2 \cdot \omega$ is the order type of the cartesian product $\{1, 2\} \times J$ (where J is the set of natural numbers) ordered as follows:

$$\langle 1, 1\rangle, \langle 2, 1\rangle, \langle 1, 2\rangle, \langle 2, 2\rangle, \ldots,$$

and hence $2 \cdot \omega = \omega$.

On the other hand, $\omega \cdot 2 = \omega + \omega$ is the order type of the product $J \times \{1, 2\}$ (see the example given above).

As we see, multiplication is not commutative.

$\omega \cdot \omega$ is the type of the set of all numbers of the form $k - 1/n$ where $k = 1, 2, \ldots$ and $n = 1, 2, \ldots$

Instead of $\omega \cdot \omega$ we write ω^2. In general, $\alpha^{n+1} = \alpha^n \cdot \alpha$.

We denote by α^ω (for $\alpha > 1$) the least of the numbers which are larger than any of the numbers α^n, where $n = 1, 2, \ldots$

More generally, the definition of exponentiation, and of many other operations, can be introduced with the aid of the concept of limit. Namely, let λ be a *limit ordinal* (>0), i. e. a number which does not possess an immediately preceding number; let φ be a function which assigns to every number $\xi < \lambda$ a certain ordinal number $\varphi(\xi)$. We denote by

$$\lim_{\xi<\lambda} \varphi(\xi)$$

the least of the numbers which are larger than all the numbers $\varphi(\xi)$.

We then define the power α^β (for $\alpha > 1$) with the aid of the formulas

1. $$\alpha^0 = 1,$$

2. $$\alpha^{\xi+1} = \alpha^\xi \cdot \alpha,$$

3. $$\alpha^\lambda = \lim_{\xi<\lambda} \alpha^\xi,$$

where λ is a limit ordinal (cf. the theorem on the definition by transfinite induction, § 7).

The arithmetic of ordinal numbers forms at present a well established theory which we shall not consider any further here. (See e. g. W. Sierpiński: *Leçons sur les nombres transfinis*, Paris, 1950, Chapter X; *Cardinal and ordinal numbers*, or F. Hausdorff, *Set theory*, Chapter III.) The facts from this theory, which we gave above, have mainly as objective to make it easy for the reader to recognize the types of well ordered countable sets; all these types can be obtained with the aid of sets of real numbers (or even with sets of rational numbers).

§ 7. Theorem on the possibility of well ordering an arbitrary set

We shall deduce this theorem, which is of fundamental importance for the theory of sets (cf. e. g. Theorem 4, § 3), from the axiom of choice. To this end, we shall prove first of all, the following theorem which is a generalization of the axiom of choice.

GENERAL PRINCIPLE OF CHOICE. *For every set A there exists a function e which assigns to every non-empty subset of the set A one of its elements, i. e.*

$$e(X) \in X \quad \textit{for every} \quad \emptyset \neq X \subset A. \tag{16}$$

Proof. Let $F(X) = \{X\} \times X$, i. e. the set $F(X)$ consists of ordered pairs of the form $\langle X, x\rangle$ where $x \in X$. Let $\boldsymbol{R}$ denote the set of values of this function, i. e. the family consisting of all the sets $F(X)$, where $\emptyset \neq X \subset A$. This is a family consisting of nonvoid disjoint sets. On the basis of the axiom of choice (Chapter III, § 7), there exists therefore a set consisting of elements, one chosen from each of the sets belonging to $\boldsymbol{R}$; this set is the desired function e.

ZERMELO THEOREM. *For every set A there exists a relation which establishes its well ordering.*

Proof. Let us take into consideration the ordinal numbers β with the following properties: there exists a function f_β whose argument runs over the set $\Gamma(\beta+1)$ and which satisfies the equalities

$$(17)\quad f_\beta(0) = e(A), \quad f_\beta(\xi) = e[A - f_\beta(\Gamma(\xi))] \quad \text{for} \quad \xi \leqslant \beta;$$

in particular

$$f_2(1) = e[A - \{e(A)\}],$$
$$f_2(2) = e(A - \{e(A), e[A - \{e(A)\}]\}).$$

The function f_β is one-to-one. For if $\xi' < \xi \leqslant \beta$, then $\xi' \in \Gamma(\xi)$ and hence $f_\beta(\xi') \in f_\beta(\Gamma(\xi))$ but $f_\beta(\xi) \in [A - f_\beta(\Gamma(\xi))]$ by (16) and (17).

It follows from this that the set of values of the function f_β, i. e. the set $f_\beta(\Gamma(\beta+1))$, is of order type $\beta+1$.

Hence, as it is seen, the numbers β form a subset Φ of the set of all order types of subsets of the set A which can be well ordered. By virtue of Theorem 3, § 4, there exist ordinal numbers which do not belong to the set Φ. Let α be the least of them. Therefore, there does not exist a function f_α satisfying conditions (17) (where we replace β by α), and on the other hand, for every $\beta < \alpha$, there exists a function f_β which satisfies these conditions.

We shall prove that the set A can be well ordered, its order type being α.

To this end, let us first note that if $\beta' \leqslant \beta$ and the function $g_{\beta'}$ has the set $\Gamma(\beta'+1)$ for its set of arguments and satisfies conditions analogous to those of (17), i. e.

$$(18)\quad g_{\beta'}(0) = e(A), \quad g_{\beta'}(\xi) = e[A - g_{\beta'}(\Gamma(\xi))] \quad \text{for} \quad \xi \leqslant \beta',$$

then for each $\xi \leqslant \beta'$ the equality

$$(19)\qquad g_{\beta'}(\xi) = f_\beta(\xi)$$

is satisfied (this means that, in the case where $\beta' = \beta$, the function f_β is uniquely determined and that in the case where $\beta' < \beta$, the function f_β is an extension of the function $f_{\beta'}$).

In fact, let us denote by $\varphi(\xi)$ the propositional function (19), taking the set $\Gamma(\beta'+1)$ for its set of arguments.

Let us apply to this function the theorem on transfinite induction (see § 2 where we substitute $\Gamma(\beta'+1)$ for A). Hence let us assume that for given $\xi \leqslant \beta'$ the condition $\gamma < \xi$ implies that $g_{\beta'}(\gamma) = f_\beta(\gamma)$ and therefore that $g_{\beta'}(\Gamma(\xi)) = f_\beta(\Gamma(\xi))$, which in turn, by virtue of (18) and (17), implies (19). By virtue of the theorem on transfinite induction, equality (19) holds for every $\xi \leqslant \beta'$.

Let us assume that

(20) $$f(\beta) = f_\beta(\beta)$$

holds for every $\beta < \alpha$.

In order to show that the set A admits a well ordering of type α, it obviously suffices to prove that the function f is one-to-one and that its set of values coincides with A.

Hence, let $\beta' < \beta$. As we proved (cf. (19)) $f_{\beta'}(\xi) = f_\beta(\xi)$ for every $\xi \leqslant \beta'$, and hence $f_{\beta'}(\beta') = f_\beta(\beta')$ in particular. But since the function f_β is one-to-one, we therefore have $f_\beta(\beta') \neq f_\beta(\beta)$, i. e. $f(\beta') \neq f(\beta)$.

It remains to prove that $f(\Gamma(\alpha)) = A$. Let us suppose that $A - f(\Gamma(\alpha)) \neq \emptyset$, and define the function f_α as follows:

$$f_\alpha(\beta) = f(\beta) \text{ for } \beta < \alpha \quad \text{and} \quad f_\alpha(\alpha) = e[A - f_\alpha(\Gamma(\alpha))].$$

As can easily be seen, the function f_α so defined satisfies condition (17) if we replace β by α in it. But this contradicts the definition of the number α.

*Remarks. The Zermelo theorem can be deduced from the following theorem (which could be stated in a still more general form):

THEOREM ON DEFINITION BY TRANSFINITE INDUCTION. *For every set A, for every number α and for every function h which assigns to subsets X of the set A elements of the same set, i.e.*

(21) $$h(X) \in A \quad \textit{for} \quad X \subset A,$$

there exists a function f defined for every $\xi \leqslant \alpha$ and satisfying the condition

(22) $$f(\xi) = h(f(\Gamma(\xi))).$$

Sketch of the proof. Let the set A and the function h be given. Let us assume that the theorem is false and that α is the least number for which there does not exist a function f satisfying condition (22). Therefore for every $\beta < \alpha$ there exists a function f satisfying the condition

$$(23) \qquad f_\beta(\xi) = h\big(f_\beta(\Gamma(\xi))\big) \quad \text{for} \quad \xi \leqslant \beta.$$

We can prove—in a manner analogous to the preceding proof—that the function f_β is uniquely determined. The function f defined by means of the formulas

$$f(\beta) = f_\beta(\beta) \text{ for } \beta < \alpha \quad \text{and} \quad f(\alpha) = h\big(f(\Gamma(\alpha))\big),$$

then satisfies the conditions of the theorem—contrary to our assumption.

Hence, our theorem has been proved.

In order to deduce the Zermelo theorem from it we substitute

$$h(X) = e(A - X) \quad \text{for} \quad X \neq A,$$

and we denote by $h(A)$ an arbitrary element of the set A. We denote by Φ the set of numbers β for which there exists a function f_β satisfying condition (23) and the inequality $f_\beta(\Gamma(\beta)) \neq A$. We assume that α is the least number which does not belong to the set Φ. Then $f(\Gamma(\alpha)) = A$, whence it easily follows that the set A can be well ordered, its order type being α.

Exercises

1. Prove that the conditions $\alpha < \Omega$ and $\beta < \Omega$ imply that $\alpha + \beta < \Omega$ and $\alpha \cdot \beta < \Omega$.

2. Every ordinal number is of the form $\lambda + n$, where λ is a limit ordinal and n is a natural number or zero.

Hint: Make use of the fact that in a well ordered set there does not exist an infinite sequence of the form $a_1 \succ a_2 \succ a_3 \succ \ldots$

3. Prove the following implications:

(a) $(\alpha < \beta) \Rightarrow (\gamma + \alpha < \gamma + \beta)$,

(b) $(\alpha \leqslant \beta) \Rightarrow (\alpha + \gamma \leqslant \beta + \gamma)$.

Does the condition $\beta > 0$ imply the inequality $\gamma < \beta + \gamma$?

4. Prove the distributive law:

$$\alpha \cdot (\beta + \gamma) = \alpha \cdot \beta + \alpha \cdot \gamma .$$

Show by means of an example that the formula $(\beta + \gamma) \cdot \alpha = \beta \cdot \alpha + \gamma \cdot \alpha$ is not true.

5. Prove that if $\alpha \geqslant \beta$ then there exists one and only one ordinal number γ such that $\alpha = \beta + \gamma$ (we call the number γ the *difference* $\alpha - \beta$ of the numbers α and β).

6. Prove that for every two ordinal numbers $\alpha \neq 0$ and β there exists a pair of numbers δ and $\varrho < \alpha$ such that

$$\beta = \alpha \cdot \delta + \varrho .$$

Here the numbers δ (*quotient*) and ϱ (*remainder*) are uniquely determined.

7. *A transfinite sequence of type* ζ is a function whose set of arguments is the set $\Gamma(\zeta)$ and whose values are ordinal numbers. A transfinite sequence φ is said to be *continuous* if for every limit ordinal $\gamma < \zeta$ the following equality holds:

$$\varphi(\gamma) = \lim_{\xi < \gamma} \varphi(\xi) .$$

Prove that the transfinite sequences $\varphi(\xi) = \alpha + \xi$ and $\varphi(\xi) = \alpha \cdot \xi$ (for $\alpha > 0$) are increasing and continuous.

8. Prove that every increasing transfinite sequence φ satisfies the inequality $\xi \leqslant \varphi(\xi)$ for every ξ.

Hint: Assuming that the theorem is false, denote by α the least number such that $\varphi(\alpha) < \alpha$.

9. Let φ be an increasing continuous transfinite sequence. Let us form the sequence

$$\alpha_0 = \alpha, \quad \alpha_1 = \varphi(\alpha_0), \quad \ldots, \quad \alpha_n = \varphi(\alpha_{n-1}), \quad \ldots$$

Let $\varkappa = \lim_{n < \omega} \alpha_n$. Prove that $\varphi(\varkappa) = \varkappa$ (under the assumption that the numbers under consideration belong to the domain of arguments of the function φ).

10. The number $\varkappa$ in Exercise 9 is said to be a *critical number* of the sequence φ. Find the critical numbers of the sequences

$$\varphi(\xi) = \alpha + \xi, \quad \varphi(\xi) = \alpha \cdot \xi, \quad \varphi(\xi) = \alpha^{\xi} .$$

11. Making use of the generalized principle of choice (see § 7) prove that every infinite cardinal number $\mathfrak{m}$ satisfies the inequality $\mathfrak{m} \geqslant \mathfrak{a}$.

Part II

TOPOLOGY

INTRODUCTION TO PART II

Topology is the study of those properties of geometric configurations which remain invariant when these configurations are subjected to one-to-one bicontinuous transformations, or homeomorphisms (see Chapter XII, § 3). We call such properties topological invariants. For example, the property of a circle to separate the plane into two regions is a topological invariant; if we transform the circle into an ellipse or into the perimeter of a triangle, this property is retained. On the other hand, the property of a curve to have a tangent line at every point is not a topological property; the circle has this property but the perimeter of a triangle does not, although it may be obtained from the circle by means of a homeomorphism.

As can already be seen from the above example topology operates with more general concepts than analysis; differential properties of a given transformation are nonessential for topology, but bicontinuity is essential. As a consequence, topology is often suitable for the solution of problems to which analysis cannot give the answer.

The generality of topological methods rests not only on the generality of the assumptions concerning the transformations considered but also on the generality of the sets considered to which these transformations are applied. These can be arbitrary point sets on the real line or in the plane, or in n-dimensional space, or still more general sets, provided only that they be sets for which—roughly speaking—it is possible to define the concept of closed set, i. e. provided that they are topological spaces. This generality has not only a methodological significance; in modern mathematics there is a characteristic tendency to confer upon the set of objects considered in a given investigation (be these functions, sequences or curves) a topology, and hence—to a geometrization or rather to a topologization—of the investigation. This gives rise to numerous applications. Thus, e. g. theorems on the existence of a solution of certain types of differential equations can be expressed as theorems on the existence of invariant points of a function space (the space of continuous functions) under continuous transformations; these theorems can be proved by topological methods in a more general form and in a simpler way than was formerly done without the aid of topology.

How much more general ought the spaces considered in topology be in order that they suffice for applications and yet, because of undue generality, they do not become too artificial? The answer to this question depends on the aims which a given topological work is to serve. Because of the limited scope and elementary character of this book it seemed appropriate to limit ourselves to the spaces called metric (whose definition is given in Chapter IX, § 1). Their generality is sufficient for the majority of important applications; in particular, subsets of n-dimensional Euclidean space, sequence spaces (of Hilbert and Fréchet), and the space of continuous functions are metric spaces; at the same time, the very concept of a metric space is especially simple and geometrically clear.

In Chapters IX-XII we give the fundamental concepts with which we must deal in all parts of topology. The reader knows many of these concepts from analysis, in relation to the space of real or complex numbers (such as accumulation point, neighborhood, closed set, and so on); this refers especially to Chapter XII which contains theorems on continuous functions. Theorems known from analysis, e. g. on uniform continuity, uniform convergence, the Darboux property, are proved here (and in Chapters XV and XVI) under significantly more general hypotheses.

This permits us to recognize the proper extent of these theorems (which also is of didactic significance).

In the further chapters (XIII-XVIII) we gradually confine ourselves to more specific spaces: we give the important properties of separable spaces (still embracing the majority of spaces arising in applications), complete spaces (with the Baire theorem and its consequences), compact spaces (which form the generalization of closed bounded subsets of Euclidean space), connected spaces (connectedness is the precise statement of the concept of the continuity of a set) and locally connected spaces (as it turns out, curves, surfaces, multi-dimensional varieties or manifolds, with which we have to deal in differential geometry are as a rule locally connected continua).

Chapter XIX contains results from dimension theory. The concept of dimension—even though it dates from antiquity (it appears already in Euclid's *Elements*)—was properly defined only in recent times and this thanks to the use of topological methods. The limitations imposed on the present volume have forced us to refrain from giving some of the proofs.

We shall concern ourselves in more detail with the properties of the n-dimensional simplex, which is the fundamental concept of classical multi-dimensional geometry, in Chapter XX. In particular, we give a proof of the renowned fixed point theorem, due to L. E. J. Brouwer, which has such extensive applications in the theory of differential equations.

Chapter XXI contains, in a very general outline, an introduction to homology theory which forms a fundamental part of *algebraic topology* (for more details, see the bibliography at the end of this Introduction). The latter has various applications in differential and algebraic geometry, the calculus of variations, and in other branches of analysis. This chapter depends on Chapter XX (viz., on the concept of simplex), in contrast, however, to the other chapters of this book, use is made here of algebraic concepts, especially from the theory of groups. This is the origin of the name algebraic topology in contrast to set-theoretic topology, in which we make use of the concepts and theorems of set theory. Worthy of remark is the relation of the individual branches of mathematics which we observe here: topology, being a powerful tool for functional analysis and for various branches of classical analysis, which in its turn is connected, because of its applications, with technology and the natural sciences, itself makes use of the methods of algebra and the theory of sets.

Finally, the last chapter, XXII, conceptually closely related to geometry, concerns theorems on the separation of the plane. Here is given a detailed proof of the Jordan theorem which is a classical theorem of analysis.

In its initial stages, set-theoretic and algebraic topology developed entirely independently and possessed completely different thematic. Set-theoretical topology, formerly called the theory of point sets, and concerning arbitrary subsets of Euclidean space, was begun by G. Cantor, the creator of the theory of sets (circa 1880). Algebraic topology was created by H. Poincaré in the last years of the past century; its objects were n-dimensional polygons and polyhedra. Some reconciliation of these two theories came rather late, about 35 years ago; this was, to a large degree, the work of P. S. Aleksandrov. This period was preceded by the transition from the investigation of subsets of Euclidean space in set-theoretic topology to the investigation of arbitrary topological spaces. This extension of the thematics of topology appeared to a significant degree in connection with the new mathematical investigations concerning the concept of function space and infinite-dimensional spaces introduced by Hilbert.

In the last thirty years or so there has appeared an unusually rich flourishing of topology; many fundamental problems of topology have been solved and new methods developed. Topology, which until recently was a conglomeration of loosely related theorems, became a systematic science, and topological methods penetrated into many other domains of mathematics.

We can recommend the following books to the reader who wishes to increase his knowledge of topology:

P. S. Aleksandrov, *Combinatorial Topology*, Graylock, Rochester 1956 and 1957.

P. S. Aleksandrov and H. Hopf, *Topologie, I*, Edwards, Ann Arbor 1945.

N. Bourbaki, *Topologie Générale*, Actualités Scientifiques N 1045, 1084, 1142, 1143, 1235, Paris 1949-1958.

S. Eilenberg and N. Steenrod, *Foundations of Algebraic Topology*, Princeton 1952.

F. Hausdorff, *Set Theory*, Chelsea, New York 1957.

W. Hurewicz and H. Wallman, *Dimension Theory*, Princeton 1948.

J. L. Kelley, *General Topology*, Van Nostrand, New York 1955.

K. Kuratowski, *Topologie*, Monografie Matematyczne, Warszawa-Wrocław, vol. I, fourth ed. 1958, vol. II, third ed. 1961.

S. Lefschetz, *Introduction to Topology*, Princeton Univ. Press, Princeton 1949.

M. H. A. Newman, *Elements of the Topology of Plane Sets of Points*, Cambridge Univ. Press, Cambridge 1952.

G. Nöbeling, *Grundlagen der Analytischen Topologie*, Springer, Berlin 1954.

L. S. Pontrjagin, *Topological Groups*, Princeton Univ. Press., Princeton 1939.

L. S. Pontrjagin, *Foundations of Combinatorial Topology*, Graylock, Rochester 1952.

H. Seifert and W. Threlfall, *Lehrbuch der Topologie*, Chelsea, New York 1947.

W. Sierpiński, *General Topology*, Univ. of Toronto Press, Toronto 1952.

A. H. Wallace, *An Introduction to Algebraic Topology*, Pergamon Press, London 1957.

G. T. Whyburn, *Analytic Topology*, Coll. Public., New York 1942.

R. L. Wilder, *Topology of Manifolds*, Coll. Public., New York 1949.

We wish to quote also the following elementary books:

E. M. Patterson, *Topology*, Interscience Publ., New York 1956.

G. L. Spencer and D. W. Hall, *Elementary Topology*, John Wiley, New York 1955.

R. Vaidyanathaswamy, *Treatise on Set Topology*, Part I, Indian Mathematical Society, Madras 1947.

CHAPTER IX

METRIC SPACES

§ 1. Metric spaces

Definition. A set X is said to be a *metric space* if to every pair of its elements, i. e. to every pair of *points* x, y belonging to the set X, there is assigned a real number $|x-y| \geqslant 0$, called the *distance from the point* x *to the point* y, which satisfies the following three conditions:

(1) $$|x-y| = 0 \text{ if and only if } x = y\,,$$

(2) $$|x-y| = |y-x|\,,$$

(3) $$|x-y| + |y-z| \geqslant |x-z|\,;$$

the last condition is the so-called *triangle inequality.*

It follows immediately from this definition that every subset of a metric space is itself a metric space (the definition of distance remaining the same).

Examples. 1. Every set of real or complex numbers forms a metric space if the distance between two numbers x and y is understood to be the absolute value of the difference of these numbers. This justifies the symbol we are using for the distance.

2. Euclidean n-space, $\mathcal{E}^n$, whose points are sequences of n real numbers $(x_1, x_2, \ldots, x_n)$, is a metric space under the usual definition of the distance from the point $x = (x_1, x_2, \ldots, x_n)$ to the point $y = (y_1, y_2, \ldots, y_n)$ given by the Pythagorean formula

(4) $$|x-y| = \Big\{\sum_{i=1}^{n} |x_i - y_i|^2\Big\}^{1/2}.$$

This same formula "metrizes" the *cartesian product* $X_1 \times X_2 \times \ldots \times X_n$ of any n metric spaces, $X_1, X_2, \ldots, X_n$.

3. *Hilbert space.* This space is the set of all sequences of real numbers $x = (x_1, x_2, \ldots, x_i, \ldots)$ such that the series $\sum_{i=1}^{\infty} x_i^2$ is convergent. Here the distance between two such sequences is understood to be

$$(5) \qquad |x-y| = \left\{\sum_{i=1}^{\infty} |x_i - y_i|^2\right\}^{1/2}.$$

4. The set of continuous real valued functions defined on the closed interval $0 \leqslant x \leqslant 1$ forms a metric space if the distance between two functions f and g is defined by the formula

$$(6) \qquad |f-g| = \sup |f(x) - g(x)|, \quad \text{where} \quad 0 \leqslant x \leqslant 1.$$

5. An arbitrary set can be considered to be a metric space if we assume that the distance between each pair of distinct points is 1.

§ 2. Diameter of a set. Bounded spaces

The least upper bound of the distances $|x-y|$ between all pairs of points x and y in the metric space X is called the *diameter* of the space X and is denoted by the symbol $\delta(X)$. If X is a circle or a sphere, then its diameter $\delta(X)$ is the diameter in the usual sense.

Metric spaces with finite diameter are said to be *bounded.*

For example, the closed interval $0 \leqslant x \leqslant 1$ is bounded. The same is true of a square and the n-dimensional cube. On the other hand, the half-line $x \geqslant 0$, the real line, and the space $\mathcal{E}^n$ are examples of unbounded spaces.

§ 3. The Hilbert cube

Under the assumption that the spaces $X_1, X_2, \ldots, X_m, \ldots$ are uniformly bounded (i. e. the upper bound of their diameters is finite; see also Chapter XII, § 4, Remark), we define the distance between two points $x = (x_1, x_2, \ldots, x_m, \ldots)$ and $y = (y_1, y_2, \ldots, y_m, \ldots)$ of the infinite cartesian product $X_1 \times X_2 \times \ldots \times X_m \times \ldots$ by means of the formula

$$(7) \qquad |x-y| = \sum_{m=1}^{\infty} (1/2^m)|x_m - y_m| .$$

We shall leave it to the reader to prove that the distance defined in this way satisfies conditions (1)-(3), i. e. that the space $X_1 \times X_2 \times \ldots$ is metric.

We denote the closed interval $0 \leqslant x \leqslant 1$ by $\mathcal{J}$. The space $\mathcal{H} = \mathcal{J} \times \mathcal{J} \times \ldots$ is called the *Hilbert cube*; it is a space all "coordinates" x_m of whose points $x = (x_1, x_2, \ldots, x_m, \ldots)$ are contained in the closed interval $[0, 1]$. The space $\mathcal{H}$, or the infinite power of the closed interval $[0, 1]$, is clearly the natural generalization of the n-dimensional cube.

Exercises

1. Let $\mathcal{E}^2$ be the complex number plane; for points $z, z' \in \mathcal{E}^2$ (where $z \neq z'$) let $||z-z'||$ be defined as follows: in case the line zz' goes through the origin of the coordinate system, take $||z-z'|| = |z-z'|$, and in the contrary case take $||z-z'|| = |z|+|z'|$, where $|z|$ denotes as always the absolute value of z.

Prove that the function $||z-z'||$ can be treated as the distance of z from z', i. e. that it satisfies the conditions of a metric space.

2. Show that if the sets A and B are not void and if $A \subset B$, then $\delta(A) \leqslant \delta(B)$.

3. Prove the inequality

$$\delta(A \cup B) \leqslant \delta(A) + \delta(B)$$

under the assumption that $A \cap B \neq \emptyset$.

4. Let X be a metric space and let $a \in X$. We assign to each point $p \in X$ the function f_p defined as follows:

$$f_p(x) = |x-p| - |x-a| ;$$

prove that $|f_p - f_q| = |p-q|$, where the distance between functions is defined by means of formula (6).

5. Let X and Y be two metric spaces. Let Φ denote the set of all bounded functions which map the space X into subsets of the space Y (we say that the function f is bounded provided that the diameter $\delta[f(X)]$ is finite). Prove that if we define the distance $|f-g|$ for $f, g \in \Phi$ by means of formula (6), the set Φ becomes a metric space (i. e. that conditions (1)-(3) are satisfied).

CHAPTER X

LIMIT OF A SEQUENCE OF POINTS. CLOSURE OF A SET

We define the concept of the limit of a sequence of points, which is a fundamental concept in topology, by making use of the concept of the limit of a sequence of real numbers which is known from elementary analysis.

§ 1. Convergence of a sequence of points

Definition. A sequence of points $p_1, p_2, \ldots, p_n, \ldots$ of a metric space is *convergent* to the point p of this space if the sequence of real numbers $|p_n - p|$ is convergent to zero. We then call the point p the *limit* of the sequence $p_1, p_2, \ldots, p_n, \ldots$ and we write $p = \lim\limits_{n\to\infty} p_n$.

Using the symbolism of logic, we write this definition in the following form:

$$(1)\qquad (\lim_{n\to\infty} p_n = p) \equiv (\lim_{n\to\infty} |p_n - p| = 0)$$

$$(2)\qquad \equiv \bigwedge_\varepsilon \bigvee_k \bigwedge_n [(n > k) \Rightarrow (|p_n - p| < \varepsilon)] .$$

The definition of the convergence of a sequence of points in a metric space can be given in another form, very suitable for considerations in the sequel, by introducing the concept of sphere.

An *(open) spherical neighborhood of* p with radius $\varepsilon > 0$, or more briefly $K(p, \varepsilon)$, is the set of points x whose distance from the point p is less than ε:

$$(3)\qquad K(p, \varepsilon) = \underset{x}{E}(|x - p| < \varepsilon) .$$

In the space of real numbers an open spherical neighborhood is an open interval and in the plane it is a circular disk without the boundary. Hence our terminology corresponds to Euclidean 3-space.

§ 2. Properties of the limit

THEOREM 1. *A necessary and sufficient condition that* $\lim_{n\to\infty} p_n = p$, *is that every spherical neighborhood* K *of* p *contains all the points of the sequence* $p_1, p_2, \ldots$, *with perhaps the exception of a finite number* (i. e. there exists a k such that $p_n \in K$ for all $n > k$).

In order to prove this we substitute $p_n \in K(p, \varepsilon)$ into formula (2) instead of $|p_n - p| < \varepsilon$ (which we can do by virtue of (3)).

THEOREM 2. *Every convergent sequence is bounded*; in other words: *the set of terms in a convergent sequence is bounded.*

For let $p = \lim_{n\to\infty} p_n$ and let Z be the set of terms of the sequence $p_1, p_2, \ldots, p_n, \ldots$ By virtue of our assumption there exists a k such that for $n > k$ we have $|p_n - p| < 1$. Let ϱ denote the maximal of the $k+1$ numbers

$$|p_1 - p|, |p_2 - p|, \ldots, |p_n - p|, 1.$$

Hence we have $|p_n - p| \leqslant \varrho$ for every n. Therefore

$$|p_n - p_m| \leqslant |p_n - p| + |p - p_m| \leqslant 2\varrho, \quad \text{i. e.} \quad \delta(Z) \leqslant 2\varrho.$$

The proofs of the following theorems do not deviate from the proofs given in elementary analysis for sequences of real numbers.

THEOREM 3. *If* $p_n = p$ *for* $n = 1, 2, \ldots$, *then* $\lim_{n\to\infty} p_n = p$.

THEOREM 4 (ON SUBSEQUENCES). *If* $\lim_{n\to\infty} p_n = p$ *and* $k_1 < k_2 < \ldots$, *then*

$$\lim_{n\to\infty} p_{k_n} = p.$$

THEOREM 5. *Every sequence* $p_1, p_2, \ldots$, *which is not convergent to* p, *contains a subsequence none of whose subsequences is convergent to* p.

THEOREM 6. *Neither the convergence of a sequence nor its limit depend on the initial finite number of terms of this sequence.*

This means that the addition or the omission of a finite number of terms of a convergent sequence does not affect either its convergence or the value of its limit.

THEOREM 7. *If* $\lim_{n\to\infty} p_n = p = \lim_{n\to\infty} q_n$, *then the sequence* $p_1, q_1, p_2, q_2, \ldots$ *is convergent to* p.

§ 3. Limit in the cartesian product

Let $Z = X \times Y$ be the cartesian product of the metric spaces X and Y.

THEOREM 1. *A necessary and sufficient condition that a sequence of points* $z_n = \langle x_n, y_n \rangle$ *of the space* $X \times Y$ *be convergent to the point* $z = \langle x, y \rangle$ *is that* $\lim_{n\to\infty} x_n = x$ *and* $\lim_{n\to\infty} y_n = y$.

Proof. Let $\lim_{n\to\infty} z_n = z$ and let $\varepsilon > 0$. Hence there exists a k such that $|z_n - z| < \varepsilon$ for $n > k$. But since

$$|z_n - z| = \{|x_n - x|^2 + |y_n - y|^2\}^{1/2} \geqslant |x_n - x|$$

(cf. Chapter IX, § 2, (4)), we also have $|x_n - x| < \varepsilon$ for $n > k$, i. e. $\lim_{n\to\infty} x_n = x$.

In an analogous manner we can prove that $\lim_{n\to\infty} y_n = y$.

Let us assume conversely that $\lim_{n\to\infty} x_n = x$ and $\lim_{n\to\infty} y_n = y$. Let $\varepsilon > 0$. Then there exists a k such that for $n > k$ we have

$$|x_n - x| < \varepsilon \quad \text{and} \quad |y_n - y| < \varepsilon,$$

whence

$$|z_n - z| = \{|x_n - x|^2 + |y_n - y|^2\}^{1/2} < \varepsilon\sqrt{2}\,.$$

Therefore $\lim_{n\to\infty} z_n = z$.

THEOREM 2. *Let* $X_1, X_2, \ldots, X_m, \ldots$ *be uniformly bounded spaces* (see also Chapter XII, § 4, Remark). *Let* $\varrho > \delta(X_m)$ *for* $m = 1, 2, \ldots$ *Let* $x^n = (x_1^n, x_2^n, \ldots, x_m^n, \ldots)$ *for* $n = 1, 2, \ldots$ *be a point of the space* $X_1 \times X_2 \times \ldots \times X_m \times \ldots$ (*i. e.* $x_m^n \in X_m$ *for* $m = 1, 2, \ldots$), *metrized with the aid of formula* (7) *of Chapter* IX, § 3. *A necessary and sufficient condition that this sequence be convergent to the point* $x = (x_1, x_2, \ldots, x_m, \ldots)$ *is that* $\lim_{n\to\infty} x_m^n = x_m$ *for* $m = 1, 2, \ldots$, *i. e.*

$$(\lim_{n\to\infty} x^n = x) \equiv \bigwedge_m (\lim_{n\to\infty} x_m^n = x_m).$$

Proof. Let $\lim_{n\to\infty} x^n = x$ and let $\varepsilon > 0$. Therefore, for a fixed m there exists a k such that

$$|x^n - x| < \varepsilon/2^m$$

for $n > k$.

Since, however,

$$(1/2^m)|x_m^n - x_m| \leqslant |x^n - x|$$

by (7) (Chapter IX, § 3), we have

$$|x_m^n - x_m| \leqslant 2^m |x^n - x| < 2^m \cdot \varepsilon/2^m = \varepsilon$$

for $n > k$.

This means that

(4) $$\lim_{n\to\infty} x_m^n = x_m.$$

Let us assume next that equality (4) holds for $m = 1, 2, \ldots$

Let $\varepsilon > 0$. Let i be a natural number such that

(5) $$1/2^i < \varepsilon.$$

Applying equality (4) for $m = 1, 2, \ldots, i$, there exists a k such that for $n > k$ the inequalities

(6) $$|x_1^n - x_1| < \varepsilon,\ |x_2^n - x_2| < \varepsilon,\ \ldots,\ |x_i^n - x_i| < \varepsilon$$

hold. Therefore, because of (5) and (6),

$$|x^n - x| = \sum_{m=1}^{\infty} (1/2^m)|x_m^n - x_m| = \sum_{m=1}^{i} (1/2^m)|x_m^n - x_m| +$$

$$+ \sum_{m=i+1}^{\infty} (1/2^m)|x_m^n - x_m| < \sum_{m=1}^{i} (\varepsilon/2^m) + \sum_{m=i+1}^{\infty} \delta(X_m)/2^m < \varepsilon + \varepsilon \cdot \varrho$$

for all $n > k$, i. e. $|x^n - x| < \varepsilon(1 + \varrho)$. It follows from this that $\lim_{n\to\infty} x^n = x$.

§ 4. Closure of a set

Let A be a subset of a given metric space. We denote by $\bar{A}$ a subset of this space, called the *closure of the set* A, defined in the following way: a point p is in the set $\bar{A}$ if and only if there exists a sequence of points $p_1, p_2, \ldots, p_n, \ldots$ in the set A such that $\lim_{n\to\infty} p_n = p$.

THEOREM. $p \in \bar{A}$ *if and only if*

$$(7) \qquad K \cap A \neq \emptyset$$

for every open spherical neighborhood K of p.

For, if $p = \lim_{n\to\infty} p_n$, where $p_n \in A$, then $K \cap A \neq \emptyset$ by virtue of Theorem 1, § 2.

Next, let us assume that condition (7) is satisfied for every K. Let $K_n = K(p, 1/n)$. By assumption, $K_n \cap A \neq \emptyset$, i. e., for every n there exists a point $p_n \in K_n \cap A$. By the definition of K_n we have $|p_n - p| < 1/n$, and therefore $p = \lim_{n\to\infty} p_n$. Inasmuch as $p_n \in A$ we have $p \in \bar{A}$.

Remark. The above theorem can be formulated as follows: *A necessary and sufficient condition that the point p does not belong to the set $\bar{A}$ is, that there exist a spherical neighborhood of p which is disjoint from the set A.*

§ 5. Four fundamental properties of the closure

We shall prove the following properties of the operation $\bar{A}$:

$$\text{(I)} \qquad \overline{A \cup B} = \bar{A} \cup \bar{B},$$

$$\text{(II)} \qquad A \subset \bar{A},$$

$$\text{(III)} \qquad \bar{\emptyset} = \emptyset,$$

$$\text{(IV)} \qquad \overline{(\bar{A})} = \bar{A}.$$

Proof of property (I). Let $p \in \overline{A \cup B}$. This means that $p = \lim_{n\to\infty} p_n$, where $p_n \in A \cup B$. It follows from this that there exists a sequence of indices $k_1 < k_2 < \ldots$ such that for every n we have $p_{k_n} \in A$ or for every n we have

$p_{k_n} \in B$. Since $p = \lim_{n\to\infty} p_{k_n}$ (by virtue of Theorem 4, § 2), in the first case we obtain $p \in \bar{A}$, and in the second case $p \in \bar{B}$. Hence, in every case we have $p \in \bar{A} \cup \bar{B}$.

We have thus proved that

$$\overline{A \cup B} \subset \bar{A} \cup \bar{B}. \tag{8}$$

In order to prove the converse inclusion we shall show that

$$(A \subset B) \Rightarrow (\bar{A} \subset \bar{B}), \tag{I'}$$

i. e. that the condition

$$A \subset B \tag{9}$$

implies the condition

$$\bar{A} \subset \bar{B}. \tag{10}$$

For, if $p \in \bar{A}$, then $p = \lim_{n\to\infty} p_n$, where $p_n \in A$. Because of the inclusion (9) we deduce from this that $p_n \in B$ and hence that $p \in \bar{B}$.

Since $A \subset A \cup B$ and $B \subset A \cup B$, we deduce from (I′) that

$$\bar{A} \subset \overline{A \cup B} \quad \text{and} \quad \bar{B} \subset \overline{A \cup B},$$

and hence, adding these two inclusions memberwise, we obtain

$$\bar{A} \cup \bar{B} \subset \overline{A \cup B}. \tag{11}$$

Inclusions (8) and (11) yield equality (I).

In order to prove inclusion (II) it suffices to note that if $p \in A$ then $p = \lim_{n\to\infty} p_n$, where $p_n = p$ for $n = 1, 2, \ldots$ (see Theorem 3, § 2).

Formula (IV) remains to be proved. By virtue of inclusion (II) we have $\bar{A} \subset \overline{(\bar{A})}$. Therefore, it suffices to prove that $\overline{(\bar{A})} \subset \bar{A}$.

Hence, let $p \in \overline{(\bar{A})}$. By virtue of the theorem of § 4, for every spherical neighborhood K of p we have $K \cap \bar{A} \neq \emptyset$. Hence, let $q \in K \cap \bar{A}$. Let us choose a spherical neighborhood L of q such that $L \subset K$ (to this end it suffices that the radius of L be less than the difference of two numbers: the radius of K and the distance of q from p). Since $q \in \bar{A}$, L is a sphere with center q, and hence (by virtue of the theorem of § 4) we have $L \cap A \neq \emptyset$. But since $L \subset K$, we therefore have $(L \cap A) \subset (K \cap A)$, whence $K \cap A \neq \emptyset$. We deduce from this that $p \in \bar{A}$ (by virtue of the very same theorem of § 4).

Remark. Properties (I)-(IV), which belong to the closure (of a set lying in a metric space), defined above, can be taken as the axioms of a topological space, if we understand by a *topological space* a set in which the operation of closure has been defined and which assigns to each subset A of this space some subset $\bar{A}$ of the same space in such a manner that conditions (I)-(IV) are satisfied. Every metric space in which closure has been defined in the manner given in § 4 is therefore a topological space.

In the sequel, we shall consider mainly metric spaces; however, we shall introduce many theorems making use of formulas (I)-(IV) only. These theorems will therefore be true in every topological space.

§ 6. Further algebraic properties of the operation of closure

Let X denote the metric space under consideration. Then the following formulas hold:

1. $\bar{X} = X$.

This formula follows immediately from the definition of closure.

2. $\bar{A} - \bar{B} \subset \overline{A - B}$.

Proof. $A \cup B = (A - B) \cup B$, and therefore $\overline{A \cup B} = \overline{(A - B) \cup B}$. From this, by virtue of formula (I), we have $\bar{A} \cup \bar{B} = \overline{A - B} \cup \bar{B}$ and hence $\bar{A} \subset \overline{A - B} \cup \bar{B}$, whence $\bar{A} - \bar{B} \subset \overline{A - B}$.

3. $\overline{A \cap B} \subset \bar{A} \cap \bar{B}$.

Proof. Since $A \cap B \subset A$ and $A \cap B \subset B$, we have, by virtue of property (I′), $\overline{A \cap B} \subset \bar{A}$ and $\overline{A \cap B} \subset \bar{B}$, and therefore $\overline{A \cap B} \subset \bar{A} \cap \bar{B}$.

More generally, the following formula is valid:

4. $\overline{\bigcap_t A_t} \subset \bigcap_t \bar{A}_t$,

where the variable t ranges over an arbitrary set T.

Proof. Since for every $s \in T$ we have $\bigcap_t A_t \subset A_s$, hence by virtue of (I′) we have $\overline{\bigcap_t A_t} \subset \bar{A}_s$, and from this we get $\overline{\bigcap_t A_t} \subset \bigcap_s \bar{A}_s$. Replacing the index s by t we obtain formula 4.

5. $\bigcup_t \bar{A}_t \subset \overline{\bigcup_t A_t}$.

Proof. For every s we have $A_s \subset \bigcup_t A_t$, and hence by virtue of (I′) we have $\bar{A}_s \subset \overline{\bigcup_t A_t}$, and $\bigcup_s \bar{A}_s \subset \overline{\bigcup_t A_t}$. From this we obtain formula 5.

6. *The closure of a set consisting of a single point is this same set:*

$$\overline{\{p\}} = \{p\}.$$

This property is not a consequence of formulas (I)-(IV) [1]; it follows however immediately from the definition of closure. For, if $q = \lim_{n\to\infty} q_n$, where $q_n \in \{p\}$, then $q_n = p$ for $n = 1, 2, \ldots$, and hence by Theorem 3, § 2 $\lim_{n\to\infty} q_n = p$, i. e. $p = q$.

§ 7. Accumulation points and isolated points

A point p is said to be an *accumulation point* of the set A if it is the limit of a sequence of points belonging to A and distinct from p. Every point of the set A which is not an accumulation point of A is called an *isolated point* of A.

For example, the point 0 is (the only) accumulation point of the set consisting of the points $1, 1/2, 1/3, \ldots, 1/n, \ldots$; all the points of this set are its isolated points.

The following theorems are easily proved:

THEOREM 1. *A necessary and sufficient condition that the point p be an accumulation point of the set A is that every spherical neighborhood of p contain some point, distinct from p, of the set A.*

[1]) Topological spaces satisfying Theorem 6 are called $\mathcal{T}_1$-spaces.

THEOREM 2. *A necessary and sufficient condition that the point p be an isolated point of the set A is that there exist a spherical neighborhood K of p such that $K \cap A = \{p\}$.*

§ 8. Derived set

The set of all accumulation points of the set A is called the *derived set* of A and is denoted by A^d.

The derived set has the following easily proved properties.

1. $\bar{A} = A \cup A^d$.
2. $\overline{A^d} = A^d$.
3. $(A \cup B)^d = A^d \cup B^d$.
4. $\bigcup_t A_t^d \subset (\bigcup_t A_t)^d$.
5. $A^{dd} \subset A^d$.

On the other hand—in distinction from the closure—the second derived set need not necessarily be equal to the first. If, for example, A consists of the points $1, 1/2, 1/3, \ldots$, then A^d consists of the point 0, and A^{dd} is the null set. If A is the set of numbers of the form $1/n+1/m$ $(n, m = 1, 2, \ldots)$, then $A^d \neq A^{dd} \neq A^{ddd} = \emptyset$.

Exercises

1. Prove Theorems 3-7, § 2.

2. A $\mathcal{L}^*$ space is a set in which to certain sequences $p_1, p_2, \ldots$ of elements of this set, called *convergent sequences*, there is assigned an element $p = \lim_{n\to\infty} p_n$, called the *limit of the sequence*, in such a way that Theorems 3-5, § 2, are true. Hence, metric spaces are $\mathcal{L}^*$ spaces. Prove that Theorems 6 and 7, § 2, are valid in $\mathcal{L}^*$ spaces.

3. Let a $\mathcal{L}^*$ space be given. If $\lim_{n\to\infty} p_n = p$ and the sequence $q_1, q_2, \ldots$ is obtained from the sequence $p_1, p_2, \ldots$ by finite repetition of its elements, then $\lim_{n\to\infty} q_n = p$.

4. Let Φ denote the space of all real valued continuous functions defined on the closed interval [0, 1] (Chapter IX, § 1, Example 4). Show that the equality $f = \lim_{n\to\infty} f_n$, where $f_n \in \Phi$, holds if and only if the sequence of functions $f_1, f_2, \ldots$ is uniformly convergent to the function f.

CHAPTER XI

VARIOUS TYPES OF SETS

§ 1. Closed sets and open sets

A set A is said to be *closed* if $\bar{A} = A$, that is (because of Chapter X, § 5, (II)) if $\bar{A} \subset A$, or in other words: if the conditions $\lim_{n\to\infty} x_n = x$ and $x_n \epsilon A$ imply that $x \epsilon A$.

A set A is said to be *open* if its complement is closed, that is if $\overline{X-A} = X-A$, or in other words if $A = X - \overline{X-A}$, where X is the entire space.

EXAMPLES. 1. The null set is a closed set, i. e. $\bar{\emptyset} = \emptyset$ (Chapter X, § 5, property (III)); the entire space is a closed set (Chapter X, § 6, property 1). It also follows from this that the null set and the entire space are open sets.

2. In the space of real numbers the closed interval $a \leqslant x \leqslant b$ is a closed set. Our terminology is therefore in agreement with the terminology used in analysis. On the other hand, the open interval $a < x < b$ for $a < b$ is an open set which is not closed.

3. If f is a continuous real valued function defined on the closed interval $a \leqslant x \leqslant b$, then this function, i. e. the set of points

$$A = \underset{x,y}{E}\{[y = f(x)] \wedge (a \leqslant x \leqslant b)\},$$

is a closed set.

For, let $p \epsilon \bar{A}$, i. e. $p = \lim_{n\to\infty} p_n$, where $p_n \epsilon A$. The points p_n are therefore of the form

$$p_n = \langle x_n, f(x_n)\rangle, \tag{1}$$

$$a \leqslant x_n \leqslant b. \tag{2}$$

Let $p = \langle x, y\rangle$. Since $p = \lim_{n\to\infty} p_n$, we have

$$\lim_{n\to\infty} x_n = x\,, \tag{3}$$

$$\lim_{n\to\infty} f(x_n) = y\,. \tag{4}$$

It follows from (2) and (3) that $a \leqslant x \leqslant b$.

But because of the continuity of the function f, it follows from (3) that

$$\lim_{n\to\infty} f(x_n) = f(x)\,,$$

and hence $y = f(x)$ by virtue of (4), i. e. $p = \langle x, f(x)\rangle$ and by the definition of the set A we have $p \in A$.

We have thus proved that $\bar{A} \subset A$, i. e. that the set A is closed.

4. Every finite set is closed.

We omit the easy proof of this assertion. A proof can be based on property 6 of Chapter X, § 6, and on formula (I) of Chapter X, § 5.

5. The set of integers, as well as each of its subsets, is closed in the space of real numbers.

6. The derived set A^d is a closed set (see Chapter X, § 8, property 2).

7. If p is an isolated point of the space then the set $\{p\}$ is open (and also closed).

§ 2. Operations on closed sets and open sets

THEOREM 1. *The union of two closed sets is a closed set.*

For, if the sets A and B are closed, i. e. $\bar{A} = A$ and $\bar{B} = B$, then

$$\overline{A \cup B} = \bar{A} \cup \bar{B} = A \cup B\,.$$

This theorem can be generalized (by induction) to an arbitrary *finite* number of sets. The union of an infinite number of closed sets may be a non closed set: if, e. g. $A_n = \{1/n\}$ then the union $A_1 \cup A_2 \cup \ldots$ is not a closed set (in the space of real numbers), since the point 0 does not belong to it but it belongs to its closure.

THEOREM 2. *The intersection of an arbitrary number of closed sets is a closed set.*

In fact, if the sets A_t are closed, i. e. $\bar{A}_t = A_t$, then by formula 4 of Chapter X, § 6, we have

$$\overline{\bigcap_t A_t} \subset \bigcap_t \bar{A}_t = \bigcap_t A_t,$$

and hence the set $\bigcap_t A_t$ is closed.

THEOREM 1′. *The intersection of a finite number of open sets is an open set.*

THEOREM 2′. *The union of an arbitrary number of open sets is an open set.*

These properties follow from properties 1 and 2 using de Morgan formulas (see Chapter II, § 4, (30) and Chapter IV, § 2, (4)):

$$X - A \cap B = (X - A) \cup (X - B), \quad X - \bigcup_t A_t = \bigcap_t (X - A_t)$$

For, if the sets A and B are open, then the sets $X - A$ and $X - B$ are closed, and hence the set $X - A \cap B = (X - A) \cup (X - B)$ is also closed, i. e. the set $A \cap B$ is open. The generalization of the theorems to the case of an arbitrary finite number of sets is immediate.

If the sets A_t are open, i. e. the sets $X - A_t$ are closed, then the set $X - \bigcup_t A_t = \bigcap_t (X - A_t)$ is closed, and hence the set $\bigcup_t A_t$ is open.

Remark. Theorems 1, 1′ and 2, 2′ are examples of a so-called *duality* in topology: to every theorem on closed sets there corresponds, by virtue of the de Morgan formulae, a theorem on open sets, and conversely.

§ 3. Interior and boundary of a set. Neighborhood of a point

Definitions. For an arbitrary set A, the set

$$\mathrm{Int}(A) = X - \overline{X - A}$$

is called the *interior* of the set A, and the set

$$\mathrm{Fr}(A) = \bar{A} \cap \overline{X - A}$$

is called the *boundary* of the set A.

Let us analyze the above definitions more closely.

The condition $p \in X - \overline{X-A}$ means that $p \notin \overline{X-A}$. Hence, a point p belongs to the set $\mathrm{Int}(A)$ if and only if there exists a spherical neighborhood K of p such that $K \cap (X-A) = \emptyset$, i. e. $K \subset A$ (cf. Chapter X, § 4, Remark). Interior points of a set A (i. e. those belonging to the interior of the set) are therefore the points p for which there exists a spherical neighborhood contained in the set A.

By definition, a set A is open if and only if $A = X - \overline{X-A}$, i. e. if $A = \mathrm{Int}(A)$. Hence, for every point p of an open set A, there exists a sphere, with center at p, lying in the set A. This property also characterizes open sets.

It follows from this that $K(p, \varepsilon)$ is an open set. For if $x \in K(p, \varepsilon)$, then $K(x, \varepsilon - |x-p|) \subset K(p, \varepsilon)$.

As follows from the definition (cf. the theorem in Chapter X, § 4), the boundary points p of the set A have the property that every $K(p, \varepsilon)$ has points in common with the set A, as well as with the complement of A.

The interior of the closed interval $a \leqslant x \leqslant b$ in the space of real numbers is the open interval $a < x < b$ and its boundary is the set consisting of its endpoints a and b.

The interior of the closed disk $E_x\{|x-p| \leqslant \varrho\}$ on the plane is the open disk $E_x\{|x-p| < \varrho\}$ and its boundary is the circumference $E_x\{|x-p| = \varrho\}$.

A set A is said to be a *neighborhood* of a point p if $p \in \mathrm{Int}(A)$, i. e. if p is an interior point of the set A. Hence an open set is a neighborhood of each of its points. Every neighborhood of the point p contains an open neighborhood of the point p, namely its interior.

We say, more generally, that A is a *neighborhood of the set* B if $B \subset \mathrm{Int}(A)$.

§ 4. Dense sets and boundary sets

A set A is said to be *dense* if $\bar{A} = X$. A set A is said to be a *boundary set* if its complement is a dense set,

i. e. if $\overline{X-A} = X$. (A set whose closure is a boundary set is also said to be a *nowhere dense* set.)

Obviously, every set which contains a dense set is dense and a subset of a boundary set is a boundary set.

In the space $\mathcal{E}$ of all real numbers, the set of rational numbers is both a dense and a boundary set. In the plane $\mathcal{E}^2$ a straight line is a boundary set.

It can be easily proved (applying the theorem of Chapter X, § 4) that the following theorems are valid:

THEOREM 1. *A set A is dense if and only if in every spherical neighborhood there exist points which belong to A.*

THEOREM 2. *A set A is a boundary set if and only if in every spherical neighborhood there exist points which do not belong to A.*

THEOREM 3. *A closed set A is a boundary set if and only if for every spherical neighborhood K there exists a spherical neighborhood $L \subset K$ such that $L \cap A = \emptyset$.*

The union of two boundary sets might not be a boundary set. For example, the set of all rational numbers and the set of all irrational numbers are boundary sets (in the space of real numbers), but their union is not a boundary set.

On the other hand, the following theorem can be proved:

THEOREM 5. *If a set A is a boundary set and the set B is a closed boundary set, then $A \cup B$ is a boundary set.*

Hint for the proof. Applying Formula 2 of Chapter X, § 6, we have

$$X-B = \overline{X-A}-\bar{B} \subset \overline{(X-A)-B} = \overline{X-(A \cup B)}.$$

§ 5. Sets dense in themselves

A set each of whose points is an accumulation point of this set is said to be a set *dense in itself*.

Hence these sets are characterized by the inclusion

$$A \subset A^d \tag{1}$$

or—what amounts to the same thing—by the condition that they do not contain any isolated points.

THEOREM 1. *The closure of a set dense in itself is dense in itself.*

Proof. Let A be a set which is dense in itself and therefore satisfying formula (1). From this, by virtue of formula (1) of Chapter X, § 8, we have

$$A^d = A \cup A^d = \bar{A}, \tag{2}$$

and therefore, applying formulas 3 and 5 of Chapter X, § 8, we obtain

$$(\bar{A})^d = (A \cup A^d)^d = A^d \cup A^{dd} = A^d,$$

whence by (2), we have $(\bar{A})^d = \bar{A}$. Hence, the set $\bar{A}$ satisfies condition (1).

THEOREM 2. *The union of an arbitrary number of sets which are dense in themselves is a set dense in itself.*

For, if $A_t \subset A_t^d$, then, by virtue of formula (4) of Chapter X, § 8, we have

$$\bigcup_t A_t \subset \bigcup_t A_t^d \subset (\bigcup_t A_t)^d.$$

THEOREM 3. *Each space is the union of two sets of which one is closed and dense in itself and the other does not contain any non-empty subset which is dense in itself*[1]).

Proof. Let C denote the union of all subsets of the given space which are dense in themselves. It follows from Theorem 2 that the set C is dense in itself and therefore, by virtue of Theorem 1, the set $\bar{C}$ is also dense in itself and hence it is a subset of the set C. Thus $\bar{C} \subset C$, i. e. the set C is closed. Finally, the set $X - C$, being disjoint from C, does not contain non-empty sets which are dense in themselves.

---

[1]) Sets which are simultaneously closed and dense in themselves are also called *perfect sets*. They are therefore characterized by the equality $A = A^d$. Sets which do not contain any non-empty subset which is dense in itself are also called *scattered sets*.

* § 6. Borel sets

Borel sets are sets which belong to the smallest family $\boldsymbol{R}$ of subsets of a given space satisfying the following conditions:

(a) *every closed set belongs to* $\boldsymbol{R}$,

(b) *if* $X_n \in \boldsymbol{R}$ *for* $n = 1, 2, \ldots$, *then* $\bigcup_{n=1}^{\infty} X_n \in \boldsymbol{R}$,

(c) *if* $X_n \in \boldsymbol{R}$ *for* $n = 1, 2, \ldots$, *then* $\bigcap_{n=1}^{\infty} X_n \in \boldsymbol{R}$.

A family of Borel sets is therefore, in the sense of the terminology of Chapter IV, § 7, a Borel family generated by the family of closed sets.

The union of a countable number of closed sets is called an F_σ-set. The intersection of a countable number of open sets is called a G_δ-set.

It follows directly from the definition that every F_σ-set is a Borel set. We shall show in the sequel that also every G_δ-set is a Borel set (see Chapter XII, § 8, Remarks).

Making use of ordinal numbers we can classify Borel sets in classes $\boldsymbol{R}_\alpha$, where $\alpha < \Omega$, in the following manner.

1. The class $\boldsymbol{R}_0$ is the family of all closed sets.

2. For $\alpha = \lambda + n > 0$, where λ is a limit ordinal and n is a nonnegative integer, the class $\boldsymbol{R}_\alpha$ is the family of all sets of the form

$$\bigcap_{k=1}^{\infty} X_k \quad \text{or} \quad \bigcup_{k=1}^{\infty} X_k$$

according to whether n is even or odd, and the sets X_1, $X_2, \ldots$ belong to classes of indices smaller than α.

Therefore, in particular, the class $\boldsymbol{R}_1$ is the family of all F_σ-sets. The class $\boldsymbol{R}_2$ is the family of intersections of a countable number of F_σ-sets (they are the so-called $F_{\sigma\delta}$-sets), and so forth.

It can be proved that for every $\alpha < \Omega$ there exists in the space of real numbers a set of the class $\boldsymbol{R}_\alpha$ which does not belong to any class with index smaller than α.

R e m a r k. If we start with open sets, instead of closed sets (cf. condition (a)), we obtain the Borel family generated by the family of open sets (which, as can be proved, is identical with the Borel family, considered above, generated by the family of closed sets; see Chapter XII, § 7). Here the open sets form the zero class, the G_δ-sets form the first class, the $G_{\delta\sigma}$-sets form the second class, and so forth. This classification is dual to the classification previously considered.

Exercises

1. Prove that if the set G is open, then the following rules are valid for every set X:

(a) $$G \cap \overline{X} \subset \overline{G \cap X},$$

(b) $$\overline{G \cap \overline{X}} = \overline{G \cap X}.$$

2. Prove the formulas:

(a) $\mathrm{Int}(X \cap Y) = \mathrm{Int}(X) \cap \mathrm{Int}(Y)$,

(b) $X \subset Y$ implies $\mathrm{Int}(X) \subset \mathrm{Int}(Y)$,

(c) $\bigcup_t \mathrm{Int}(X_t) \subset \mathrm{Int}(\bigcup_t X_t)$,

(d) $\mathrm{Fr}(X) = X \cap \overline{X^c} \cup (\overline{X} - X)$,

(e) $\overline{X} = X \cup \mathrm{Fr}(X)$,

(f) $\mathrm{Fr}(X \cup Y) \cup \mathrm{Fr}(X \cap Y) \cup (\mathrm{Fr}(X) \cap \mathrm{Fr}(Y)) = \mathrm{Fr}(X) \cup \mathrm{Fr}(Y)$,

(g) $\mathrm{Fr}[\mathrm{Int}(X)] \subset \mathrm{Fr}(X)$,

(h) $\mathrm{Int}(X) \cap \mathrm{Fr}(X) = \emptyset$.

3. Prove that: (a) the complement of a G_δ-set is an F_σ-set, (b) the union of an infinite sequence of F_σ-sets is an F_σ-set; the intersection of two F_σ-sets is an F_σ-set. State theorems on G_δ sets which are the duals of (b) (use the de Morgan rules).

4. Since an arbitrary subset E of a metric space $\mathfrak{X}$ is also a metric space, we can define for every set $A \subset E$ the closure of A in the space E or the so-called *relative closure* of A in E as follows: we put a point p into the relative closure of the set A in E if $p \in E$ and $p = \lim_{n\to\infty} p_n$, where $p_n \in A$. This means that $p \in \overline{A} \cap E$.

The set $\overline{A} \cap E$ is therefore the relative closure of the set A in E.

Prove the following theorems (for topological spaces, assuming that $\overline{A} \cap E$ is by definition the relative closure of A in E):

(a) The relative closure satisfies axioms I-IV relativized to the set E, i. e. for arbitrary sets $A \subset E$ and $B \subset E$, we have

$$(\mathrm{I}_E)\quad \overline{A \cup B} \cap E = (\overline{A} \cap E) \cup (\overline{B} \cap E), \qquad (\mathrm{II}_E)\quad A \subset (\overline{A} \cap E),$$

$$(\mathrm{III}_E)\quad \overline{\emptyset} \cap E = \emptyset, \qquad (\mathrm{IV}_E)\quad \overline{\overline{A} \cap E} \cap E = \overline{A} \cap E.$$

(b) The set A is open in E if

$$A = E - \overline{E - A},$$

and A is closed in E if

$$\bar{A} \cap E = A.$$

(c) A necessary and sufficient condition that the set A be closed (open) in E is, that it be the intersection of the set E and a closed (open) set.

(d) The relative boundary of the set A in E is the set

$$\mathrm{Fr}_E(A) = \bar{A} \cap E \cap \overline{E - A},$$

and the relative interior of the set A in E is

$$\mathrm{Int}_E(A) = E - \overline{E - A}.$$

5. Show that if the set A is closed in the space X and the set B is closed in the space Y, then the set $A \times B$ is closed in the space $X \times Y$.

Prove the analogous theorem on open sets.

6. Let $A \subset X$, $B \subset Y$. Prove the following formulas:

$$\mathrm{Int}(A \times B) = \mathrm{Int}(A) \times \mathrm{Int}(B),$$
$$\mathrm{Fr}(A \times B) = [\mathrm{Fr}(A) \times B] \cup [A \times \mathrm{Fr}(B)].$$

7. A necessary and sufficient condition that the cartesian product $A \times B$ be dense in itself is that one of the sets A and B be dense in itself.

8. Every open subset of a dense in itself space is dense in itself.

9. If the sets A and $X - A$ are boundary sets, then the space X is dense in itself.

10. The set $\mathrm{Int}[\mathrm{Fr}(A)]$ is dense in itself.

11. By a *Hausdorff space* we understand an arbitrary set X in which to every element p there are assigned certain subsets of the set X—called the *neighborhoods* of p—in such a way that the following four conditions are satisfied:

A. Every point $p \in X$ belongs to each of its neighborhoods.

B. If U and V are neighborhoods of the point p, then there exists a neighborhood of p contained in $U \cap V$.

C. If U is a neighborhood of p and $q \in U$, then there exists a neighborhood of q contained in U.

D. If $p \neq q$, then there exist disjoint neighborhoods U of p and V of q.

Prove that 1. every metric space is Hausdorff (where the neighborhoods of the point p are the open sets which contain p) and 2. every Hausdorff space satisfies conditions (I)-(IV) of Chapter X, § 5, if closure in this space is defined as follows: $p \in \bar{X}$ if and only if every neighborhood U of the point p satisfies the inequality $U \cap X \neq \emptyset$.

We call a topological space satisfying condition D a $\mathfrak{T}_2$-space. Give an example of a $\mathfrak{T}_1$-space which is not $\mathfrak{T}_2$.

Prove that statement 1. can be strengthened as follows: every $\mathcal{T}_2$-space is Hausdorff.

12. Prove that the concept of a topological space (see § 5, X, Remark) is equivalent to the following. The term "open set" is considered as primitive term and the following axioms are assumed:

1. The union of an arbitrary number of open sets is open;
2. The intersection of two open sets is open;
3. The null set is open;
4. The space is open.

The closure of A is, by definition, the intersection of all closed sets (i. e. of complements of open sets) containing A.

13. Similarly, prove that the concept of topological space can be defined considering $\mathrm{Int}(A)$ as primitive term and assuming the following axioms:

$$\mathrm{Int}(A \cap B) = \mathrm{Int}(A) \cap \mathrm{Int}(B), \quad \mathrm{Int}(A) \subset A,$$
$$\mathrm{Int}(X) = X, \quad \mathrm{Int}[\mathrm{Int}(A)] = \mathrm{Int}(A).$$

14. A family of open non-void sets is called a *base* of the given space if every open set is the union of a certain number of sets belonging to this family (comp. § 1, XIII, Theorem 2).

A family of sets is called a *subbase* if the family of finite intersections of its elements is a base.

Let $\{X_t\}$, where $t \in T$, be a given family of topological $\mathcal{T}_1$-spaces. Show that the cartesian product $\boldsymbol{P}_t X_t$ (cf. § 8, IV), becomes a $\mathcal{T}_1$-space by assuming that the sets of the form

$$\mathfrak{G} = E_{\mathfrak{z}}(\mathfrak{z}^t \in G),$$

where G is open in X_t, form a subbase.

15. Prove that in the case of metric spaces and of T finite (or countable) the above definition of open sets agrees with their definition based on the concept of distance given by formula (7), § 3, IX.

16. A family $\{X_t\}$ of subsets of a given space is called *locally finite*, if for each point of the space, there is a neighborhood which has points in common but with a finite number of sets X_t. Show, under this assumption, that

$$\overline{\bigcup_t X_t} = \bigcup_t \bar{X}_t.$$

17. Let X be a topological space and ϱ an equivalence relation (comp. Exercise 9, Chapter V). We define a topology in the quotient space X/ϱ assuming that a subset $\boldsymbol{R}$ of X/ϱ is open if and only if the set $S(\boldsymbol{R})$ is open (in X). Show that X/ϱ is a topological space.

18. A relation ϱ is called *closed* if the set $E_{x,y}\, x\varrho y$ is closed in the product space $X \times X$.

Show that if the quotient space X/ϱ is a $\mathcal{T}_2$-space then the relation ϱ is closed.

CHAPTER XII

CONTINUOUS MAPPINGS

§ 1. Continuous mappings

Definition. We say that a function f, defined for every point x of the space X and having values $f(x)$ in the space Y, is *continuous at the point* x_0 if the condition

(1) $$\lim_{n\to\infty} x_n = x_0$$

implies

(2) $$\lim_{n\to\infty} f(x_n) = f(x_0)$$

for every sequence of points $x_1, x_2, \ldots, x_n, \ldots,$ where $x_n \in X$.

This definition is analogous to the definition of the continuity of a real valued function of a real variable, which is known in classical analysis as Heine's definition of the continuity of a function. We shall prove that it is equivalent to the following (Cauchy) definition.

THEOREM. *A necessary and sufficient condition for the function f to be continuous at the point $x_0 \in X$ is that for every $\varepsilon > 0$, there exist a number $\delta > 0$ such that the condition*

(3) $$|x - x_0| < \delta$$

implies

(4) $$|f(x) - f(x_0)| < \varepsilon$$

for every $x \in X$.

Using the symbolism of logic, we can write this condition in the following form:

(5) $$\bigwedge_{\varepsilon} \bigvee_{\delta} \bigwedge_{x} \{(|x - x_0| < \delta) \Rightarrow (|f(x) - f(x_0)| < \varepsilon)\}.$$

Proof. Let us first assume that the function f is continuous at the point x_0 and suppose that condition (5) is not satisfied, i. e. that there exists an $\varepsilon > 0$ such that for arbitrary $\delta > 0$ there exists an x for which $|x-x_0| < \delta$ but $|f(x)-f(x_0)| \geqslant \varepsilon$, i. e.

$$\bigvee_\varepsilon \bigwedge_\delta \bigvee_x (|x-x_0| < \delta) \wedge \big(|f(x)-f(x_0)| \geqslant \varepsilon\big) .$$

Let us take $\delta = 1/n$. There exists (by the axiom of choice) a sequence of points $x_1, x_2, \ldots, x_n, \ldots$ such that

$$|x_n - x_0| < 1/n \tag{6}$$

and

$$|f(x_n) - f(x_0)| \geqslant \varepsilon . \tag{7}$$

Equality (1) follows from inequality (6) and hence, the function f being continuous at the point x_0, we have equality (2). This equality is however in contradiction with inequality (7). Thus, the supposition that condition (5) is not satisfied has led us to a contradiction.

Next, let us assume that the function f satisfies condition (5). Hence for a given number $\varepsilon > 0$, there exists a number $\delta > 0$ satisfying the implication given in formula (5). Let us assume that condition (1) is satisfied. Then there exists a k such that $|x_n - x_0| < \delta$ for $n > k$. Therefore $|f(x_n)-f(x_0)| < \varepsilon$. This means that equality (2) holds and hence the function f is continuous at the point x_0.

§ 2. Functions which are continuous at every point

Such functions are called, briefly, *continuous* functions.

The set of all continuous functions f defined for every $x \in X$ and having values $f(x)$ in the space Y is denoted by the symbol Y^X. [We also denote this set by the symbol $(Y^X)_{\text{top}}$ in order to distinguish it from the symbol used in set theory for the set of all functions f mapping X into Y (see Chapter VI, § 2). Since, however, we shall consider only continuous functions in the sequel we shall omit, in order to simplify our symbolism, the index "top", keeping in mind that the symbol Y^X is used in the topological sense.]

THEOREM 1. *A necessary and sufficient condition for the function f to be continuous, i. e. that $f \in Y^X$, is that for every closed set B contained in the space Y, the set $f^{-1}(B)$ be closed (in the space X); in other words, that the inverse image of a closed set be a closed set.* (The meaning of the symbol f^{-1} was given in Chapter IV, § 4.)

Proof. Let us assume that the function f is continuous and that $\bar{B} = B$. Let us also assume that condition (1) is satisfied where

(8) $x_n \in f^{-1}(B)$, i. e. $f(x_n) \in B$ for $n = 1, 2, \ldots$

Since the function f is continuous, formula (2) holds and therefore $f(x_0) \in \bar{B}$; but since $\bar{B} = B$, it follows from this that $f(x_0) \in B$, i. e. that $x_0 \in f^{-1}(B)$.

Thus the set $f^{-1}(B)$ is closed.

Next, let us assume that the function f is not continuous. We have to define a closed set $B \subset Y$ such that the set $f^{-1}(B)$ is not closed.

By assumption, there exists a sequence $x_1, x_2, \ldots$ satisfying condition (1), but which does not satisfy condition (2). We deduce from this (cf. Chapter X, § 2, Theorem 1) that there exists an open spherical neighborhood K of $f(x_0)$ and a sequence of indices $k_1 < k_2 < \ldots$ such that for all n we have

(9) $$f(x_{k_n}) \notin K\,.$$

Let $B = Y - K$. The set B is therefore closed. At the same time, by virtue of (9) we have

(10) $f(x_{k_n}) \in B$, i. e. $x_{k_n} \in f^{-1}(B)$ for $n = 1, 2, \ldots,$

and

(11) $f(x_0) \in K$, i. e. $f(x_0) \notin B$, hence $x_0 \notin f^{-1}(B)$.

Since $x_0 = \lim_{n\to\infty} x_{k_n}$ (by (1)), the set $f^{-1}(B)$ is not closed.

COROLLARY 1. *A necessary and sufficient condition that the function f be continuous is that the inverse image of every open set be open.*

We obtain easy proof of this corollary from the formula

$$f^{-1}(Y-B) = X-f^{-1}(B)$$

(cf. Chapter IV, § 4, (16)).

COROLLARY 2. *If f is a continuous real valued function then the sets*

$$E_x[f(x) \leqslant a], \quad E_x[f(x) \geqslant a], \quad E_x[a \leqslant f(x) \leqslant b]$$

are closed and the sets

$$E_x[f(x) < a], \quad E_x[f(x) > a], \quad E_x[a < f(x) < b]$$

are open.

This is true because these sets are inverse images of the closed sets

$$E_y(y \leqslant a), \quad E_y(y \geqslant a), \quad E_y(a \leqslant y \leqslant b)$$

and of the open sets

$$E_y(y < a), \quad E_y(y > a), \quad E_y(a < y < b),$$

respectively.

THEOREM 2. *If $f \in Y^X$, then f is a closed set in the space $X \times Y$.*

The proof does not differ from the proof given in Chapter XI, § 1, Example 3, for the special case where X denotes the closed interval $a \leqslant x \leqslant b$ and Y is the set of all real numbers.

§ 3. One-to-one functions. Homeomorphisms

As stated in Chapter V, § 1, f is *one-to-one* if for every two points $x \neq x'$ we have $f(x) \neq f(x')$, i. e. if

(12) $$[f(x) = f(x')] \Rightarrow (x = x').$$

For every one-to-one function f there exists an *inverse function* $g = f^{-1}$ defined (for $y \in f(X)$) by the equivalence

(13) $$[g(y) = x] \equiv [y = f(x)].$$

If the function f is continuous, one-to-one and its inverse f^{-1} is also continuous, then we say that f is a *homeomorphism*.

We say that the spaces X and Y are *homeomorphic* and we write

$$X \underset{\text{top}}{=} Y$$

if there exists a homeomorphic function f which maps X onto the entire space Y, i. e. $Y = f(X)$.

It is clear that

1. $(f^{-1})^{-1} = f$,

2. if f is a homeomorphism then f^{-1} is a homeomorphism,

3. the homeomorphism relation is reflexive, symmetric and transitive.

THEOREM 1. *A necessary and sufficient condition for the function f to be a homeomorphism is that the conditions* (1) *and* (2) *be equivalent, i. e. that we have the equivalence*

$$(14) \qquad (\lim_{n\to\infty} x_n = x_0) \equiv [\lim_{n\to\infty} f(x_n) = f(x_0)] .$$

Proof. Let us assume that the function f is a homeomorphism. Then, f being continuous, we have

$$(15) \qquad (\lim_{n\to\infty} x_n = x_0) \Rightarrow [\lim_{n\to\infty} f(x_n) = f(x_0)] ,$$

and f being one-to-one we have for $g = f^{-1}$ (cf. (13)):

$$(16) \qquad x_n = g(y_n) \quad \text{and} \quad y_n = f(x_n) .$$

Since the function g is continuous by assumption, we therefore have

$$(17) \qquad (\lim_{n\to\infty} y_n = y_0) \Rightarrow [\lim_{n\to\infty} g(y_n) = g(y_0)] ,$$

i. e.

$$(18) \qquad [\lim_{n\to\infty} f(x_n) = f(x_0)] \Rightarrow (\lim_{n\to\infty} x_n = x_0) .$$

Formulas (15) and (18) yield the equivalence (14).

Conversely, if we assume the equivalence (14), then obviously formula (15) holds, and therefore the function f is continuous.

At the same time, formula (18) holds also, whence it follows that the function f is one-to-one. For let x be such that

$$f(x) = f(x_0) \tag{19}$$

and set

$$x_n = x \quad \text{for} \quad n = 1, 2, \ldots \tag{20}$$

Hence we have $\lim_{n\to\infty} f(x_n) = f(x)$, whence by virtue of (19), $\lim_{n\to\infty} f(x_n) = f(x_0)$ and by (18) $\lim_{n\to\infty} x_n = x_0$.

On the other hand it follows from formula (20) that $\lim_{n\to\infty} x_n = x$. From this we have $x = x_0$.

Hence we have proved that the equality $x = x_0$ follows from equality (19). This means, according to (12), that the function f is one-to-one.

Let us therefore set $g = f^{-1}$. Applying formulas (16) and (18) (which is satisfied by assumption), we obtain formula (17). This formula means that the function g is continuous.

Therefore f is a homeomorphism.

THEOREM 2. *A necessary and sufficient condition for a one-to-one function f to be a homeomorphism is that both the images and the inverse images of closed sets be closed sets.*

Proof. Let us assume that the function f is a homeomorphism. Let $g = f^{-1}$. Hence the function g is continuous and therefore by virtue of Theorem 1, § 2, for every closed subset A of the space X the set $g^{-1}(A)$ is closed. Since, however, $g^{-1} = f$ (cf. 1), this means that the set $f(A)$, i. e. the image of the set A, is a closed set.

Also, the inverse images of closed sets are closed sets because the function f is continuous (cf. Theorem 1, § 2).

Conversely, let us assume that the set $f(A)$, as well as the set $f^{-1}(B)$ are closed, provided that the sets

$A \subset X$ and $B \subset Y$ are closed. Since $f = g^{-1}$, it follows from this (by the theorem which we have already cited above) that the functions g and f are continuous, i. e. that f is a homeomorphism.

Remark. As we have already mentioned in the introduction, topology is the study of the invariants of homeomorphisms, i. e. of those properties which—if they belong to a given space—then they hold in every space which is homeomorphic with it. We can prove in general (making use of Theorem 1, § 3) that every property which can be formulated in terms of the concept of limit and in terms of the theory of sets is an invariant of homeomorphisms.

§ 4. Examples of homeomorphisms

1. Let $a \leqslant x \leqslant b$ and $c \leqslant y \leqslant d$, where $a < b$ and $c < d$, be two given closed intervals of real numbers. The function

$$y = \{(d-c)/(b-a)\}x + (bc-ad)/(b-a)$$

is a homeomorphism which maps the first interval onto the second. Hence, any two closed intervals are homeomorphic.

This same function maps the open interval $a < x < b$ homeomorphically onto the open interval $c < y < d$.

2. The function $y = \tan x$ maps the open interval $-\pi/2 < x < \pi/2$ homeomorphically onto the entire set of real numbers. Its inverse is the function $x = \arctan y$.

3. A necessary and sufficient condition for a continuous real valued function, defined on the closed interval $a \leqslant x \leqslant b$, to be a homeomorphism, is that it be strictly monotonic.

4. Let us consider in Euclidean 3-space $\mathcal{E}^3$ the surface of the sphere $x^2+y^2+(z-1)^2 = 1$ and let us draw a line, which is not parallel to the XY-plane, from the point $b = (0, 0, 2)$. Let us assign to the point p of intersection of this line with the surface of the sphere, the point $f(p)$ which is the point of intersection of this line with the plane $z = 0$.

The function f so defined is, as is easy to verify, a homeomorphism which maps the surface of a sphere with the point b removed onto the entire plane. Hence the plane is homeomorphic to the surface of the sphere with one point removed. One makes use of this fact in the theory of analytic functions when it is said that the plane of complex numbers is completed with "the point at infinity" to the surface of the sphere.

Remark 1. In the definition of homeomorphism, the condition of continuity of the inverse map is essential, which means that the continuity of the mapping f does not imply the continuity of the mapping f^{-1}. For example, the function $z = e^{2\pi ix}$ maps the set $0 \leqslant x < 1$ onto the set of complex numbers lying on the circle with equation $|z| = 1$ in a continuous and one-to-one manner. However, the inverse mapping is not continuous at the point $z = 1$.

5. THEOREM. *Every metric space is homeomorphic to a bounded space.*

Let X be a metric space. Let us introduce into it a "new distance" by assuming that $\|x-y\| = |x-y|$ if $|x-y| \leqslant 1$, but $\|x-y\| = 1$ if $|x-y| > 1$.

It is easy to verify that the distance $\|x-y\|$ satisfies conditions (1)-(3) given in the definition of a metric space (Chapter IX, § 1).

In introducing the new distance $\|x-y\|$ between points of the space X, we have transformed this space into a metric space X^*. Let us denote this transformation by f. This function, i. e. $f(x) = x$, is a homeomorphism. This follows from the remark that the conditions

$$\lim_{n\to\infty} \|x_n - y\| = 0 \quad \text{and} \quad \lim_{n\to\infty} |x_n - y| = 0$$

are equivalent.

Since for every two points x and y we have $\|x-y\| \leqslant 1$, hence the space X^* is bounded; namely we have $\delta(X^*) \leqslant 1$.

Remark 2. When, in Chapter IX, § 3, we considered the space $X_1 \times X_2 \times \ldots \times X_m \times \ldots$ we assumed that the spaces X_m were bounded in common. Making use of the theorem we just proved, we can omit this assumption by defining the distance between two points

$$x = (x_1, x_2, \ldots, x_m, \ldots) \quad \text{and} \quad y = (y_1, y_2, \ldots, y_m, \ldots)$$

by the formula

$$|x-y| = \sum_{m=1}^{\infty} (1/2^m)\, \|x_m - y_m\| .$$

Theorem 2 of Chapter X, § 3, also remains valid without the assumption of boundedness.

§ 5. Sequences of functions. Uniform convergence

Let $f_1, f_2, \ldots, f_n, \ldots$ be a given sequence of functions defined on the space X, with values belonging to the space Y. As in analysis, we say that this sequence is *uniformly convergent* to the limit f if for every $\varepsilon > 0$ there exists a k such that for all $n \geqslant k$ and for every $x \in X$ the inequality

$$(21) \qquad |f_n(x) - f(x)| < \varepsilon$$

holds, i. e. if

$$\bigwedge_\varepsilon \bigvee_k \bigwedge_x \bigwedge_n \big[(n \geqslant k) \Rightarrow \big(|f_n(x) - f(x)| < \varepsilon\big)\big] .$$

We shall now prove a theorem which is a generalization of a theorem known from analysis.

THEOREM 1. *The limit of a uniformly convergent sequence of continuous functions is a continuous function.*

Suppose $f_1, f_2, \ldots$ is a uniformly convergent sequence of continuous functions defined in the metric space X with values in the space Y. Let

$$f(x) = \lim_{n\to\infty} f_n(x) .$$

Let $\varepsilon > 0$ be a given number and let $x_0 \in X$ be a given point. Hence, there exists a k such that for every $x \in X$

the inequality

$$(22) \qquad |f_k(x) - f(x)| < \varepsilon$$

holds.

Since the function f_k is continuous at the point x_0, there exists a $\delta > 0$ such that

$$(23) \qquad |f_k(x) - f_k(x_0)| < \varepsilon$$

provided that $|x - x_0| < \delta$. By inequality (22) we have

$$(24) \qquad |f_k(x_0) - f(x_0)| < \varepsilon .$$

We deduce from the inequalities (22), (23) and (24) that the condition $|x - x_0| < \delta$ implies $|f(x) - f(x_0)| < 3\varepsilon$. It follows that f is continuous at the point x_0.

§ 6. Continuity of functions in cartesian products. Functions of several variables

Let $w = f(x, y)$, where $x \in X$, $y \in Y$ and $w \in W$. The function f is a function of the two variables x and y. However, this same function can be considered as a function of one variable, namely the variable $z = \langle x, y \rangle$ running over the cartesian product $Z = X \times Y$.

By the definition of continuity, the function f is continuous at the point $z_0 = \langle x_0, y_0 \rangle$ if

$$\text{(i)} \qquad (\lim_{n\to\infty} z_n = z_0) \Rightarrow [\lim_{n\to\infty} f(z_n) = f(z_0)] .$$

Since the equality $\lim_{n\to\infty} z_n = z_0$ is equivalent to the conjunction $\lim_{n\to\infty} x_n = x_0$ and $\lim_{n\to\infty} y_n = y_0$ (cf. Chapter X, § 3, Theorem 1), condition (i) for the continuity of the function f can be formulated as follows:

$$\text{(ii)} \quad (\lim_{n\to\infty} x_n = x_0) \wedge (\lim_{n\to\infty} y_n = y_0) \Rightarrow [\lim_{n\to\infty} f(x_n, y_n) = f(x_0, y_0)] .$$

Similar remarks can be made about functions of three variables, and more generally, of a finite number of variables. They can also be applied to functions of an infinite number of variables. Thus, the following theorem holds:

THEOREM 1. *Let* $y = f(x)$, *where* $x \in X_1 \times X_2 \times \ldots \times \times X_m \times \ldots$, *i. e.* $x = (x_1, x_2, \ldots, x_m, \ldots)$ *and* $x_m \in X_m$. *A necessary and sufficient condition for the function* f *to be continuous at the point* $x^0 = (x_1^0, x_2^0, \ldots)$, *is that the system of equalities*

$$\lim_{n\to\infty} x_m^n = x_m^0, \quad \text{where} \quad m = 1, 2, \ldots,$$

imply the equality

$$\lim_{n\to\infty} f(x^n) = f(x^0), \quad \text{where} \quad x^n = (x_1^n, x_2^n, \ldots).$$

The proof of this theorem—as in the case of two variables—follows easily from Theorem 2 of Chapter X, § 3 (see also § 4, Remark 2).

Next, we shall consider functions whose values (and not the arguments, as before) belong to a cartesian product.

Suppose f is a function defined in the space T with values belonging to the cartesian product $X \times Y$ of the spaces X and Y. Since $f(t) \in X \times Y$ for every $t \in T$, we have $f(t) = \langle x(t), y(t) \rangle$, where $x(t) \in X$, $y(t) \in Y$. The functions x and y (of the variable t) map the space T onto subsets of the spaces X and Y, respectively.

In the particular case where X and Y denote the space of real numbers, f is a complex valued function.

THEOREM 2. *A necessary and sufficient condition for the function* f *to be continuous is, that the functions* x *and* y *be continuous.*

Proof. Assume the functions x and y are continuous. Let

$$\lim_{n\to\infty} t_n = t; \tag{25}$$

then

$$\lim_{n\to\infty} x(t_n) = x(t) \quad \text{and} \quad \lim_{n\to\infty} y(t_n) = y(t), \tag{26}$$

and hence, by Theorem 1 of Chapter X, § 3, we have

$$(27) \qquad \lim_{n\to\infty} \langle x(t_n), y(t_n)\rangle = \langle x(t), y(t)\rangle ,$$

i. e.

$$(28) \qquad \lim_{n\to\infty} f(t_n) = f(t) ,$$

and therefore the function f is continuous.

On the other hand, if f is continuous then condition (25) implies (28), i. e. (27), and therefore the equations (26) hold. Hence the functions x and y are also continuous.

Now let f be a function defined in the space T with values belonging to the space $X_1 \times X_2 \times \ldots \times X_m \times \ldots$ We can represent the function f in the following way:

$$f(t) = \big(x_1(t), x_2(t), \ldots, x_m(t), \ldots\big) ,$$

where x_m is a mapping of T into X_m.

THEOREM 3. *A necessary and sufficient condition for the function f to be continuous is that the functions x_m be continuous for $m = 1, 2, \ldots$*

Proof. Let us assume that the functions x_m are continuous. Then equation (25) implies

$$(29) \qquad \lim_{n\to\infty} x_m(t_n) = x_m(t) \quad \text{for} \quad m = 1, 2, \ldots ,$$

and hence (cf. Chapter X, § 3, Theorem 2):

$$(30) \qquad \lim_{n\to\infty} \big(x_1(t_n), x_2(t_n), \ldots\big) = \big(x_1(t), x_2(t), \ldots\big) ,$$

i. e.

$$(31) \qquad \lim_{n\to\infty} f(t_n) = f(t) .$$

We deduce from this that the function f is continuous.

On the other hand, it follows—assuming the function f is continuous—that condition (25) implies condition (31), i. e. (30). This means that condition (29) is satisfied and hence the functions x_m $(m = 1, 2, \ldots)$ are continuous.

Continuity of the function $|x-y|$. The distance $|x-y|$ between the points x and y of the metric space X is a function of two variables (with non-negative real values); hence we can consider it to be a function defined on the product $X \times X$.

THEOREM 4. *The function* $|x-y|$ *is continuous.*

Proof. Let

$$\lim_{n\to\infty} x_n = x\,, \qquad \lim_{n\to\infty} y_n = y$$

and let $\varepsilon > 0$ be given. Then there exists a k such that for $n > k$ we have

$$|x-x_n| < \varepsilon\,, \qquad |y_n - y| < \varepsilon\,. \tag{32}$$

From the triangle inequality we obtain (see Fig. 5):

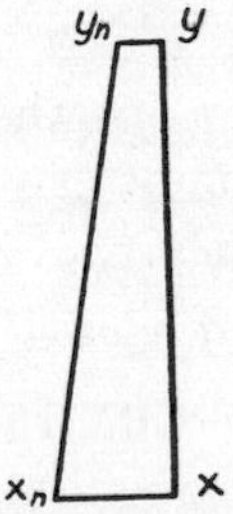

FIG. 5

$$|x-y| \leqslant |x-x_n| + |x_n - y_n| + |y_n - y|\,. \tag{33}$$

It follows from inequalities (32) and (33) that

$$|x-y| < |x_n - y_n| + 2\varepsilon\,. \tag{34}$$

Similarly, from the inequality

$$|x_n - y_n| \leqslant |x_n - x| + |x-y| + |y_n - y|$$

we obtain the inequality

$$|x_n - y_n| < |x-y| + 2\varepsilon\,. \tag{35}$$

By inequalities (34) and (35) we have for $n > k$

$$\big||x_n - y_n| - |x-y|\big| < 2\varepsilon\,.$$

This means that $\lim_{n\to\infty} |x_n - y_n| = |x-y|$ and hence the function $|x-y|$ is continuous.

§ 7. Applications. Distance between a point and a set

The distance between the point x and the non-empty set A is defined to be the number

$$\text{(36)} \quad \varrho(x, A) = \text{greatest lower bound of the numbers } |x-a|, \text{ where } a \in A.$$

We assume, moreover, that $\varrho(x, \emptyset) = 1$. Let us note that:

THEOREM 1. *If* $A = \{y\}$, *then* $\varrho(x, A) = |x-y|$.

THEOREM 2. *If* $\emptyset \neq A \subset B$ *then* $\varrho(x, B) \leqslant \varrho(x, A)$.

THEOREM 3. $[\varrho(x, A) = 0] \equiv (x \in \bar{A})$.

In fact, if $x \in \bar{A}$, then for every $\varepsilon > 0$ there exists a point $a \in A$ such that $|x-a| < \varepsilon$. This means that $\varrho(x, A) = 0$.

Conversely, if $\varrho(x, A) = 0$, then for every $\varepsilon > 0$ there exists a point $a \in A$ such that $|x-a| < \varepsilon$, and hence $x \in \bar{A}$.

From this it follows that:

THEOREM 4. *If* A *is a closed set then*

$$[\varrho(x, A) = 0] \equiv (x \in A).$$

THEOREM 5. *The function* $\varrho(x, A)$ *is continuous (for fixed* A*).*

Proof. The theorem is obvious if the set A is empty. Because of this, we can assume that $A \neq \emptyset$. Let $\delta > 0$ and let

$$\text{(37)} \qquad |x-x'| < \delta.$$

By virtue of (36), there exists a point $a \in A$ (see Fig. 6) such that

$$\text{(38)} \qquad |x-a| \leqslant \varrho(x, A) + \delta.$$

It follows from (37) and (38) that

$$\text{(39)} \quad \varrho(x', A) \leqslant |x'-a| \leqslant |x-a| + |x-x'| < \varrho(x, A) + \delta + \delta.$$

Similarly, we have

$$\text{(40)} \qquad \varrho(x, A) < \varrho(x', A) + 2\delta.$$

Inequalities (39) and (40) yield

(41) $$|\varrho(x, A) - \varrho(x', A)| < 2\delta .$$

This means that inequality (37) implies inequality (41). Hence the function $\varrho(x, A)$ is continuous.

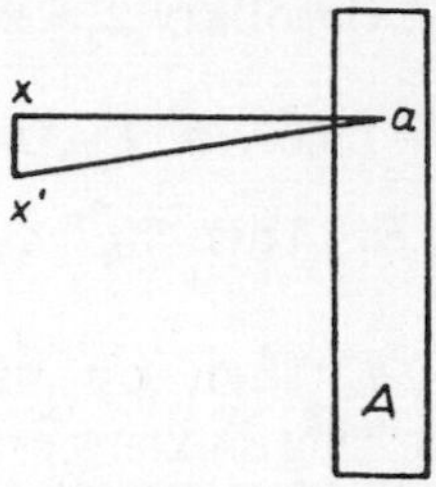

FIG 6

THEOREM 6. *For every pair of disjoint closed sets A and B, there exists a pair of disjoint open sets G and H such that*

(42) $$A \subset G \quad \textit{and} \quad B \subset H .$$

(The property of a space expressed in this theorem is called *normality* of the space).

Proof. Let

$$G = \underset{x}{E}[\varrho(x, A) < \varrho(x, B)] , \quad H = \underset{x}{E}[\varrho(x, B) < \varrho(x, A)] .$$

The sets G and H are open. In fact, by virtue of the continuity of the functions $\varrho(x, A)$ and $\varrho(x, B)$, the function $f(x) = \varrho(x, B) - \varrho(x, A)$ is also continuous. As

$$G = \underset{x}{E}[\varrho(x, B) - \varrho(x, A) > 0] ,$$

the set G is open (cf. Corollary 2, § 2). Similarly, the set H is open.

The proof of the equality $G \cap H = \emptyset$ is immediate.

Finally, the formulas (42) hold. For, if $x \in A$, then by virtue of Theorem 4 we have $\varrho(x, A) = 0$, but $\varrho(x, B) \neq 0$, because x does not belong to B (since $A \cap B = \emptyset$). Therefore, $\varrho(x, A) < \varrho(x, B)$, and from this it follows that $x \in G$.

This means that $A \subset G$. Similarly, $B \subset H$.

*THEOREM 7. *Every closed set is a G_δ-set.*

Proof. Let $F = \overline{F}$. Let us set

$$K(F, \varepsilon) = \underset{x}{E}[\varrho(x, F) < \varepsilon].$$

In view of the continuity of the function $\varrho(x, F)$ the set $K(F, \varepsilon)$ is open (cf. Corollary 2, § 2). We shall show that

$$F = \bigcap_{n=1}^{\infty} K(F, 1/n).$$

In fact, if $x \in F$, then $\varrho(x, F) = 0$ and hence $x \in K(F, 1/n)$.

Conversely, if $x \notin F$, then by virtue of Theorem 4, $\varrho(x, F) > 0$ and hence there exists an n such that $\varrho(x, F) > 1/n$; therefore $x \notin K(F, 1/n)$.

Remarks. If follows immediately from Theorem 7 that every open set is an F_σ-set (and hence every G_δ-set is an $F_{\sigma\delta}$-set). It also follows that condition (a) in the definition of Borel sets (Chapter XI, § 6) can be replaced by:

(a′) *every open set belongs to* $\boldsymbol{R}$.

*§ 8. Extension of continuous functions. Tietze theorem [1])

LEMMA 1. *For every pair of disjoint closed sets A and B in the metric space X, there exists a continuous real valued function f defined on the entire space X and satisfying the following conditions:*

$$f(x) = \begin{cases} -1 & \text{for} \quad x \in A, \\ 1 & \text{for} \quad x \in B, \end{cases} \tag{43}$$

$$-1 < f(x) < 1 \quad \text{for} \quad x \notin A \cup B. \tag{44}$$

It is easy to prove, using Theorems 3-5, § 7, that the function f defined by the formula

$$f(x) = \{\varrho(x, A) - \varrho(x, B)\}/\{\varrho(x, A) + \varrho(x, B)\}$$

satisfies the conditions set forth in the lemma.

[1]) We shall make use of Tietze theorem in the last chapter.

LEMMA 2. *If f is a continuous real valued function defined on a closed subset of the metric space X such that $|f(x)| \leqslant \mu$ $(\neq 0)$, then there exists a continuous function g defined on the entire space X and satisfying the following conditions:*

$$|g(x)| \leqslant (1/3)\mu \quad \textit{for all} \quad x \in X, \tag{45}$$

$$|g(x)| < (1/3)\mu \quad \textit{for all} \quad x \in X-F, \tag{46}$$

$$|f(x)-g(x)| \leqslant (2/3)\mu \quad \textit{for all} \quad x \in F. \tag{47}$$

Proof. Let

$$A = \underset{x}{E}[f(x) \leqslant (-1/3)\mu] \quad \text{and} \quad B = \underset{x}{E}[f(x) \geqslant (1/3)\mu].$$

The sets A and B are disjoint and closed (see Corollary 2, § 2). The function

$$g(x) = (1/3)\mu\{\varrho(x, A)-\varrho(x, B)\}/\{\varrho(x, A)+\varrho(x, B)\} \tag{48}$$

satisfies the required conditions in virtue of Lemma 1.

TIETZE EXTENSION THEOREM. *Every continuous real valued function f defined on a closed subset F of the metric space X can be extended to the entire space X; i. e. there exists a real valued function f^* defined on the entire space X such that*

$$f^*(x) = f(x) \quad \textit{for} \quad x \in F. \tag{49}$$

Moreover, if f is bounded:

$$|f(x)| \leqslant \mu (\neq 0) \quad \textit{for every} \quad x \in F, \tag{50}$$

then

$$|f^*(x)| < \mu \quad \textit{for every} \quad x \in X-F. \tag{51}$$

Proof. Consider first the case where the function f is bounded and hence satisfies inequality (50). We define a sequence of continuous functions $g_0, g_1, \ldots$ inductively. Let $g_0(x) = 0$ for every $x \in X$. For given $n \geqslant 0$ let us assume that the functions $g_0(x), \ldots, g_n(x)$ satisfy the inequality

$$\left|f(x)-\sum_{i=0}^{n} g_i(x)\right| \leqslant (2/3)^n\mu \quad \text{for} \quad x \in F. \tag{52}$$

In the case $n = 0$ this inequality reduces to inequality (50).

Replacing in the assumptions of Lemma 2: $f(x)$ by $f(x) - \sum_{i=0}^{n} g_i(x)$ and μ by $(2/3)^n\mu$, we obtain a continuous function g_{n+1} defined on the space X and satisfying the following conditions:

$$(53) \qquad |g_{n+1}(x)| \leqslant (2^n/3^{n+1})\mu \quad \text{for} \quad x \in X,$$

$$(54) \qquad |g_{n+1}(x)| < (2^n/3^{n+1})\mu \quad \text{for} \quad x \in X - F,$$

$$(55) \qquad \left| f(x) - \sum_{i=0}^{n+1} g_i(x) \right| \leqslant (2/3)^{n+1}\mu \quad \text{for} \quad x \in F.$$

Thus the continuous functions g_n are defined for all $n = 0, 1, 2, \ldots$

For every $x \in X$ let us set

$$(56) \qquad f^*(x) = \sum_{i=0}^{\infty} g_i(x).$$

It follows from inequalities (52)-(54) that the series (56) is uniformly convergent in the space X; and hence by virtue of Theorem 1, § 5, the function f is continuous.

Moreover, condition (52) implies condition (49), and because of inequality (54), we have for $x \in X - F$:

$$|f^*(x)| = \left| \sum_{i=0}^{\infty} g_i(x) \right| \leqslant \sum_{i=0}^{\infty} |g_{i+1}(x)| < \mu \sum_{i=0}^{\infty} (2^i/3^{i+1}) = \mu,$$

and therefore inequality (51) is also satisfied.

Thus the theorem has been proved for the case where the function f is bounded.

If f is unbounded, we first apply the homeomorphism h which maps the space of all real numbers onto the open interval $-1 < y < 1$, e. g. $h(x) = (2/\pi)\arctan x$. The function hf (the composition of the functions f and h) is continuous and bounded; hence there exists by virtue of the part of the theorem already proved a continuous function h^* defined on the space X and such that

$$h^*(x) = hf(x) \text{ for } x \in F, \quad |h^*(x)| < 1 \text{ for } x \in X.$$

Now let

$$f^*(x) = h^{-1}h^*(x)$$

for every $x \in X$. The function f^* is continuous and for every $x \in F$ we have

$$f^*(x) = h^{-1}hf(x) = f(x).$$

Thus the theorem has been proved in all generality.

COROLLARY 1. *Every continuous function defined on a closed subset F of a metric space X with values belonging to one of the spaces $\mathcal{E}^n$, $\mathcal{J}^n$, $\mathcal{E}\times\mathcal{E}\times\ldots$, $\mathcal{H}$ can be extended to the entire space X.*

We shall prove this corollary, e. g. for the Hilbert cube $\mathcal{H} = \mathcal{J}\times\mathcal{J}\times\ldots$ The proof in the other cases is analogous.

For every $x \in F$ we have $f(x) \in \mathcal{J}\times\mathcal{J}\times\ldots$, and hence

$$f(x) = [f_1(x), f_2(x), \ldots, f_n(x), \ldots],$$

where $f_n(x)$ is the n-th coordinate of the point $f(x)$ in the Hilbert cube, hence a continuous function with real values. Extending each of the functions f_n to a continuous function f_n^* defined on the entire space X, we obtain a function

$$f^*(x) = [f_1^*(x), f_2^*(x), \ldots, f_n^*(x), \ldots]$$

which is the extension of the function f (see Theorem 3, § 6).

COROLLARY 2. *Every continuous function f defined on a closed subset F of a metric space X with values belonging to the sphere $\mathcal{S}_n$ (i. e. to the set of points $x_1^2 + \ldots + x_{n+1}^2 = 1$ of the space $\mathcal{E}^{n+1}$) can be extended to some neighborhood of the set F (with respect to the space X).*

Proof. By virtue of Corollary 1 there exists an extension $f^* \in (\mathcal{E}^{n+1})^X$ of the function f. Let us set

$$G = E_x[f^*(x) \neq 0].$$

Because of the continuity of the function f^*, G is an open set containing the set F (since $|f^*(x)| = |f(x)| = 1$ for $x \in F$). Thus the function

$$g(x) = f^*(x)/|f^*(x)|$$

is the required extension of the function f onto the set G which assumes values belonging to $\mathcal{S}_n$.

Remarks. Spaces which can be substituted in Corollary 1 for $\mathcal{E}^n$, $\mathcal{J}^n$, etc., are called *absolute retracts.* Spaces which in Corollary 2 can be substituted for $\mathcal{S}_n$ are called *neighborhood retracts.* (These concepts were introduced by K. Borsuk.)

This terminology is connected with the concept of retraction. We say, namely, that a subset R of the space X is a *retract* of this space if there exists a continuous transformation f of the space X onto the set R such that $f(x) = x$ for $x \in R$ (this transformation is called a *retraction*; a projection is an example of a retraction).

Thus, an absolute retract is, as can be proved, a space which is a retract of every other space containing it and in which it is closed. A neighborhood retract is not a retract of the entire space, but of some one of its neighborhoods in this space.

These concepts are important generalizations of the concepts of classical n-dimensional geometry: the n-dimensional cube is an absolute retract, every n-dimensional polyhedron is (as can be proved) a neighborhood retract.

Exercises

1. Prove that a necessary and sufficient condition that the function f defined in the space X with values in the space Y be continuous at the point $x \in X$ is that for every set $B \subset Y$ the condition $f(x) \in \mathrm{Int}(B)$ implies the condition $x \in \mathrm{Int}(f^{-1}(B))$; similarly, that it is necessary and sufficient that the implication $[x \in \overline{f^{-1}(B)}] \Rightarrow [f(x) \in \bar{B}]$ hold for every set $B \subset Y$.

Hint: Make use of Theorem 1, § 2.

2. Prove: a necessary and sufficient condition for the function f to be continuous is that every set $A \subset X$ satisfy the inclusion $f(\bar{A}) \subset \overline{f(A)}$;

similarly: it is necessary and sufficient that every set $B \subset Y$ satisfy the inclusion $\overline{f^{-1}(B)} \subset f^{-1}(\bar{B})$.

3. Prove that the composition of two continuous functions is a continuous function.

4. Let the sets A and B be both open or both closed, and let f be a function defined on the set $A \cup B$. Prove that if the function f is continuous on the set A and on the set B, then it is also continuous on the set $A \cup B$.

5. Let f be a function defined on the space X. If the space X is a union of open sets G_t, and if on each of these sets individually the function f is continuous, then f is continuous on the entire space X.

6. Let f be a function defined on the space X. If $X = \bigcup_{n=1}^{\infty} A_n$ where $A_n \subset \mathrm{Int}(A_{n+1})$ and if the function f is continuous on each of the sets A_n, then it is continuous on the entire space X.

7. Prove: a necessary and sufficient condition for the one-to-one function f to be a homeomorphism, is that the condition $f(\bar{A}) = \overline{f(A)}$ be satisfied for arbitrary set A; similarly: it is necessary and sufficient that the condition $f^{-1}(\bar{B}) = \overline{f^{-1}(B)}$ be satisfied for arbitrary set B.

Hint: Make use of Exercise 2.

8. If the function f defined on the space X is continuous, then the set $\underset{x,y}{E}[y = f(x)]$ is homeomorphic to X.

9. The set of all sequences of natural numbers forms a metric space (the so-called *Baire space*), if for the distance between distinct sequences $x = (m_1, m_2, \ldots)$ and $y = (n_1, n_2, \ldots)$ we take the number $1/r$, where r is the smallest index such that $m_r \neq n_r$. Show that this space is homeomorphic to the set of all irrational numbers of the interval $[0, 1]$.

Hint: Assign the continued fraction

$$f(x) = \frac{1|}{|m_1} + \frac{1|}{|m_2} + \ldots$$

to the sequence of natural numbers $x = (m_1, m_2, \ldots)$.

10. A necessary and sufficient condition for the limit $f(x) = \lim_{n\to\infty} f_n(x)$ of the sequence of continuous functions $f_1, f_2, \ldots$ defined in the space X to be a continuous function is, that the space X, for every $\varepsilon > 0$, be representable as a union of open sets $A_n(\varepsilon)$, where

$$A_n(\varepsilon) = \underset{x}{E}\{|f_n(x) - f(x)| < \varepsilon\}\cdot$$

Hint: In order to show the continuity of the function f under the assumption of our condition at an arbitrary point $x_0 \in X$, we find an index n_0 such that $x_0 \in A_{n_0}(\varepsilon/3)$. Further, we make use of the fact that the set $A_{n_0}(\varepsilon/3)$ is open and that the function f_{n_0} is continuous.

11. Introducing a "new" distance into the metric space X with the aid of the formula

$$\varphi(x, y) = |x-y|/\{1+|x-y|\},$$

we have defined a homeomorphic transformation of X onto X.

Deduce from this that the set of all sequences with real terms $x = (x_1, x_2, \ldots, x_m, \ldots)$ is a metric space under the following definition of distance:

$$|x-y| = \sum_{m=1}^{\infty} (1/2^m)|x_m - y_m|/\{1+|x_m-y_m|\}$$

(this is the so-called *Fréchet space*).

12. Let F be a closed subset of the space X, and let

$$f(x) = 1/\varrho(x, F) \quad \text{for} \quad x \in X-F.$$

Prove that the set

$$\underset{x,y}{E}[y = f(x)] \wedge (x \notin F)$$

is closed in the space $X \times \mathcal{E}$.

Deduce from this that every open set in X is homeomorphic to a closed subset of the space $X \times \mathcal{E}$ (making use of Exercise 8).

Generalize this corollary to the difference of closed sets.

13. Let Q be a G_δ subset of the space X, i. e. $Q = G_1 \cap G_2 \cap \ldots \cap G_n \cap \ldots$, where G_n is an open set. Let

$$f_n(x) = 1/\varrho(x, X-G_n) \text{ for } x \in G_n, \quad \text{and} \quad f(x) = [f_1(x), f_2(x), \ldots].$$

Prove that the set

$$\underset{x,y}{E}[y = f(x)] \wedge (x \in Q)$$

is closed in the space $X \times \mathcal{E} \times \mathcal{E} \times \mathcal{E} \times \ldots$

Deduce from this that every G_δ-set is homeomorphic to a closed subset of the space $X \times \mathcal{E} \times \mathcal{E} \times \mathcal{E} \times \ldots$

14. Let $\boldsymbol{R}$ denote a family of nonvoid closed bounded subsets of a metric space X. By the *distance of two sets* $A, B \in \boldsymbol{R}$ we understand the maximum of the two numbers

$$\text{least upper bound}_{x \in A}\, \varrho(x, B) \quad \text{and} \quad \text{least upper bound}_{y \in B}\, \varrho(y, A).$$

Prove that the distance defined in this way, which we denote by the symbol $\operatorname{dist}(A, B)$, metrizes the set $\boldsymbol{R}$ (i. e. it satisfies conditions (1)-(3) of Chapter IX, § 1).

15. Show that in Theorem 6, § 7, it is possible to replace the assumption that the sets A and B are disjoint and closed, by a weaker assumption, namely that $\bar{A} \cap B = \emptyset = A \cap \bar{B}$.

16. Prove that if $X = G \cup H$, where G and H are open sets, then there exist closed sets A and B such that

$$X = A \cup B, \quad A \subset G \quad \text{and} \quad B \subset H.$$

17. For every pair of closed subsets A and B of the space X there exists a pair of closed sets P and Q such that

$$P \cup Q = X, \quad P \cap (A \cup B) = A, \quad Q \cap (A \cup B) = B.$$

Hint: Consider the sets

$$\underset{x}{E}[\varrho(x, A) \leqslant \varrho(x, B)] \quad \text{and} \quad \underset{x}{E}[\varrho(x, B) \leqslant \varrho(x, A)].$$

18. Prove the following generalization of Theorem 6, § 7: for every finite system of closed sets $F_1, F_2, \ldots, F_n$ satisfying the equality $F_1 \cap F_2 \cap \ldots \cap F_n = \emptyset$ there exists a system of open sets $G_1, G_2, \ldots, G_n$ such that

$$G_1 \cap G_2 \cap \ldots \cap G_n = \emptyset \quad \text{and} \quad F_i \subset G_i \text{ for } i = 1, 2, \ldots, n.$$

Hint: Consider the sets

$$H_{ij} = \underset{x}{E}[\varrho(x, F_i) < \varrho(x, F_j)] \quad \text{and} \quad G_i = H_{i1} \cup H_{i2} \cup \ldots \cup H_{in}.$$

In order to prove that $G_1 \cap G_2 \cap \ldots \cap G_n = \emptyset$ we consider for each point x the maximum of the numbers $\varrho(x, F_1), \ldots, \varrho(x, F_n)$; if it is the number $\varrho(x, F_i)$ then $x \notin G_i$.

19. Deduce the following corollary from the preceding theorem: if the open sets $G_1, G_2, \ldots, G_n$ satisfy the equality $X = G_1 \cup G_2 \cup \ldots \cup G_n$, then there exist closed sets $F_1, F_2, \ldots, F_n$ which satisfy the conditions

$$F_1 \cup F_2 \cup \ldots \cup F_n = X \quad \text{and} \quad F_i \subset G_i \text{ for } i = 1, 2, \ldots, n.$$

20. Show that the Hilbert cube $\mathcal{H}$ is homeomorphic to the subset of the Hilbert space (cf. Chapter IX, § 1, Example 3) composed of points $x = (x_1, x_2, \ldots, x_i, \ldots)$ such that $0 \leqslant x_i \leqslant 1/i$.

21. Show that Lemma 1 of § 8 can be strengthened as follows: if $f(x) = -1$ then $x \in A$, if $f(x) = 1$ then $x \in B$.
Hint: Use Theorem 7, § 7.

CHAPTER XIII

SEPARABLE SPACES

§ 1. Separable spaces

Definition. A space is said to be *separable* if it contains a countable dense subset.

Hence, a space is separable if it contains a sequence of points $p_1, p_2, \ldots$ such that every point p is of the form

$$p = \lim_{n\to\infty} p_{k_n}.$$

The space of all real numbers is a separable space, for the set of rational numbers is countable and dense. An example of a space which is not separable, is an arbitrary uncountable set in which $|x-y| = 1$ for every pair of points $x \neq y$.

We say that a sequence of non-empty open sets $G_1, G_2, \ldots$ forms a *base* of the space if for every point p of the space and for every $\varepsilon > 0$ there exists an n such that

$$(1) \qquad p \in G_n \quad \text{and} \quad \delta(G_n) < \varepsilon.$$

In the space of all real numbers the open intervals $r < x < s$ with rational endpoints r and s form a base. The set of these intervals is countable, and for every real number x and for every $\varepsilon > 0$, there exist rational r and s such that $r < x < s$ and $s - r < \varepsilon$.

THEOREM 1. *Every separable metric space has a base. Conversely, if a space contains a base, then this space is separable.*

Proof. Let $p_1, p_2, \ldots$ be a dense sequence in the given metric space. Let us consider the spherical neighborhoods of the points p_n with rational radii:

$$K_{n,r} = \underset{x}{E}(|x - p_n|) < r).$$

The set of these neighborhoods is countable (cf. Theorem 3, Chapter V, § 3) and forms a base.

In fact, for an arbitrary point p and every number $\varepsilon > 0$, there exists a point p_n such that $|p-p_n| < \varepsilon$. Let r be a rational number such that $|p-p_n| < r < \varepsilon$. Then $p \in K_{n,r}$ and $\delta(K_{n,r}) < 2\varepsilon$, and hence the sets $K_{n,r}$ form a base.

In order to prove the second part of the theorem, choose a point p_n in every G_n. The set of these points is countable and dense in the space.

THEOREM 2. *If $G_1, G_2, \ldots$ is a base of the given space then every open set H is the union of a certain number of sets belonging to this base.*

Proof. Let $p \in H$. Since the set H is open, there exists a spherical neighborhood K of p such that $K \subset H$. By virtue of our assumption, there exists a set G_n such that $p \in G_n$ and $\delta(G_n) < \frac{1}{2}\delta(K)$, and therefore $G_n \subset K$. Thus, for every point $p \in H$, there exists an index $n(p)$ such that $p \in G_{n(p)} \subset H$. Hence H is the union of the sets $G_{n(p)}$ for all points $p \in H$.

THEOREM 3 (Lindelöf). *In a separable space, every family of open sets H_t where $t \in T$ (T is an arbitrary set) contains a (finite or infinite) sequence $t_1, t_2, \ldots$ such that*

$$\bigcup_n H_{t_n} = \bigcup_t H_t .$$

In other words: *every noncountable covering consisting of open sets contains a countable covering.*

Proof. Let $G_1, G_2, \ldots$ be a base of the space. Let $k_1, k_2, \ldots$ be a sequence consisting of numbers i such that G_i is contained in some one of the sets H_t. Therefore to each k_n there corresponds a certain index t_n such that $G_{k_n} \subset H_{t_n}$. We therefore have

$$\bigcup_n G_{k_n} \subset \bigcup_n H_{t_n} \subset \bigcup_t H_t . \tag{2}$$

It remains to prove the inclusion

$$\bigcup_t H_t \subset \bigcup_n H_{t_n} . \tag{3}$$

Let $p \in H_t$. Since the sequence $G_1, G_2, \ldots$ forms a base there exists an i such that $p \in G_i \subset H_t$. Therefore, the number i belongs to the sequence $k_1, k_2, \ldots$, whence

$$p \in \bigcup_n G_{k_n} \quad \text{and hence} \quad p \in \bigcup_n H_{t_n}$$

by virtue of (2). Inclusion (3) is therefore proved.

§ 2. Properties of separable spaces

THEOREM 1. *Every subset Z of a separable metric space X is a separable metric space.*

Proof. Let $G_1, G_2, \ldots$ be a basis of the space X. It is easily seen that the sequence of the non-empty sets $H_n = Z \cap G_n$ is a base of Z.

THEOREM 2. *The cartesian product of two or a finite number of separable spaces is a separable space.*

Proof. If the spaces X and Y are separable, and $P = (p_1, p_2, \ldots)$ is dense in X, and $Q = (q_1, q_2, \ldots)$ is dense in Y, then the set

$$(4) \qquad P \times Q = (\langle p_1, q_1\rangle, \langle p_1, q_2\rangle, \langle p_2, q_1\rangle, \langle p_2, q_2\rangle, \ldots, \langle p_i, q_j\rangle, \ldots)$$

is dense in the space $X \times Y$.

For, if $\langle p, q\rangle \in X \times Y$, then p and q are of the form

$$(5) \qquad p = \lim_{n\to\infty} p_{k_n} \quad \text{and} \quad q = \lim_{n\to\infty} q_{r_n},$$

whence

$$\langle p, q\rangle = \lim_{n\to\infty} \langle p_{k_n}, q_{r_n}\rangle,$$

i. e. the point $\langle p, q\rangle$ is the limit of a sequence of points belonging to the sequence (4).

The generalization of the proof to the case of a finite number of sets is immediate.

THEOREM 3. *If the spaces $X_1, X_2, \ldots$ are separable, then the space $X_1 \times X_2 \times \ldots$ is also separable. In particular, the Hilbert cube $\mathcal{H}$ is separable.*

Proof. Let R_m be a countable set dense in the space X_m (e. g. let R_m be the set of rational numbers on the closed interval $\mathcal{J}=[0,1]$ if $X_m=\mathcal{J}$). Let a_m be a fixed point of the set R_m (e. g. let $a_m=0$, if $X=\mathcal{J}$). Let us consider the set Q of all sequences $(p_1, p_2, \ldots)$ such that

1. $p_m \in R_m$ for every m,
2. $p_m = a_m$ for sufficiently large m.

Every sequence belonging to the set Q is a point of the space $X_1 \times X_2 \times \ldots$ Obviously Q is countable (cf. Theorem 5, Chapter V, § 3).

We shall prove that the set Q is dense. Let $x=(x_1, x_2, \ldots) \in X_1 \times X_2 \times \ldots$ Since $\bar{R}_m = X_m$, we therefore have for every m

$$x_m = \lim_{n\to\infty} r_m^n, \tag{6}$$

where $r_m^n \in R_m$. Let us consider the sequence of points belonging to Q:

$$p^1 = (r_1^1, a_2, a_3, a_4, \ldots),$$
$$p^2 = (r_1^2, r_2^2, a_3, a_4, \ldots),$$
$$\ldots\ldots\ldots\ldots\ldots\ldots$$
$$p^n = (r_1^n, r_2^n, \ldots, r_n^n, a_{n+1}, a_{n+2}, \ldots),$$
$$\ldots\ldots\ldots\ldots\ldots\ldots\ldots\ldots\ldots$$

By virtue of (6) we have $x = \lim_{n\to\infty} p^n$, which was to be proved.

§ 3. Theorems on powers in separable spaces

THEOREM 1. *Every separable space has power $\leqslant \mathfrak{c}$.*

Proof. Let $p_1, p_2, \ldots$ be a sequence dense in the space. Therefore, to every point x there corresponds a sequence of natural numbers $k_1, k_2, \ldots$ such that $x = \lim_{n\to\infty} p_{k_n}$. Thus, there are at most as many points in the space as there are infinite sequences consisting of natural numbers, i. e. at most $\mathfrak{c}$ (cf. Chapter VI, § 4, (42)).

THEOREM 2. *The number of open sets in a separable space is at most $\mathfrak{c}$.*

The same applies to *closed sets.*

Proof. Let $G_1, G_2, \ldots$ be a base of the space. By virtue of Theorem 2, § 1, to every open set H there corresponds a sequence of natural numbers $k_1, k_2, \ldots$ such that

$$H = \bigcup_{n=1}^{\infty} G_{k_n} .$$

It follows from this that the number of open sets is at most that of all sequences of natural numbers, i. e. at most $\mathfrak{c}$.

The second part of the theorem follows immediately from the first, for, if we assign to each open set its complement, then we map the family of open sets onto the family of closed sets in a one-to-one manner.

*Remark. More generally, we can prove that *the family of all Borel subsets of a separable space has power* $\leqslant \mathfrak{c}$. Hence, every separable space of power $\mathfrak{c}$ contains non-Borel sets; and furthermore, since the family of all subsets of this space has power $2^{\mathfrak{c}}$, the family of non-Borel subsets has power $> \mathfrak{c}$ (and therefore, e. g. on the real line there exist more non-Borel than Borel sets).

THEOREM 3. *Every family* $\boldsymbol{R}$ *of disjoint open subsets of a separable space is countable.*

Proof. Let $p_1, p_2, \ldots$ be a sequence dense in the space under consideration. Hence, if H is a non-empty set belonging to the family $\boldsymbol{R}$, then there exists an index n such that $p_n \in H$; we denote this index by $n(H)$; if $\emptyset \in \boldsymbol{R}$ then we put $n(\emptyset) = 0$. We have therefore assigned to each non-empty set H belonging to $\boldsymbol{R}$ a number $n(H)$ such that

$$p_{n(H)} \in H . \tag{7}$$

Distinct numbers correspond to distinct sets. For if $n(H_1) = n(H_2)$, then by (7) we have

$$p_{n(H_1)} \in H_1 \cap H_2 ,$$

which is possible only if $H_1 = H_2$ (because the sets belonging to the family $\boldsymbol{R}$ are disjoint).

Therefore, there are at most as many elements of the family $\boldsymbol{R}$ as there are non-negative integers, which was to be proved.

THEOREM 4. *The set of isolated points of a separable space is countable.*

Proof. Since each isolated point of the space constitutes an open set of the space (see Chapter XI, § 1), it follows that the one-element sets, whose single element is an isolated point, form a family of disjoint open sets. This family is countable by virtue of Theorem 3, and hence the set of isolated points is also countable.

COROLLARY. *Let Z be a subset of a separable space. Then the set of isolated points of Z is countable.*

In fact, the set Z, being a subset of a separable space, can itself be considered to be a separable space (by virtue of Theorem 1, § 2).

THEOREM 5. *If the spaces X and Y are separable, then the space Y^X (i. e. the set of continuous functions which map the space X onto subsets of the space Y) has power $\leqslant \mathfrak{c}$.*

Proof. By virtue of Theorem 2, Chapter XII, § 2, if $f \in Y^X$, then f is a closed set in the space $X \times Y$; but since the latter space is separable (Theorem 2, § 2), the family of all its closed subsets has power $\leqslant \mathfrak{c}$ (Theorem 2).

Remark. If the space Y has power $\mathfrak{c}$, then the space Y^X has the same power, because the set of constant functions is then of power $\mathfrak{c}$. Under the assumption that the space X also has power $\mathfrak{c}$, we note that there are more discontinuous than continuous functions, because the set of all functions mapping X into the subsets of Y has power $\mathfrak{c}^{\mathfrak{c}} > \mathfrak{c}$ (cf. Chapter VI, § 4, (45)).

§ 4. URYSOHN THEOREM. *Every separable metric space X is homeomorphic to a subset of the Hilbert cube $\mathcal{H}$.*

We write this symbolically as

$$X \underset{\text{top}}{\subset} \mathcal{H}.$$

Proof. By Theorem 5 of § 4, Chapter XII, we can assume that

$$\delta(X) \leqslant 1 .$$

Let $p_1, p_2, \ldots$ be a sequence of points dense in the space X. To each $x \in X$ we assign the point of the Hilbert cube with "coordinates": $|x-p_1|, |x-p_2|, \ldots$, i. e.

(8) $$h(x) = (|x-p_1|, |x-p_2|, \ldots, |x-p_n|, \ldots) .$$

The functions

(9) $$h_n(x) = |x-p_n|$$

are continuous (Chapter XII, § 6, Theorem 4), and therefore, by Theorem 3, Chapter XII, § 6, the function h is also continuous. We shall prove that this function is a homeomorphism.

We assume that

(10) $$\lim_{k\to\infty} h(x_k) = h(x) .$$

We must show that

(11) $$\lim_{k\to\infty} x_k = x .$$

Let $\varepsilon > 0$. Since the sequence $p_1, p_2, \ldots$ is dense in the space X, there exists a point p_j such that

(12) $$|x-p_j| < \varepsilon .$$

It follows from formulas (10) and (8) that

$$\lim_{k\to\infty} h_j(x_k) = h_j(x) .$$

Because of (9) this means that

$$\lim_{k\to\infty} |x_k-p_j| = |x-p_j| ;$$

therefore, there exists a k_0 such that

(13) $$|x_k-p_j| < |x-p_j| + \varepsilon$$

provided that $k > k_0$.

By the inequalities (12) and (13), we therefore have

$$|x-x_k| \leqslant |x-p_j|+|p_j-x_k| < 3\varepsilon$$

for $k > k_0$. This means that formula (11) is valid.

Remark. As every subset of the Hilbert cube is a separable metric space, it follows from the above theorem that *from the topological point of view separable metric spaces are equivalent to subsets of the Hilbert cube.*

*§ 5. Condensation points. The Cantor-Bendixson theorem

A point p of a set A is said to be a *condensation point* of A if every spherical neighborhood of p contains a noncountable set of points of the set A.

We denote the set of condensation points of the set A by the symbol A^0.

Every condensation point of the set A is an accumulation point of A, i. e.

(14) $$A^0 \subset A^d.$$

It is also easy to prove that the set A^0 is closed, i. e.

(15) $$A^0 = \overline{A^0},$$

and that

(16) $$(A \cup B)^0 = A^0 \cup B^0.$$

The following generalization of Theorem 4, § 3, is valid.

THEOREM 1. *In a separable space the set of points of an arbitrary set A which are not condensation points of the set, i. e. the set $A-A^0$, is countable.*

Proof. Let $G_1, G_2, \ldots$ be a base of the space. Let $p \in A-A^0$. Then there exists a spherical neighborhood K of p such that $A \cap K$ is countable. At the same time, there exists an index $n(p)$ such that $p \in G_{n(p)} \subset K$, whence $A \cap G_{n(p)} \subset A \cap K$, and therefore the set $A \cap G_{n(p)}$ is countable.

Since the union of a countable number of countable sets is countable (Chapter V, § 3, Theorem 4), the set

$$S = \bigcup_p A \cap G_{n(p)},$$

where $p \in A - A^0$, is countable. Now, $A - A^0 \subset S$, for $p \in A \cap G_{n(p)}$. Therefore the set $A - A^0$ is countable.

Since a countable set clearly has no point of condensation, it follows from the theorem that

$$(A - A^0)^0 = \emptyset . \tag{17}$$

From this we deduce that

$$X^0 = X^{00} \tag{18}$$

where X denotes the space. In fact, the identity $X = X^0 \cup (X - X^0)$ yields, by virtue of (16) and (17), that

$$X^0 = X^{00} \cup (X - X^0)^0 = X^{00} .$$

THEOREM 2. *Every separable space X which does not contain non-empty sets dense in themselves (i. e. a space which is "scattered") is countable.*

Proof. By virtue of (18) and (14), we have $X^0 = X^{00} \subset X^{0d}$; i. e. $X^0 \subset X^{0d}$, which means that the set X^0 is dense in itself. Therefore $X^0 = \emptyset$ by hypothesis, it follows $X = X - X^0$, and this last set is countable by virtue of Theorem 1.

THEOREM 3 (Cantor-Bendixson). *Every separable space is the union of two disjoint sets, one dense in itself and closed (i. e. perfect) and the other countable.*

This is an immediate consequence of the preceding theorem and of Theorem 3, Chapter XI, § 5.

Exercises

1. Show that the space considered in Exercise 1, Chapter IX, is not separable.

Hint: Show that there exists a continuum of disjoint open sets in this space.

2. Prove that $A^0 - B^0 \subset (A - B)^0$.

3. Prove the rules

$$(\bigcap_t A_t)^0 \subset \bigcap_t A_t^0 , \qquad \bigcup_t A_t^0 \subset (\bigcup_t A_t)^0 .$$

4. Let there be assigned to every ordinal number $\xi < \alpha$ an open set A_ξ lying in the separable space X, so that $A_{\xi+1} \subset A_\xi$ and $A_{\xi+1} \neq A_\xi$.

Prove that $a < \Omega$ (i. e. that there is but a countable number of sets A_ξ).

Hint: Let $G_1, G_2, \ldots$ be a base of the space X. Assign to each ξ (with perhaps the exception of the last one) a number $n(\xi)$ such that

$$G_{n(\xi)} \subset A_\xi \quad \text{and} \quad G_{n(\xi)} - A_{\xi+1} \neq \emptyset .$$

5. Prove the analogous theorem obtained by making the assumption that the sets A_ξ are closed.

6. Deduce the following corollary from the above theorem: every set of real numbers which is well ordered with respect to the "less than" relation is countable.

7. The derived sets of transfinite order are defined inductively by means of the formulas

$$X^{(1)} = X^d, \quad X^{(\xi+1)} = (X^\xi)^d, \quad X^\lambda = \bigcap_{\xi<\lambda} X^{(\xi)} \quad (\lambda \text{ a limit ordinal}).$$

Prove (making use of Exercise 5) that beginning with some $a < \Omega$ the derived sets of all orders are equal.

8. Deduce the Cantor-Bendixson theorem from the above theorem making use of Theorem 4, § 3.

9. If the sets $R_1, R_2, \ldots$ form a base of the space X and the sets $S_1, S_2, \ldots$ form a base of the space Y, then the sets $R_m \times S_n$ $(m = 1, 2, \ldots;\ n = 1, 2, \ldots)$ form a base of the space $X \times Y$.

10. A space is said to be *locally separable* at the point p if there is a separable neighborhood of p. Give an example of a metric space which is locally separable at none of its points.

Hint: Use a construction analogous to the construction used in Exercise 1, Chapter IX.

CHAPTER XIV

COMPLETE SPACES

§ 1. Complete spaces

Definition. We say that a sequence of points $p_1, p_2, \ldots$ in a metric space is a *Cauchy sequence* if for every $\varepsilon > 0$ there exists a k such that for every $n > k$ we have

$$(1) \qquad |p_n - p_k| < \varepsilon ,$$

i. e. if

$$\bigwedge_\varepsilon \bigvee_k \bigwedge_n [(n > k) \rightarrow (|p_n - p_k| < \varepsilon)] .$$

A metric space is said to be *complete* if every Cauchy sequence $p_1, p_2, \ldots$ is convergent, that is, there exists a point p of this space such that $p = \lim_{n\to\infty} p_n$.

The space of all real numbers is complete according to the known Cauchy theorem from analysis. Let us note that completeness is not a topological property of the space. The space of all real numbers is homeomorphic to the open interval $0 < x < 1$ (cf. Chapter XII, § 4) which is not a complete space inasmuch as the sequence 1/2, 1/3, 1/4, ... is a Cauchy sequence but is not convergent (in this space).

THEOREM. *Every convergent sequence (in an arbitrary metric space) is a Cauchy sequence.*

Proof. In fact, if the sequence $p_1, p_2, \ldots$ is convergent to the point p, then for every $\varepsilon > 0$ there exists a k such that for every $n \geqslant k$ we have the inequality

$$(2) \qquad |p_n - p| < \varepsilon/2 .$$

In particular, for $n = k$ we have

$$(3) \qquad |p_k - p| < \varepsilon/2 .$$

For $n \geqslant k$, inequality (1) follows from the inequalities (2) and (3).

§ 2. CANTOR THEOREM. *Let $\{F_n\}$ be a given decreasing sequence of non-empty closed sets in a complete space:*

$$F_1 \supset F_2 \supset \ldots \supset F_n \supset F_{n+1} \supset \ldots \tag{4}$$

If

$$\lim_{n\to\infty} \delta(F_n) = 0\,, \tag{5}$$

then

$$\bigcap_{n=1}^{\infty} F_n \neq \emptyset\,. \tag{6}$$

Proof. Let $p_n \in F_n$. Then $p_1, p_2, \ldots$ is a Cauchy sequence. In fact, by virtue of (5), there exists for every $\varepsilon > 0$ a k such that $\delta(F_n) < \varepsilon$ provided $n \geqslant k$.

By (4), we also have $p_n \in F_n \subset F_k$, and hence for $n \geqslant k$, we have

$$p_n, p_k \in F_k\,, \qquad \text{whence} \qquad |p_n - p_k| \leqslant \delta(F_k) < \varepsilon\,;$$

i. e. $p_1, p_2, \ldots$ is a Cauchy sequence. Since the space is complete, this sequence is convergent. Hence, let $p = \lim\limits_{n\to\infty} p_n$.

For every m, the terms of the sequence $p_1, p_2, \ldots$ with the exception of at most the first $m-1$ terms belong to F_m, and since the set F_m is closed, the limit of this sequence also belongs to F_m, i. e.

$$p \in F_m \quad \text{for} \quad m = 1, 2, \ldots, \quad \text{i. e.} \quad p \in \bigcap_{m=1}^{\infty} F_m\,.$$

Remark. The set $\bigcap_{m=1}^{\infty} F_m$ consists of only one point p.

§ 3. BAIRE THEOREM. *In a non-empty complete space the union*

$$E = F_1 \cup F_2 \cup \ldots \cup F_k \cup \ldots \tag{7}$$

of closed boundary sets cannot fill the entire space; furthermore, this union is a boundary set[1]).

Proof. In order to prove that the set E is a boundary set in the space X, it suffices to show that every spherical

[1]) Sets of the form (7) (where the sets F_k are closed boundary sets), as well as all their subsets, are said to be sets of the *first category*.

neighborhood S_0 of an arbitrary point contains points of the set $X-E$ (see Theorem 2, Chapter XI, § 4).

Since the closed set F_1 is a boundary set, there exists a point in S_0 with a spherical neighborhood S_1 such that $\bar{S}_1 \subset S_0$ and $\bar{S}_1 \cap F_1 = \emptyset$ (see Chapter XI, § 4, Theorem 3). Clearly, we can assume that $\delta(S_1) < 1$.

Similarly, we find an S_2 such that $\bar{S}_2 \subset S_1$, $\bar{S}_2 \cap F_2 = \emptyset$ and $\delta(S_2) < 1/2$.

Continuing in this manner, we obtain a sequence of spherical neighborhoods which satisfy the conditions

$$S_0 \supset \bar{S}_1 \supset \bar{S}_2 \supset \ldots \supset \bar{S}_n \supset \ldots , \tag{8}$$

$$\bar{S}_n \cap F_n = \emptyset \tag{9}$$

and

$$\delta(S_n) < 1/n , \quad \text{whence} \quad \lim_{n\to\infty} \delta(S_n) = 0 . \tag{10}$$

From the Cantor theorem, we deduce by virtue of (8) and (10) that there exists a point p belonging to all the sets $\bar{S}_n$. Therefore (by (9))

$$p \in \bigcap_{n=1}^{\infty} \bar{S}_n \subset \bigcap_{n=1}^{\infty} (X-F_n) = X - \bigcup_{n=1}^{\infty} F_n ,$$

hence by (7) $p \in X-E$. Also $p \in S_0$.

This completes the proof of the Baire theorem.

Remarks. 1. Since a subset of a boundary set is a boundary set, Baire theorem can also be stated in the following manner: in a complete space every set of the first category is a boundary set.

2. It follows from the Baire theorem that every nonvoid complete dense in itself space is noncountable.

In fact, if the space were countable: $X = (p_1, p_2, \ldots)$, then it would be the union of a sequence of sets each consisting of one point: $X = \{p_1\} \cup \{p_2\} \cup \ldots$ But each of these sets is a closed boundary set, inasmuch as each of the points p_n is an accumulation point of the space X (cf. Chapter XI, § 4, Theorem 4).

Since the space $\mathcal{E}$ of real numbers is complete and dense in itself, we have thus obtained a new proof of the inequality $\mathfrak{c} > \mathfrak{a}$.

3. The set of irrational numbers is not an F_σ-set in the space $\mathcal{E}$ (and therefore the set of rational numbers is not a G_δ-set).

For, if the opposite were true, the set of irrational numbers would be the union of a countable number of closed boundary sets (because the set of irrational numbers is itself a boundary set). But since the set of rational numbers is the union of a countable number of one-element sets—and hence of closed boundary sets—the entire space $\mathcal{E}$ could be represented as the union of a countable number of closed boundary sets; but this contradicts Baire theorem.

Exercises

1. Show by means of an example that Baire theorem is not valid in arbitrary metric spaces.

2. The cartesian product $X \times Y$ of two complete spaces, metrized with the aid of the formula

$$|\langle x_1, y_1\rangle - \langle x_2, y_2\rangle| = \{|x_1 - x_2|^2 + |y_1 - y_2|^2\}^{1/2},$$

is complete.

3. The cartesian product $X_1 \times X_2 \times X_3 \times \dots$ of complete spaces is complete if the distance between two points $x = (x_1, x_2, \dots)$ and $y = (y_1, y_2, \dots)$ is defined by the formula

$$|x - y| = \sum_{n=1}^{\infty} (1/2^n)|x_n - y_n|/(1 + |x_n - y_n|).$$

4. Prove that every G_δ-set lying in a complete space is homeomorphic to a complete space (Aleksandrov theorem).

Hint: Use Exercises 3 and 12, Chapter XII.

5. Let X be a metric space and let Y be a complete space. Prove that the space Φ of all bounded mappings of the space X onto subsets of the space Y, metrized by formula (6), Chapter IX, § 1, is complete (cf. Exercise 5, Chapter IX).

6. Making use of the preceding exercise and Theorem 1, Chapter XII, § 5, prove that a subset of the space Φ consisting of all continuous mappings forms a complete space.

7. Prove that every metric space is isometric with a subset of some complete space.

Hint: Use the preceding exercise and Exercise 4, Chapter IX.

CHAPTER XV

COMPACT SPACES

The concept of a complete space arises from a generalization of the Cauchy theorem; in an analogous way, the idea of compact space arises from a generalization of the Bolzano-Weierstrass theorem.

§ 1. Compact spaces

Definition. A metric space is said to be *compact* if we can select from each sequence of points $p_1, p_2, \dots$ of this space a subsequence which is convergent to some point p of this space; i. e. if there exists a sequence of indices

(1) $$k_1 < k_2 < \dots$$

and a point p such that

(2) $$\lim_{n\to\infty} p_{k_n} = p.$$

When we say that a set A (situated in a metric space) is compact, we understand by this that the set A treated as a space forms a compact space; strictly speaking, that every sequence of points belonging to the set A contains a subsequence which converges to a point which also belongs to the set A.

EXAMPLE. The classical Bolzano-Weierstrass theorem states that the closed interval $a \leqslant x \leqslant b$ is a compact set. With the aid of this theorem it is easy to prove that the closed square in the plane, and more generally the closed cube in Euclidean n-space, is a compact space.

As we shall show, compact spaces situated in Euclidean n-space are identical with the closed and bounded sets in this space.

§ 2. Properties of compact metric spaces

THEOREM 1. *A compact space is complete.*

Proof. Let us assume the sequence $p_1, p_2, \ldots$ is a Cauchy sequence. We shall show that it is convergent.

By assumption, for a given $\varepsilon > 0$, there exists a j such that for $n > j$ we have the inequality

$$|p_n - p_j| < \varepsilon . \tag{3}$$

Since the space is compact, we can select a subsequence from the sequence $p_1, p_2, \ldots$ which satisfies conditions (1) and (2).

We shall prove that

$$\lim_{n\to\infty} p_n = p . \tag{4}$$

By virtue of (2) there exists an $m > j$ such that

$$|p_{k_m} - p| < \varepsilon . \tag{5}$$

Since (because of (1)) $k_m \geqslant m > j$, we therefore have by (3):

$$|p_{k_m} - p_j| < \varepsilon . \tag{6}$$

Adding inequalities (3), (5) and (6) memberwise, we obtain

$$|p_n - p| < 3\varepsilon \quad \text{for} \quad n > j ,$$

which proves equality (4).

THEOREM 2. *Every compact space is separable. Furthermore, for every number $\varepsilon > 0$, there exists a finite number of points $A_\varepsilon = \{p_1, p_2, \ldots, p_k\}$ such that*

$$\varrho(x, A_\varepsilon) < \varepsilon , \tag{7}$$

i. e. such that every point x is at a distance less than ε from some point of the set A_ε.

We define the set A_ε inductively. Let p_1 be an arbitrary point of our space. Let p_2 be an arbitrary point such that $|p_1 - p_2| \geqslant \varepsilon$, provided that such a point p_2 exists; if such a point does not exist, then we take $A_\varepsilon = \{p_1\}$.

In general, p_n is a point such that

$$(8) \qquad |p_n - p_m| \geqslant \varepsilon \quad \text{for all} \quad m < n,$$

provided that such a point p_n exists; if such a point does not exist we take $A_\varepsilon = \{p_1, \ldots, p_{n-1}\}$.

The sequence $p_1, p_2, \ldots$ constructed in this manner must be finite; for in the contrary case, it should contain a convergent subsequence (by virtue of the compactness assumption), which however is impossible because it follows from condition (8) that no subsequence of $p_1, p_2, \ldots$ is a Cauchy sequence, and hence it cannot be convergent.

We have thus defined the set A_ε. It remains to show that the space is separable.

Let $B = A_1 \cup A_{1/2} \cup \ldots \cup A_{1/n} \cup \ldots$ This set is countable. It is dense in the space because for every x and every n we have $\varrho(x, B) \leqslant \varrho(x, A_{1/n}) < 1/n$ (by virtue of (7) and Theorem 2, Chapter XII, § 7); this means that there exists a point $b \in B$ such that $|x - b| < 1/n$. And therefore $x \in \bar{B}$.

THEOREM 3. *Every compact space X is bounded.*

Proof. Let us put $\varepsilon = 1$ in Theorem 2. It follows that $\delta(X) < \delta(A_1) + 2$.

THEOREM 4. *A compact subset A of an arbitrary space X is a closed set.*

Proof. Let us assume that the set A is not closed. Then there exists a sequence of points belonging to A and converging to a point p which does not belong to A. Then every subsequence of this sequence is also convergent to p; hence the set A is not compact (because the point p does not belong to it).

THEOREM 5. *Every closed subset F of a compact space X is compact.*

Proof. Let $p_1, p_2, \ldots$ be an arbitrary sequence of points in the set F. Since X is a compact space, we can choose from this sequence a subsequence which satisfies conditions (1) and (2).

On the other hand, since F is closed, condition (2) yields that $p \in F$, which proves the compactness of the set F.

§ 3. The Cantor and Borel theorems

1. CANTOR THEOREM. *In a compact space every decreasing sequence of non-empty closed sets*

$$F_1 \supset F_2 \supset \dots \supset F_n \supset \dots \tag{9}$$

satisfies the inequality

$$\bigcap_{n=1}^{\infty} F_n \neq \emptyset . \tag{10}$$

The course of the proof is similar to that of the proof of the Cantor theorem for complete spaces. Namely, let p_n be an arbitrarily chosen point in the set F_n. From the sequence $\{p_n\}$ we choose a subsequence $p_{k_1}, p_{k_2}, \dots$ which is convergent to some point p of our space (i. e. which satisfies equality (2)).

Since, by virtue of (9), each of the sets F_n contains almost all of the terms of the sequence $p_1, p_2, \dots$, and hence, also almost all of the terms of the sequence $p_{k_1}, p_{k_2}, \dots$, we therefore have $p \in F_n$ because the sets F_n are closed.

This means that inequality (10) is satisfied.

We shall deduce the following theorem from the Cantor theorem:

2. BOREL THEOREM. *Let X be a compact space and let*

$$X = \bigcup_{n=1}^{\infty} G_n , \tag{11}$$

where the G_n are open sets. Then there exists an index m such that

$$X = G_1 \cup \dots \cup G_m . \tag{12}$$

Remark. We can formulate the Borel theorem as follows: *every countable covering of a compact space by open sets contains a finite covering.*

Proof. Let us assume that such an index does not exist and let us set

$$F_n = X - (G_1 \cup G_2 \cup \dots \cup G_n) . \tag{13}$$

Therefore, F_n is a non empty closed set (being the complement of an open set).

By virtue of (13), condition (9) is satisfied and therefore according to the Cantor theorem inequality (10) holds. From this and the de Morgan laws we deduce that

$$X \neq X - \bigcap_{n=1}^{\infty} F_n = \bigcup_{n=1}^{\infty} (X - F_n).$$

At the same time, by (13), we have

$$\bigcup_{n=1}^{\infty} (X - F_n) = \bigcup_{n=1}^{\infty} (G_1 \cup G_2 \cup \ldots \cup G_n),$$

and therefore

$$\bigcup_{n=1}^{\infty} (G_1 \cup G_2 \cup \ldots \cup G_n) \neq X.$$

But by virtue of (11) we have

$$X = \bigcup_{n=1}^{\infty} G_n \subset \bigcup_{n=1}^{\infty} (G_1 \cup G_2 \cup \ldots \cup G_n),$$

i. e. $\bigcup_{n=1}^{\infty} (G_1 \cup G_2 \cup \ldots \cup G_n) = X$.

We have thus arrived at a contradiction. This completes the proof of the Borel theorem.

Remark. Conversely, it would be possible in an equally simple manner to deduce the Cantor theorem from the Borel theorem (the Borel and Cantor theorems are dual of one another).

The following theorem is a sharpening of the Borel theorem:

3. Borel-Lebesgue theorem. *Every covering of a compact space by open sets contains a finite covering.*

Proof. Let us set

$$X = \bigcup_t G_t.$$

Since the space X is separable, being compact (cf. Theorem 2, § 2), we may apply Lindelöf theorem (Chapter XIII, § 1, Theorem 3), by virtue of which any covering of the space X by open sets G_t contains a countable covering:

$$X = \bigcup_{n=1}^{\infty} G_{t_n}.$$

Applying Borel theorem in turn to this covering, we choose a finite covering $G_{t_1}, G_{t_2}, \ldots, G_{t_n}$:

$$X = G_{t_1} \cup G_{t_2} \cup \ldots \cup G_{t_n}.$$

Remarks. 1. As the Borel theorem is dual to the Cantor theorem, so the Borel-Lebesgue theorem is dual to the following theorem (due to Riesz) which establishes a generalization of the Cantor theorem:

If a family of closed subsets F_t *of a compact space* X *is such that*

$$F_{t_1} \cap F_{t_2} \cap \ldots \cap F_{t_k} \neq \emptyset$$

for every finite system of indices, then

$$\bigcap_t F_t \neq \emptyset .$$

The proof does not present any difficulties; we base our arguments on the Borel-Lebesgue theorem (and put $G_t = X - F_t$).

2. The Borel-Lebesgue theorem can be given the following somewhat more general form:

Let a family of open sets G_t *and a compact set* A, *where*

$$A \subset \bigcup_t G_t ,$$

be given in an (arbitrary) space X; *then there exists a finite system of indices* $t_1, t_2, \ldots, t_n$, *such that*

$$A \subset G_{t_1} \cup G_{t_2} \cup \ldots \cup G_{t_n} .$$

THEOREM 4. *In a compact space, the family of sets which are simultaneously open and closed is countable.*

Proof. Since a compact space is separable (see Theorem 2, § 2) it contains a sequence of open sets $G_1, G_2, \ldots$ such that every non-empty open set H is the union of a certain number of these sets (see Chapter XIII, § 1, Theorem 2). If, moreover, the set H is closed, then we can assume that this number is finite (by virtue of Borel theorem). Hence to every open-closed set H we can assign a finite system of natural numbers $k_1, k_2, \ldots, k_n$ in such a way that

$$H = G_{k_1} \cup G_{k_2} \cup \ldots \cup G_{k_n} .$$

To distinct sets H there obviously correspond distinct systems of natural numbers. Hence, there are at most as many open-closed sets as there are finite systems of natural numbers, and the number of the latter is countable (see Chapter V, § 3, Theorem 5)

§ 4. Continuous mappings of compact spaces

THEOREM 1. *The continuous image of a compact space is a compact space, i. e. compactness is an invariant of continuous mappings.*

Proof. Suppose $f(X) = Y$, where f is a continuous function and X is a compact space. We have to show that the space Y is also compact.

Let $y_1, y_2, \ldots$ be an arbitrary sequence of points of the space Y. Since every point of the space Y is the image of some point of the space X, there exists a sequence of points $x_1, x_2, \ldots$ belonging to X such that $y_n = f(x_n)$.

Since the space X is compact, the sequence $x_1, x_2, \ldots$ contains a convergent subsequence $x_{k_1}, x_{k_2}, \ldots$:

$$\lim_{n\to\infty} x_{k_n} = x \in X .$$

Because of the continuity of f, it follows from this that

$$\lim_{n\to\infty} f(x_{k_n}) = f(x) , \quad \text{i. e.} \quad \lim_{n\to\infty} y_{k_n} = f(x) \in Y ,$$

which proves the compactness of the space Y.

THEOREM 2. *If X is a compact space, $F = \overline{F} \subset X$ and f is a continuous function defined on X, then $f(F)$ is a closed subset of the space $f(X)$.*

In other words, $\overline{F} = F$ *implies* $\overline{f(F)} = f(F)$.

Proof. By virtue of Theorem 5, § 2, F is compact, and therefore by Theorem 1 the set $f(F)$ is compact and hence, by Theorem 4, § 2, it is a closed subset of the space $f(X)$.

Remark. It is essential to make the compactness assumption in Theorem 2. In fact, consider the following example: let $X =$ the plane, $F =$ hyperbola $y = 1/x$ and let f denote the projection of the plane onto the x-axis, i. e. $f(x, y) = x$.

THEOREM 3. *If the continuous and one-to-one function f maps a compact space X onto Y, then f is a homeomorphism.*

Proof. We have to show that the inverse function $g = f^{-1}$ is continuous, i. e. (cf. Chapter XII, § 2, Theorem 1) that if F is an arbitrary closed subset of the space X then the set $g^{-1}(F)$ is closed in Y. But $g^{-1} = f$ and hence $g^{-1}(F) = f(F)$ and, by Theorem 2, $f(F)$ is closed in Y.

THEOREM 4 (Generalization of the Weierstrass theorem). *Every continuous real valued function f defined on a compact space X is bounded and attains its least upper and greatest lower bounds.*

Proof. The set $f(X)$ is, by virtue of Theorem 1, a compact subset of the set of real numbers and hence (cf. Theorems 3 and 4, § 2) it is a closed and bounded set. Since the set $f(X)$ is closed, the least upper bound m_0 and the greatest lower bound m_1 of the function f belong to $f(X)$. Therefore, there exist an x_0 such that $m_0 = f(x_0)$ and an x_1 such that $m_1 = f(x_1)$, which was to be proved.

We introduce the concept of uniform continuity in a way similar to the way it is done in analysis.

We say, namely, that the function f defined on the space X with values in the space Y is *uniformly continuous*, if for every $\varepsilon > 0$ there exists a $\delta > 0$ (depending only on ε) such that the condition $|x'-x''| < \delta$ implies the inequality $|f(x')-f(x'')| < \varepsilon$ for arbitrary pairs of points x', x'' of the space X; we write this condition symbolically in the form

$$\bigwedge_{\varepsilon} \bigvee_{\delta} \bigwedge_{x'} \bigwedge_{x''} \{[|x'-x''| < \delta] \Rightarrow [|f(x')-f(x'')| < \varepsilon]\}.$$

Continuity in the usual sense follows from uniform continuity. The converse theorem is not true as shown by:

$$y = 1/x \quad (0 < x < 1), \qquad y = e^x \quad (-\infty < x < +\infty).$$

On the other hand, the following theorem is valid in compact spaces:

THEOREM 5 (Generalization of Heine theorem on uniform continuity). *A continuous function f defined on a compact space X is uniformly continuous.*

Proof. Let us assume the contrary, that the function f is not uniformly continuous. Hence there exists an $\varepsilon > 0$ such that for every $\delta > 0$ there exists a pair of points x', x'' in the space X which satisfies the conditions

$$|x'-x''| < \delta \quad \text{and} \quad |f(x')-f(x'')| \geqslant \varepsilon,$$

i. e.

$$\bigvee_{\varepsilon} \bigwedge_{\delta} \bigvee_{x'} \bigvee_{x''} \{[|x'-x''| < \delta] \wedge [|f(x')-f(x'')| \geqslant \varepsilon]\}.$$

From this it follows in particular for $\delta = 1/n$ that there exists a pair of points x'_n, x''_n such that:

(14) $$|x'_n - x''_n| < 1/n,$$

(15) $$|f(x'_n)-f(x''_n)| \geqslant \varepsilon.$$

Since the space X is compact, we can select a convergent subsequence $x'_{k_1}, x'_{k_2}, \ldots$ from the sequence $x'_1, x'_2, \ldots$ Let

(16) $$\lim_{n\to\infty} x'_{k_n} = x.$$

It follows from conditions (14) and (16) that

(17) $$\lim_{n\to\infty} x''_{k_n} = x.$$

Since the function f is continuous, we deduce from equalities (16) and (17) that

$$\lim_{n\to\infty} f(x'_{k_n}) = f(x) \quad \text{and} \quad \lim_{n\to\infty} f(x''_{k_n}) = f(x),$$

whence

$$\lim_{n\to\infty} |f(x'_{k_n}) - f(x''_{k_n})| = 0,$$

which is a contradiction of inequality (15).

*THEOREM 6 (on continuous convergence). *A necessary and sufficient condition for a sequence of continuous functions $f_1, f_2, \ldots$ defined on a compact space X to be uniform-*

ly convergent to the function f, is that the condition

(18) $$\lim_{n\to\infty} x_n = x$$

imply

(19) $$\lim_{n\to\infty} f_n(x_n) = f(x).$$

[We say that the sequence of functions $f_1, f_2, \ldots$ is *continuously convergent* if condition (18) implies condition (19).]

Proof. *Necessity.* Let us assume that the sequence $f_1, f_2, \ldots$ is uniformly convergent to the function f. Let $\varepsilon > 0$. Hence, there exists a k such that

(20) $$|f_n(x) - f(x)| < \varepsilon$$

for all x and for $n > k$.

Let us assume (18) is satisfied. We must prove equality (19).

Applying (20), we have

(21) $$|f_n(x_n) - f(x_n)| < \varepsilon$$

for $n > k$.

Since the function f is continuous, being the limit of a uniformly convergent sequence of continuous functions (cf. Chapter XII, § 5, Theorem 1), therefore by (18), we have

(22) $$|f(x_n) - f(x)| < \varepsilon$$

for sufficiently large n.

From inequalities (21) and (22) we deduce for sufficiently large n

$$|f_n(x_n) - f(x)| < 2\varepsilon,$$

which proves that equality (19) is satisfied.

Sufficiency. Let us assume that the sequence of continuous functions f_n is continuously convergent to the function f, but that it is not uniformly convergent. Hence

$$\bigvee_\varepsilon \bigwedge_n \bigvee_x \bigvee_k \{(k > n) \wedge [|f_k(x) - f(x)| \geqslant \varepsilon]\},$$

i. e. for some $\varepsilon > 0$ and for every natural number n we can choose a point x_n and an index k_n in such a way that

$$k_1 < k_2 < \ldots < k_n < \ldots, \tag{23}$$

$$|f_{k_n}(x_n) - f(x_n)| \geqslant \varepsilon \quad \text{for} \quad n = 1, 2, \ldots \tag{24}$$

The space X being compact, we can choose a convergent subsequence from the sequence $x_1, x_2, \ldots$ Clearly, we can assume that the points x_n are so chosen that the sequence $x_1, x_2, \ldots$ is convergent. Now, let the equality (18) be satisfied. We shall prove that

$$\lim_{n\to\infty} f_{k_n}(x_n) = f(x). \tag{25}$$

Let us construct the sequence $x_1', x_2', \ldots$ in the following way:

$$x_m' = x_n \quad \text{for} \quad k_{n-1} < m \leqslant k_n \quad (\text{where } k_0 = 0). \tag{26}$$

Obviously

$$\lim_{m\to\infty} x_m' = \lim_{n\to\infty} x_n = x.$$

From this, by virtue of the continuous convergence of the sequence $f_1, f_2, \ldots$, we have

$$\lim_{m\to\infty} f_m(x_m') = f(x),$$

and hence

$$\lim_{n\to\infty} f_{k_n}(x_{k_n}') = f(x). \tag{27}$$

But since, by virtue of (26) $x_{k_n}' = x_n$, (27) yields (25).

Since the sequence $\{f_m\}$ is continuously convergent, we have

$$\lim_{m\to\infty} f_m(x_0) = f(x_0)$$

for fixed x_0. Therefore, for every n we have

$$\lim_{m\to\infty} f_m(x_n) = f(x_n),$$

whence we deduce that the inequality

$$|f_{m_n}(x_n) - f(x_n)| < 1/n \tag{28}$$

holds for some increasing sequence of indices

(29) $$m_1 < m_2 < \ldots < m_n < \ldots$$

We showed above that conditions (18) and (23) imply (25). Therefore, taking (29) into account, we have

(30) $$\lim_{n\to\infty} f_{m_n}(x_n) = f(x).$$

Formulas (25) and (30) yield

$$\lim_{n\to\infty} |f_{k_n}(x_n) - f_{m_n}(x_n)| = 0,$$

whence by virtue of (29) we have

$$\lim_{n\to\infty} |f_{k_n}(x_n) - f(x_n)| = 0;$$

but this contradicts inequality (24).

This also concludes the proof of the theorem.

§ 5. Cartesian multiplication of compact spaces

THEOREM 1. *The cartesian product $X \times Y$ of the compact spaces X and Y is a compact space.*

Proof. Let $z_n = \langle x_n, y_n \rangle \in X \times Y$, i. e. $x_n \in X$, $y_n \in Y$. We must show that the sequence $z_1, z_2, \ldots$ contains a convergent subsequence.

We can choose a convergent subsequence from the sequence $x_1, x_2, \ldots$ since the space X is compact. Hence, let

(31) $$\lim_{n\to\infty} x_{k_n} = x.$$

Similarly, since the space Y is compact we can select a convergent subsequence from the sequence $y_{k_1}, y_{k_2}, \ldots$ Let

(32) $$\lim_{n\to\infty} y_{r_{k_n}} = y.$$

By (31) we have

(33) $$\lim_{n\to\infty} x_{r_{k_n}} = x.$$

Because of (32) and (33) we get

$$\lim_{n\to\infty} \langle x_{r_{k_n}}, y_{r_{k_n}} \rangle = \langle x, y \rangle, \qquad \text{i. e.} \qquad \lim_{n\to\infty} z_{r_{k_n}} = z.$$

We have thus selected a convergent subsequence from the sequence $z_1, z_2, \ldots$; this completes the proof.

In an analogous manner it can be proved that the cartesian product of an arbitrary finite number of compact spaces is a compact space.

Remark. In particular, the n-dimensional cube $\mathcal{J}^n$ is a compact space. It follows from this that *for subsets of Euclidean space $\mathcal{E}^n$, the concept of a compact set coincides with the concept of a closed bounded set.* For, every bounded subset of the space $\mathcal{E}^n$ lies in a sufficiently large cube (cf. also Theorems 3 and 4, § 2), and therefore—being a closed subset of a compact space—is compact (Theorem 5, § 2).

THEOREM 2. *If the spaces $X_1, X_2, \ldots$ are compact, then the space $X_1 \times X_2 \times \ldots$ is also compact.*

Proof. Let $p_1, p_2, \ldots$ be a sequence of points belonging to the space $X_1 \times X_2 \times \ldots$ Hence

$$p_n = (\overset{1}{x}_n, \overset{2}{x}_n, \ldots, \overset{m}{x}_n, \ldots), \quad \text{where} \quad \overset{m}{x}_n \in X \quad \text{for} \quad n, m = 1, 2, \ldots$$

Since the space X_1 is compact, there exists a sequence of natural numbers

$$(34) \qquad 1 < k_1 < k_2 < \ldots$$

such that the sequence $\overset{1}{x}_{k_1}, \overset{2}{x}_{k_2}, \ldots$ is convergent. Let

$$(35) \qquad \lim_{n\to\infty} \overset{1}{x}_{k_n} = x^1 .$$

Similarly, there exists a sequence

$$(36) \qquad 1 < j_1 < j_2 < \ldots$$

such that the sequence $\overset{2}{x}_{k_{j_1}}, \overset{2}{x}_{k_{j_2}}, \ldots$ is convergent. Let

$$(37) \qquad \lim_{n\to\infty} \overset{2}{x}_{k_{j_n}} = x^2 .$$

Continuing this process, we define an infinite sequence $x^1, x^2, x^3, \ldots$ Let us set

$$q = (x^1, x^2, x^3, \ldots) .$$

Hence we have $q \in X_1 \times X_2 \times \ldots$ We shall prove that q is the limit of the sequence

(38) $$p_1, p_{k_1}, p_{k_{j_1}}, \ldots$$

In fact, making use of formulas (34) and (36) we verify that

$$1 < k_1 < k_{j_1} < k_{j_{i_1}} < \ldots,$$

and therefore the sequence (38) is a subsequence of the sequence $p_1, p_2, p_3, \ldots$

The sequence

$$x^1_{k_1}, x^1_{k_{j_1}}, \ldots$$

is therefore a subsequence of the sequence $x^1_{k_1}, x^1_{k_2}, x^1_{k_3}, \ldots$; hence, by virtue of (35) it is convergent to x^1. Similarly the sequence

$$x^2_{k_{j_1}}, x^2_{k_{j_{i_1}}}, \ldots$$

converges to x^2 by virtue of (37).

In general, the sequence

$$x^n_1, x^n_{k_1}, x^n_{k_{j_1}}, \ldots$$

converges to x^n.

Thus, we have proved that the sequence (38), which forms a subsequence of the sequence $p_1, p_2, \ldots$, is convergent to q. This means that the space $X_1 \times X_2 \times \ldots$ is compact.

§ 6. The function space Y^X

Let X be a compact space and let Y be an arbitrary metric space. We denoted by Y^X (Chapter XII, § 2) the set of all continuous functions of the form $y = f(x)$, where $x \in X$ and $y \in Y$.

Under the assumption that X is a compact space we may consider Y^X as a metric space by defining the distance between two "points" f and g of this space by the formula (cf. Chapter IX, § 1, 4.):

(39) $$|f-g| = \text{least upper bound } |f(x)-g(x)|\,.$$

The least upper bound considered here always exists because the function $|f-g|$, being a continuous function (see Chapter XIII, § 6, Theorem 4) of the variable x which runs through the compact space X, is bounded (by Theorem 4, § 4).

Conditions (1)-(3) in the definition of a metric space (Chapter IX, § 1) follow easily from formula (39). Therefore, Y^X is indeed a metric space.

According to the definition of limit given in Chapter X, § 1, we have

$$\begin{aligned}(\lim_{n\to\infty} f_n = f) &\equiv (\lim_{n\to\infty} |f_n - f| = 0)\\ &\equiv \bigwedge_\varepsilon \bigvee_k \bigwedge_n \{(n > k) \Rightarrow [\text{l. u. b. } |f_n(x) - f(x)|] \leqslant \varepsilon\}\\ &\equiv \bigwedge_\varepsilon \bigvee_k \bigwedge_n \bigwedge_x \{(n > k) \Rightarrow |f_n(x) - f(x)| \leqslant \varepsilon\}.\end{aligned}$$

We have thus arrived at the following theorem:

THEOREM 1. *The condition* $\lim_{n\to\infty} f_n = f$ *means that the sequence of functions* $f_1, f_2, \ldots$ *is uniformly convergent to the function* f.

As can be seen from this, the convergence of the functions f_n in the space Y^X means not only that this sequence is convergent for every x, but also that it is *uniformly* convergent on the entire space X.

THEOREM 2. *If the space X is compact and the space Y is complete, then the space Y^X is complete.*

Proof. Let $f_1, f_2, \ldots$ be a Cauchy sequence of elements of the space Y^X. This means, that to every $\varepsilon > 0$, there exists a k such that the inequality

$$|f_n - f_k| < \varepsilon \tag{40}$$

holds for all $n > k$.

The sequence

$$f_1(x), f_2(x), \ldots, f_n(x), \ldots \tag{41}$$

is a Cauchy sequence for all $x \in X$, because it follows from (40) that

$$|f_n(x) - f_k(x)| \leqslant [\text{l. u. b. } |f_n(x) - f_k(x)|] = |f_n - f_k| < \varepsilon \tag{42}$$

for all $n > k$.

Hence the sequence (41) is convergent, the space Y being complete. Let us denote its limit by $f(x)$, i. e.

$$f(x) = \lim_{n\to\infty} f_n(x) .$$

We shall prove that this convergence is uniform. In fact, the inequality $|f_m(x)-f_k(x)| < \varepsilon$ holds for all $m > k$ and hence, by virtue of (42), we have

$$|f_n(x)-f_m(x)| < 2\varepsilon , \quad \text{whence} \quad |f_n(x)-\lim_{m\to\infty} f_m(x)| \leqslant 2\varepsilon ,$$

$$\text{i. e.} \quad |f_n(x)-f(x)| \leqslant 2\varepsilon .$$

Being the limit of a uniformly convergent sequence of continuous functions, the function $f = \lim_{n\to\infty} f_n$ is continuous (Chapter XII, § 5, Theorem 1), i. e. $f \in Y^X$.

Remarks. In particular, the space $\mathcal{E}^{\mathcal{I}}$, i. e. the space of all real valued continuous functions defined on the closed interval $0 \leqslant x \leqslant 1$, is complete; this space is not compact, as is shown by the example $f_n(x) = x^n$. This same remark applies to the space $\mathcal{I}^{\mathcal{I}}$.

Theorem 2 allows us to apply the Baire theorem of Chapter XIV, § 3, to function spaces (in the case where the space X is compact and the space Y is complete) for the purpose of proving existence theorems.

As an example of the numerous applications to analysis let us quote the following theorem:

BANACH THEOREM. *In the space $\mathcal{E}^{\mathcal{I}}$ the set of functions which possess a derivative at least in one point forms a boundary set.*

Banach theorem is a remarkable sharpening of Weierstrass theorem on the existence of continuous functions which do not possess a derivative at any point.

§ 7. The Cantor set

The Cantor set is the set $\mathcal{C}$ of all numbers t of the form

(43) $$t = t_1/3 + t_2/9 + \ldots + t_n/3^n + \ldots ,$$

where t_n assumes one of two values only: 0 or 2.

They are therefore numbers of the interval [0, 1] which can be written in the ternary system of calculation without using the digit 1.

For example, 1/3 belongs to C because

$$1/3 = 0/3 + 2/9 + 2/27 + \dots + 2/3^n + \dots = (0.0222\dots)_3,$$

but 1/2 does not belong to C.

We can also define the set C geometrically as follows.

Let us divide the closed interval [0, 1] into 3 equal parts and let us remove the middle open interval. We divide the remaining two intervals (0, 1/3) and (2/3, 1) into three equal parts and remove their (open) middle parts. Continuing in this way we obtain an infinite sequence of deleted intervals

$$(1/3, 2/3), (1/9, 2/9), (7/9, 8/9), (1/27, 2/27), \dots$$

Deleting from the interval [0, 1] the union of the removed intervals we obtain the set C which was defined previously arithmetically.

FIG. 7

It is therefore a *closed* set and—as is easy to see—it is dense in itself (and hence perfect), and also a *boundary set* in the interval [0, 1] (it does not contain any interval).

Next, let us note that every number of the set C possesses only one development of the form (43), where t_n is either 0 or 2 (without this last assumption this uniqueness would not hold). It follows easily from it that a necessary and sufficient condition for the sequence of numbers of the Cantor set $t^{(1)}, t^{(2)}, \dots, t^{(n)}, \dots$ to converge to t, is that the k-th digits in the development of these numbers converge to the k-th digit in the development of the number t (for $k = 1, 2, \dots$), i. e.

$$(44) \qquad (t = \lim_{n\to\infty} t^{(n)}) \equiv \bigwedge_k (t_k = \lim_{n\to\infty} t_k^{(n)}).$$

This means that the following theorem holds (cf. Chapter X, § 3, Theorem 2):

THEOREM 1. *The Cantor set is homeomorphic to the infinite power of the set consisting of two elements*:

$$\mathcal{C} \underset{\text{top}}{=} \{0, 2\} \times \{0, 2\} \times \{0, 2\} \times \ldots$$

Hence, we may identify the points of the Cantor set with sequences of zeros and twos; in other words, we identify a number belonging to $\mathcal{C}$ with the sequence of its digits in the ternary expansion (of type (43)).

We deduce from this the following theorem:

THEOREM 2. $\mathcal{C}^2 \underset{\text{top}}{=} \mathcal{C}$.

In fact, every point p of the set $\mathcal{C}^2$ can be represented in the form $p = \langle x, y \rangle$ where x and y are sequences of zeros and twos:

$$x = (x_1, x_2, \ldots) \quad \text{and} \quad y = (y_1, y_2, \ldots).$$

From these two sequences we form one: $x_1, y_1, x_2, y_2, \ldots$ and we denote this sequence by $f(p)$.

It is easy to verify that f is a homeomorphic transformation of the set $\mathcal{C}^2$ onto the set $f(\mathcal{C}^2) = \mathcal{C}$.

We could prove similarly that $\mathcal{C}^n \underset{\text{top}}{=} \mathcal{C}$ for arbitrary n. Moreover, the following theorem holds:

THEOREM 3. $\mathcal{C} \times \mathcal{C} \times \mathcal{C} \times \ldots \underset{\text{top}}{=} \mathcal{C}$.

The points p of the set $\mathcal{C} \times \mathcal{C} \times \ldots$ are sequences of points belonging to $\mathcal{C}$:

$$(45) \qquad p = [p^{(1)}, p^{(2)}, \ldots, p^{(n)}, \ldots], \qquad p^{(n)} \in \mathcal{C}.$$

In turn, $p^{(n)}$ being a point of the Cantor set, can be considered as a sequence of zeros and twos:

$$p^{(n)} = [p_1^{(n)}, p_2^{(n)}, \ldots, p_m^{(n)}, \ldots].$$

The double sequence $\{p_m^{(n)}\}$, where $n = 1, 2, \ldots$ and $m = 1, 2, \ldots$, can, by a known method (cf. Chapter V, § 3, (13) and (14)), be transformed into a single sequence

$$p_1^{(1)}, p_2^{(1)}, p_1^{(2)}, p_3^{(1)}, p_2^{(2)}, p_1^{(3)}, \ldots$$

Denoting this last sequence by $f(p)$, we obtain—as is easily proved—a homeomorphism mapping $\mathcal{C}\times\mathcal{C}\times\ldots$ onto $\mathcal{C}$.

Remark. Let us consider the (closed) "non-deleted" intervals which appear in the construction of the Cantor set, i. e.

$$(0,1/3),\ (2/3,1),$$
$$(0,1/9),\ (2/9,1/3),\ (2/3,7/9),\ (8/9,1),$$
$$\ldots\ldots\ldots\ldots\ldots\ldots\ldots\ldots\ldots$$

The intersections of these intervals with the set $\mathcal{C}$ we denote successively by $P_1, P_2, P_3, \ldots$ The following theorem holds:

THEOREM 4. *The sets $P_1, P_2, \ldots$ are open-closed in the space $\mathcal{C}$ and form a base of the space. Furthermore*

$$\lim_{n\to\infty}\delta(P_n)=0\,.$$

The proof that the sets P_n are open-closed does not offer any difficulty. In order to prove that these sets form a base of the space $\mathcal{C}$, it suffices to note that the intervals of the first row have length 1/3, those of the second 1/9, of the n-th $1/3^n$; furthermore the intervals of each row form a covering of the set $\mathcal{C}$.

§ 8. Continuous mappings of the Cantor set

THEOREM 1. *The closed interval $0\leqslant x\leqslant 1$ is a continuous image of the Cantor set.*

Proof. We define a so-called *step function* which maps the Cantor set into the interval $[0,1]$. Namely, the number $t\in\mathcal{C}$ being represented in the form (43), we set

$$\varphi(t)=\tfrac{1}{2}(t_1/2+t_2/4+\ldots+t_n/2^n+\ldots)\,. \tag{46}$$

It is easy to verify that the function φ has the same value at both endpoints of each deleted interval; we take this value as a constant value of the function f in this interval; otherwise, i. e. for $t\in\mathcal{C}$, we set $f(t)=\varphi(t)$. Figure 8 is the graph of this "step" function.

THEOREM 2. *The Hilbert cube $\mathcal{H}$ is a continuous image of the Cantor set.*

Proof. Since, by virtue of Theorem 3, § 7, the set $\mathcal{C}\times\mathcal{C}\times\mathcal{C}\times\ldots$ is a continuous image of the set $\mathcal{C}$, it suffices to prove that the space $\mathcal{H}=\mathcal{I}\times\mathcal{I}\times\mathcal{I}\times\ldots$ is

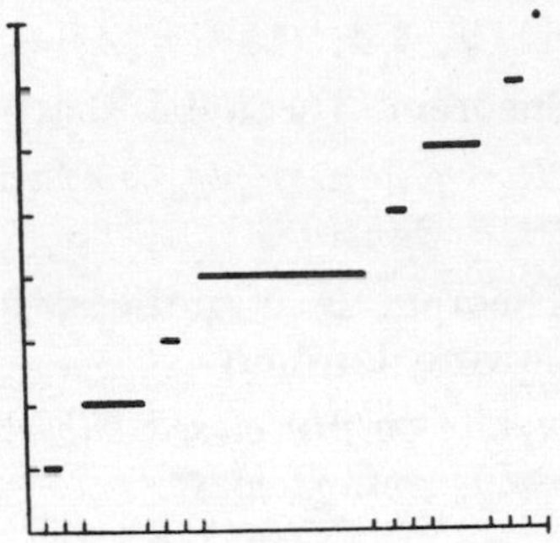

FIG. 8

a continuous image of the space $\mathcal{C}\times\mathcal{C}\times\mathcal{C}\times\ldots$ Thus, if we represent the point p of this last space in the form (45) we set

$$(47)\qquad f(p)=[\varphi(p^{(1)}),\varphi(p^{(2)}),\ldots,\varphi(p^{(n)}),\ldots],$$

where φ is the step function defined by formula (46).

The function f is continuous, as can easily be seen (cf. Chapter XII, § 6, Theorem 3). Its values are sequences of numbers belonging to the interval $[0,1]$, i. e. they are points of the space $\mathcal{H}$. Every point $x=(x_1,x_2,\ldots,x_n,\ldots)$ of this space is a value of the function f, for, by virtue of Theorem 1, for every n there exists a point $p^{(n)}\in\mathcal{C}$ such that $x_n=\varphi(p^{(n)})$; hence it suffices to define p by formula (45) in order to obtain the equality $x=f(p)$.

THEOREM 3. *Every compact space is the continuous image of some closed subset of the Cantor set.*

In fact, by virtue of the Urysohn theorem (Chapter XIII, § 4) a given compact space X can be regarded as a subset F of the Hilbert cube $\mathcal{H}$. Here, $F = \overline{F}$ because the space X is compact (cf. Theorem 4, § 2).

Let f be a function which maps the Cantor set $\mathcal{C}$ continuously onto the space $\mathcal{H}$. Let $A = f^{-1}(F)$.

Because of the continuity of the function f, the set A is closed (cf. Chapter XII, § 2, Theorem 1). At the same time (cf. Chapter IV, § 4, (18)): $f(A) = ff^{-1}(F) = F$.

*Remark. Theorem 3 can be sharpened as follows.

THEOREM 4. *Every non-empty compact space is a continuous image of the Cantor set.*

Because of Theorem 3 it suffices, for this purpose, to prove the following lemma:

LEMMA. *Every non-empty closed subset F of the Cantor set $\mathcal{C}$ is a continuous image of $\mathcal{C}$.*

Proof. Since the sequence $P_1, P_2, \ldots$ forms a base of the space $\mathcal{C}$ (see Theorem 4, § 7), the open set $\mathcal{C}-F$ is the union of a certain number of terms of this sequence. Hence, let

(48) $$\mathcal{C}-F = G_1 \cup G_2 \cup \ldots,$$

where the sets G_n belong to the sequence $P_1, P_2, \ldots$ Since we have either $P_i \cap P_j = \emptyset$ or $P_j \subset P_i$ for $i < j$, we can assume that the sets G_n are disjoint (for we can omit terms in the series (48) which are contained in the earlier terms).

We denote by p_n the point of the set F which lies nearest the set G_n, i. e. the point in which the function $\varrho(x, G_n)$ defined on the set F attains its greatest lower bound (cf. Chapter XII, § 7, Theorem 5 and Chapter XV, § 4, Theorem 4); if there is more than one such point, then we denote by p_n any one of them.

We define the function f as the retraction of the set $\mathcal{C}$ to F, namely:

$$f(x) = \begin{cases} x & \text{for} \quad x \in F, \\ p_n & \text{for} \quad x \in G_n. \end{cases}$$

Hence we have $f(\mathcal{C}) = F$. We must prove that the function f is continuous.

The sets G_n being open, the function f is obviously continuous on their union. It remains to prove that if

$$(49) \qquad \lim_{k\to\infty} x_k = x\,, \quad \text{where} \quad x_k \in \mathcal{C} - F \text{ and } x \in F\,,$$

then

$$(50) \qquad \lim_{k\to\infty} f(x_k) = f(x)\,, \quad \text{i. e.} \quad \lim_{k\to\infty} f(x_k) = x\,.$$

We denote by $n(k)$ an index such that

$$(51) \qquad x_k \in G_{n(k)}\,.$$

Since to a given G_n there can belong only a finite number of points of the sequence $x_1, x_2, \ldots$ (for $x \notin G_n$) and since (cf. Theorem 4, § 7) we have

$$\lim_{n\to\infty} \delta(P_n) = 0\,, \quad \text{and hence} \quad \lim_{n\to\infty} \delta(G_n) = 0\,,$$

we deduce from this that

$$(52) \qquad \lim_{k\to\infty} \delta(G_{n(k)}) = 0\,.$$

Let q_n denote the point of the (closed) set G_n lying nearest the point p_n. Hence we have by virtue of the definition of the points p_n and q_n

$$|p_n - q_n| = \varrho(p_n, G_n) \leqslant \varrho(x, G_n)\,,$$

and therefore

$$|p_{n(k)} - q_{n(k)}| \leqslant \varrho(x, G_{n(k)}) \leqslant |x - x_k|$$

according to (51); whence

$$|p_{n(k)} - x_k| \leqslant |p_{n(k)} - q_{n(k)}| + |q_{n(k)} - x_k| \leqslant |x - x_k| + \delta(G_{n(k)})\,.$$

And therefore by virtue of (49) and (52) we have

$$(53) \qquad \lim_{k\to\infty} p_{n(k)} = x\,.$$

At the same time, by virtue of the definition of the function f and by the formula (51) we have

$$(54) \qquad f(x_k) = p_{n(k)}\,,$$

and hence (50).

*§ 9. Bicompact spaces

A topological space (not necessarily metric) is called a *bicompact* space, if each covering by open sets contains a finite covering (i. e. if the Borel-Lebesgue theorem is satisfied, see § 3, theorem 3).

Obviously, each bicompact space is compact. But a compact space may be non-bicompact. On the other hand, a compact metric space is always bicompact (by Theorem 3, § 3).

THEOREM 1. *Every bicompact subset B of an arbitrary $\mathcal{T}_2$-space X* (see Chapter XI, exercise 11) *is closed.*

Proof. We have to prove that $X-B$ is open. Otherwise stated, we have to prove that, given a point $a \in X-B$, there exists an open set G such that

$$a \in G \subset X-B. \tag{55}$$

Now, X being a $\mathcal{T}_2$-space, for each point x of B there is a pair of open sets U_x and V_x such that

$$a \in U_x, \quad x \in V_x, \quad U_x \cap V_x = \emptyset. \tag{56}$$

Hence the sets $B \cap V_x$ form a covering of B, and (B being bicompact), there is a finite set of points $x_1, \dots, x_n$ such that

$$B = (B \cap V_{x_1}) \cup \dots \cup (B \cap V_{x_n}),$$

whence

$$B \subset V_{x_1} \cup \dots \cup V_{x_n}.$$

It follows in view of (56) that the set $G = U_{x_1} \cap \dots \cap U_{x_n}$ satisfies condition (55).

THEOREM 2. *Every closed subset F of a bicompact space X is bicompact.*

Proof. Let us set $F = \bigcup_t G_t$, where the sets G_t are open relatively to F. Let H_t be an open set in X such that $F \cap H_t = G_t$ (see Chapter XI, Exercise 4). Consider the covering of X composed of sets H_t and of the set $H = X-F$. The space X being bicompact, there exists a finite covering $H, H_{t_1}, H_{t_2}, \ldots, H_{t_n}$ of X, i. e.

$$X = H \cup H_{t_1} \cup \ldots \cup H_{t_n}, \qquad \text{whence} \qquad F = G_{t_1} \cup \ldots \cup G_{t_n},$$

and thus $G_{t_1}, \ldots, G_{t_n}$ is a finite covering of F.

THEOREM 3. *The continuous image of a bicompact space is a bicompact space.*

(Here by a continuous mapping we mean a mapping f such that $f^{-1}(G)$ is open whenever G is open; cf. Chapter XII, § 2, Theorem 2).

Proof. Let f be a continuous mapping of X onto Y. Let $\{G_t\}$ be an open covering of Y. Since $\{f^{-1}(G_t)\}$ is an open covering of X, there is a finite system $t_1, \ldots, t_n$ such that

$$X = f^{-1}(G_{t_1}) \cup \ldots \cup f^{-1}(G_{t_n}), \qquad \text{hence} \qquad Y = G_{t_1} \cup \ldots \cup G_{t_n}.$$

THEOREM 4. *Let f be a continuous mapping of a bicompact space X onto a $\mathcal{T}_2$-space Y. Then:*

1. *if F is a closed subset of X, $f(F)$ is a closed subset of Y,*
2. *if f is one-to-one, then f is a homeomorphism.*

The proof is essentially the same as the proof of Theorems 2 and 3 of § 4.

Remark. The bicompact spaces have the following important property (which we state here without proof).

TIHONOV THEOREM. *The cartesian product $P_t X_t$ of bicompact spaces is bicompact* (the product topology being defined as in Exercise 14, Chapter XI).

Exercises

1. Prove: A necessary and sufficient condition for the space X to be compact is that the derived set of every infinite set $A \subset X$ be $\neq \emptyset$.

2. Prove: A necessary and sufficient condition for a space to be compact is that it be complete and that for every $\varepsilon > 0$ it be possible to represent it as the union of a finite number of sets with diameter less than ε (spaces with this last property are said to be *totally bounded*).

3. Prove: A necessary and sufficient condition for the function f defined on an arbitrary space X (compact or not) to be uniformly continuous, is that the condition

$$\lim_{n\to\infty} |x_n - x_n'| = 0$$

imply the condition

$$\lim_{n\to\infty} |f(x_n) - f(x_n')| = 0$$

for every pair of sequences $x_1, x_2, \ldots$ and $x_1', x_2', \ldots$ of points belonging to the space X.

4. Prove: In a compact space, every sequence of functions $f_1, f_2, \ldots$ which is convergent to the function f with the property that to every $\varepsilon > 0$ there exists a $\delta > 0$ such that the condition $|x' - x''| < \delta$ implies

$$|f_n(x') - f_n(x'')| < \varepsilon \quad \text{for} \quad n = 1, 2, \ldots,$$

is uniformly convergent to f.

5. Prove that if f is a continuous mapping of the space X onto the space Y, and the sequence $A_1 \supset A_2 \supset \ldots$ is a decreasing sequence of compact subsets of the space X then

$$f\left(\bigcap_{n=1}^{\infty} A_n\right) = \bigcap_{n=1}^{\infty} f(A_n).$$

6. Prove the following *Banach Theorem* (which holds in an arbitrary complete space):

If f is a function which maps the complete space X continuously into itself, and if for every pair of points $x_1, x_2 \in X$ the inequality

$$|f(x_1) - f(x_2)| \leqslant k|x_1 - x_2|$$

holds, where k is a constant satisfying the condition $0 < k < 1$, then there exists exactly one point $x_0 \in X$ such that $f(x_0) = x_0$.

Hint: Construct inductively a sequence of points $x_1, x_2, \ldots$ in the following way: let x_1 be an arbitrary point of the space X and let $x_n = f(x_{n-1})$. Show that a sequence constructed this way is a Cauchy sequence, and then setting $x_0 = \lim_{n\to\infty} x_n$, prove that $f(x_0) = x_0$.

7. Prove using Banach theorem the following theorem on the existence of a solution of a differential equation:

Given the differential equation

$$dy/dx = f(x, y)\,, \tag{i}$$

where the function f is continuous in some plane region G and satisfies in this region the Lipschitz condition with respect to y, i. e. there exists a constant M such that the inequality

$$|f(x, y_1) - f(x, y_2)| < M|y_1 - y_2| \tag{ii}$$

holds for every pair of points $\langle x, y_1\rangle$, $\langle x, y_2\rangle \in G$. Furthermore, let $\langle x_0, y_0\rangle \in G$ be a given point. Then there exists a number $\delta > 0$ such that in the interval $x_0-\delta$, $x_0+\delta$ there exists exactly one function g satisfying equation (i), i. e.

$$\text{(iii)} \qquad dg(x)/dx = f(x, g(x)),$$

and satisfying the initial condition

$$\text{(iv)} \qquad y_0 = g(x_0).$$

Hint: Instead of the differential equation (i) we consider the equivalent integral equation

$$\text{(v)} \qquad y = y_0 + \int_{x_0}^{x} f(x, y)\,dx.$$

To each element g of the space of continuous functions $\mathcal{E}^{\mathcal{J}}$, where $\mathcal{J}$ denotes the closed interval $x_0-\delta$, $x_0+\delta$, we assign the function h_g of the variable x defined as follows:

$$\text{(vi)} \qquad h_g(x) = y_0 + \int_{x_0}^{x} f(t, g(t))\,dt.$$

Making use of (ii) we prove that for sufficiently small $\delta > 0$ the inequality

$$|h_{g_1} - h_{g_2}| \leqslant k|g_1 - g_2|, \quad \text{where} \quad 0 < k < 1,$$

holds.

Then applying Banach theorem (Exercise 6) to the space $\mathcal{E}^{\mathcal{J}}$ we deduce that there exists exactly one function g such that $h_g = g$; it is a solution of equation (v), and consequently also of equation (i), and satisfies condition (iv).

8. *Theorem on implicit definitions*. Let g be a continuous function of two variables x and y with a continuous partial derivative with respect to y in some square with center $\langle x_0, y_0\rangle$; let, also,

$$g(x_0, y_0) = 0 \quad \text{and} \quad g'_y(x_0, y_0) \neq 0.$$

Then there exists one and only one function f, continuous in a neighborhood of the point x_0, such that

$$g(x, f(x)) = 0 \quad \text{and} \quad f(x_0) = y_0;$$

in other words, the curve $E_{x,y}[g(x, y) = 0]$ is locally, at the point $\langle x_0, y_0\rangle$, the graph of a function.

Reduce the proof by means of the substitution

$$h(x, y) = y - y_0 - g(x, y)/g'_y(x_0, y_0)$$

to the following theorem:

Let h be a function of the variables x and y, which is continuous and has a continuous partial derivative with respect to y in a square K with center $\langle x_0, y_0\rangle$ and with side $2d$; let, also,

$$h(x_0, y_0) = 0 = h'_y(x_0, y_0).$$

Then, there exists one and only one function f continuous in a neighborhood of the point x_0, such that

$$\text{(vii)} \qquad f(x) = h(x, f(x)) + y_0 \quad \text{and} \quad f(x_0) = y_0.$$

Sketch of the proof. We can assume that the number d is so small that

$$|h'_y(x, y)| < \tfrac{1}{2} \quad \text{for} \quad (x, y) \in K.$$

Let I_1 denote a closed interval with center x_0 so small that

$$|h(x, y_0)| < \tfrac{1}{2}d \quad \text{for} \quad x \in I_1.$$

Let $I_2 = \underset{y}{E}(|y - y_0| < d)$.

Let us assign to each function $f \in I_2^{I_1}$, satisfying the condition $f(x_0) = y_0$, the function F_f of the variable x defined as follows:

$$F_f(x) = y_0 + h(x, f(x)) \quad \text{for} \quad x \in I_1.$$

We obtain

$$|F_{f_1}(x) - F_{f_2}(x)| = |h(x, f_1(x)) - h(x, f_2(x))|$$
$$= |f_1(x) - f_2(x)| \cdot |h'_y(x, z_x)| \leqslant \tfrac{1}{2}|f_1(x) - f_2(x)|,$$

where $f_1(x) < z_x < f_2(x)$.

We deduce from this that

$$|F_{f_1} - F_{f_2}| \leqslant \tfrac{1}{2}|f_1 - f_2|.$$

At the same time $F_f \in I_2^{I_1}$, which we prove easily by using the inequality $|h(x, y)| \leqslant |h(x, y) - h(x, y_0)| + |h(x, y_0)|$. Finally, $F_f(x_0) = y_0$.

Hence we may apply Banach theorem. It follows that there exists a function f such that $F_f = f$, i. e. satisfying conditions (vii).

9. Prove that for each metric non-compact space there is a real-valued bounded function whose least upper bound is not attained.

Hint: Use Tietze extension theorem.

10. Prove that a compact space cannot be isometric to a proper subset of itself.

11. Prove that a bicompact $\mathcal{T}_2$-space is normal.

Hint: Use a method similar to the method used in the proof of Theorem 1, § 9.

12. Let X and Y be metric spaces. Show that the set Y^X of all continuous mappings of X into Y may be considered as a topological space by defining the closure $\bar{\Phi}$ of $\Phi \subset Y^X$ as follows:

$$(f \in \bar{\Phi}) = [(f|F) \in \overline{\Phi|F} \text{ for each compact } F \subset X],$$

the topology in Y^F being defined as in § 6, formula (39), and $\Phi|F$ denoting the set of elements of Φ restricted to F.

Show that in the case where X is an open subset of a compact space, f belongs to $\bar{\Phi}$ if and only if there is a sequence of functions $f_1, f_2, \ldots$ in Φ converging uniformly to f on each compact subset of X.

CHAPTER XVI

CONNECTED SPACES

§ 1. Connected spaces

Definitions. A space X is said to be *connected* if it does not contain a subset A such that

$$(1) \qquad \emptyset \neq A \neq X$$

and

$$(2) \qquad \bar{A} \cap \overline{X-A} = \emptyset .$$

This means that a space is connected if and only if every non-empty proper subset of it has a non-empty boundary.

Let us note that a set A satisfying condition (2) is closed, for we have then $\bar{A} \cap (X-A) = \emptyset$, therefore $\bar{A} \subset A$ i. e. $\bar{A} = A$. This set is also open since the set $X-A$ is closed. It follows from this that the space is connected if and only if its only open-closed subsets are the null set and the entire space.

The connectedness of a space can also be defined in the following manner.

THEOREM 1. *A space X is connected if and only if, for every decomposition*

$$(3) \qquad X = A \cup B$$

into two nonvoid closed sets A and B, the condition

$$(4) \qquad A \cap B \neq \emptyset$$

is satisfied.

In other words, *a space is connected if and only if it cannot be represented as the union of two non-empty, disjoint and closed sets.*

Proof. Let us assume that the space X is not connected. Let the set A satisfy conditions (1) and (2).

The sets A and $B = X - A$ are then non-empty and closed, and satisfy condition (3), but do not satisfy condition (4).

Next, let us assume that the sets A and B are closed and non-empty and that condition (3) is satisfied, but that condition (4) is not satisfied, i. e. that

$$A \cap B = \emptyset\,. \tag{5}$$

It follows from (3) and (5) that $X - A = B$ and hence $\bar{A} \cap \overline{X - A} = \bar{A} \cap \bar{B} = A \cap B = \emptyset$.

Furthermore, $A \neq X$ since $B \neq \emptyset$ and $B = X - A$. The set A therefore satisfies (1) and (2), i. e. the space X is not connected.

Remark. The condition given in Theorem 1 can be formulated in the following manner: a space is connected if for each of its decompositions into two non-empty sets A and B at least one of these sets contains a point which belongs to the closure of the other set (i. e. if there exists a point p of the form $p = \lim_{n\to\infty} p_n$, where $p \in A$ and $p_n \in B$, or $p \in B$ and $p_n \in A$).

This condition allows us to make a suitable formulation of the definition of a connected set.

A set is said to be connected if this set treated as a space forms a connected space. Therefore, *a set C is connected if for each of its decompositions into two nonvoid sets A and B*:

$$C = A \cup B, \tag{6}$$

we have

$$(\bar{A} \cap B) \cup (A \cap \bar{B}) \neq \emptyset\,. \tag{7}$$

In other words, if we say that two sets A and B are *separated* provided that they satisfy the equality

$$(\bar{A} \cap B) \cup (A \cap \bar{B}) = \emptyset\,, \tag{8}$$

we may say that a set C is connected if it cannot be decomposed into two nonvoid separated sets.

We shall prove several properties of separated sets which will be useful in the sequel.

THEOREM 2. *If the sets A and B are separated and $A_1 \subset A$ and $B_1 \subset B$, then the sets A_1 and B_1 are separated.*

This is true because

$$(\bar{A}_1 \cap B_1) \cup (A_1 \cap \bar{B}_1) \subset (\bar{A} \cap B) \cup (A \cap \bar{B}) = \emptyset .$$

THEOREM 3. *If the sets A and B are separated and the sets A and C are separated, then the sets A and $B \cup C$ are separated.*

This follows from the formula

$$[\bar{A} \cap (B \cup C)] \cup [A \cap \overline{B \cup C}]$$
$$= (\bar{A} \cap B) \cup (\bar{A} \cap C) \cup (A \cap \bar{B}) \cup (A \cap \bar{C}) = \emptyset .$$

THEOREM 4. *If the sets A and B are both closed or both open, then the sets $A-B$ and $B-A$ are separated.*

Proof. We have

$$\overline{A-B} \cap (B-A) = \overline{A \cap (X-B)} \cap B \cap (X-A)$$
$$\subset \bar{A} \cap \overline{X-B} \cap B \cap (X-A) .$$

If $\bar{A} = A$, then

$$\bar{A} \cap \overline{X-B} \cap B \cap (X-A) \subset A \cap (X-A) = \emptyset .$$

If the set B is open, i. e. if the set $X-B$ is closed, then

$$\bar{A} \cap \overline{X-B} \cap B \cap (X-A) \subset (X-B) \cap B = \emptyset .$$

In an analogous way we prove that under our assumptions

$$(A-B) \cap \overline{B-A} = \emptyset ,$$

and hence the sets $A-B$ and $B-A$ are separated.

§ 2. Properties of connected spaces

THEOREM 1. *The image under a continuous mapping of a connected space is a connected space; in other words, connectedness is an invariant of continuous mappings.*

Proof. Let f be a continuous mapping of the space X and let $f(X) = Y$. Let us assume that the space Y is not connected. We shall then prove that the space X is not connected.

Hence, let A and B be nonvoid closed sets such that

(9) $$A \cup B = Y$$

and

(10) $$A \cap B = \emptyset .$$

Then by virtue of (9) (cf. Chapter IV, § 4, (16)):

$$f^{-1}(A) \cup f^{-1}(B) = f^{-1}(Y) = X .$$

The sets $f^{-1}(A)$ and $f^{-1}(B)$ are non-empty and, as the function f is continuous, they are also closed (see Chapter XII, § 2, Theorem 1); making use of (10) (cf. Chapter IV, § 4, (17)), we have

$$f^{-1}(A) \cap f^{-1}(B) = f^{-1}(A \cap B) = \emptyset .$$

Thus, the space X has been decomposed into two nonvoid disjoint closed sets. Hence, the space X is not connected.

Remarks. The only connected subsets of the space of real numbers (other than the entire space, the void set and single points) are closed or open rays, i. e. sets of the form

$$E_x(x \leqslant a), \quad E_x(x < a), \quad E_x(x \geqslant a), \quad E_x(x > a),$$

closed or open intervals, and, finally, sets of the form

$$E_x(a < x \leqslant b), \quad E_x(a \leqslant x < b) .$$

For, if the set A is not of one of these forms, then there exists a number $d \notin A$ and numbers $x_1, x_2 \in A$ such that $x_1 < d < x_2$. The set A is then the union of two non-empty sets M and N contained in the separated sets

$$E_x(x < d) \quad \text{and} \quad E_x(x > d) ,$$

respectively, and hence A is the union of two non-empty separated sets, i. e. it is not a connected set.

Now let f be a real valued continuous function defined on the connected space X. The set $f(X)$ is then, by Theorem 1, a connected subset of the set of real numbers and hence it is one of the sets we indicated above.

It follows from this that if $y_1 \in f(X)$, $y_2 \in f(X)$ and $y_1 < y_2$, then the entire interval $y_1 \leqslant y \leqslant y_2$ is contained in the set $f(X)$, or in other words, if $y_1 \leqslant y \leqslant y_2$, then $y \in f(X)$. This means that the function f has the *Darboux property*, i. e. it assumes all intermediate values in passing from one value to another. We have thus proved the following property of connected spaces:

THEOREM 2. *Every real valued continuous function defined on a connected space has the Darboux property.*

We note further that this property is characteristic of a connected space. For if a space X is not connected and A and B are non-empty disjoint closed sets such that $A \cup B = X$, then the characteristic function of the set A, i. e. the function defined by the conditions

$$f(x) = \begin{cases} 1 & \text{for} \quad x \in A, \\ 0 & \text{for} \quad x \in B, \end{cases}$$

is a real valued continuous function defined on the space X and not having the Darboux property.

THEOREM 3. *If C is connected and $C \cap A \neq \emptyset \neq C - A$, then*

$$C \cap \mathrm{Fr}(A) \neq \emptyset .$$

In other words, *if a connected set C has points in common with the set A and also with its complement, then it also has points in common with the boundary of the set A.*

Proof. By virtue of the connectedness of the set C and the equality $C = (C \cap A) \cup (C - A)$, the sets $C \cap A$ and $C - A$ are not separated, i. e.

$$(11) \qquad [\overline{C \cap A} \cap (C - A)] \cup [\overline{C - A} \cap C \cap A] \neq \emptyset ,$$

$$\text{i. e.} \qquad C \cap \left[(\overline{C \cap A} \cap (X - A)) \cup (\overline{C - A} \cap A)\right] \neq \emptyset .$$

We also have

$$\overline{C \cap A} \subset \bar{A}, \quad X - A \subset \overline{X-A}, \quad \overline{C-A} \subset \overline{X-A}, \quad A \subset \bar{A}.$$

Therefore, by (11), we have

$$\emptyset \neq C \cap \bar{A} \cap \overline{X-A} = C \cap \operatorname{Fr}(A).$$

THEOREM 4. *If the set C is connected, and $C \subset M \cup N$ and the sets M and N are separated, then $C \subset M$ or $C \subset N$.*

Proof. The sets $C \cap M$ and $C \cap N$ are separated (see Theorem 2, § 1) and $(C \cap M) \cup (C \cap N) = C$. Hence, because of the connectedness of the set C, one of these two sets is void. If $C \cap N = \emptyset$, then $C = C \cap M$, i. e. $C \subset M$. Similarly, if $C \cap M = \emptyset$, then $C \subset N$.

THEOREM 5. *If the sets C and D are connected and are not separated, then their union is connected.*

Proof. Let $C \cup D = M \cup N$, where the sets M and N are separated. We have to prove that one of them is void. By Theorem 4 we can assume that $C \subset M$. Similarly, $D \subset M$ or $D \subset N$. The inclusion $D \subset N$ does not hold, because the sets C and D would then be separated (by virtue of Theorem 2, § 1), contrary to assumption. Therefore $D \subset M$, whence $C \cup D \subset M$ and hence $N = \emptyset$.

Theorem 5 can be generalized as follows.

THEOREM 6. *If $\{C_t\}$ is a family of connected sets and if one of them, C_{t_0}, is not separated from any of the remaining sets, then the union $S = \bigcup_t C_t$ is a connected set.*

Proof. Let $S = M \cup N$, where the sets M and N are separated. We shall show that $M = \emptyset$ or $N = \emptyset$.

By virtue of Theorem 4, we can assume that $C_{t_0} \subset M$. Since the sets C_{t_0} and C_t are not separated for any t, we deduce from Theorem 5 that the sets $C_{t_0} \cup C_t$ are connected, and hence $C_{t_0} \cup C_t \subset M$ for all t, whence $S \subset M$ and therefore $N = \emptyset$.

Remark. If follows immediately from Theorem 6 that *if $\{C_t\}$ is a family of connected sets and $\bigcap_t C_t \neq \emptyset$, then the set $\bigcup_t C_t$ is connected.*

THEOREM 7. *If the set C is connected and $C \subset A \subset \bar{C}$, then the set A is also connected.*

In particular, *the closure of a connected set is connected.*

This theorem follows from the preceding theorem, C_{t_0} being the set C, and the sets of the family $\{C_t\}$, $t \neq t_0$, being the one-element sets $\{x\}$ where $x \in A$. None of the sets $\{x\}$ is separated from C because $x \in \bar{C}$. Hence, the set $C \cup \bigcup_x \{x\} = A$ is connected.

THEOREM 8. *If C is a connected subset of the connected space X and*

$$X - C = M \cup N, \tag{12}$$

where the sets M and N are separated, then the sets $C \cup M$ and $C \cup N$ are connected.

Furthermore, if the set C is closed, then the sets $C \cup M$ and $C \cup N$ are also closed.

Proof. Let us assume that

$$C \cup M = A \cup B, \tag{13}$$

where the sets A and B are separated. We have to show that $A = \emptyset$ or $B = \emptyset$.

Since we have $C \subset A \cup B$ (by virtue of (13)), we can therefore assume, by Theorem 4, that $C \subset B$. It follows from this (see Theorem 2, § 1), that the sets A and C are separated and in particular $A \cap C = \emptyset$. But since $A \subset C \cup M$, hence $A \subset M$, and since the sets M and N are separated, it follows from this that the sets A and N are separated. The set A is therefore separated from B as well as from N; it is therefore separated from $B \cup N$ (see Theorem 3, § 1).

On the other hand, by (12) and (13) we have

$$X = C \cup M \cup N = A \cup B \cup N = A \cup (B \cup N). \tag{14}$$

The space X is therefore the union of two separated sets A and $B \cup N$. Since the space is connected, one of these two sets must be void. Hence, either $A = \emptyset$ or else $B \cup N = \emptyset$, whence $B = \emptyset$.

If, moreover, $C = \bar{C}$, then by (14):

$$\overline{C \cup M} = C \cup \bar{M} = C \cup [\bar{M} \cap (C \cup M \cup N)]$$
$$= C \cup M \cup (\bar{M} \cap N) = C \cup M,$$

since $\bar{M} \cap N = \emptyset$ (M and N being separated).

Hence the set $C \cup M$ is closed.

The same argument proves that the set $C \cup N$ is connected and closed.

§ 3. Components

The component of the point p is the union of all connected sets which contain the point p.

THEOREM 1. *Each component is a connected set.*

Moreover, a component S is a *maximal* connected set, i. e. *if* C *is a connected set then*

$$(S \subset C) \Rightarrow (C = S). \tag{15}$$

Proof. Let S be the component of the point p. Therefore, S is of the form

$$S = \bigcup_t C_t,$$

where C_t is a connected set containing the point p. By virtue of Theorem 6 (see Remark following Theorem 6, § 2) S is a connected set.

Moreover, if $S \subset C$, then $p \in C$, and hence C is of the form $C = C_t$, whence $C \subset S$. Thus $C = S$.

THEOREM 2. *Each component* S *is a closed set.*

Proof. By Theorem 7, § 2, the set $\bar{S}$ is connected. But since $S \subset \bar{S}$, we have, making use of (15), $\bar{S} = S$.

THEOREM 3. *Two distinct components are always separated.*

Proof. If the components S_1 and S_2 are not separated, then the set $S_1 \cup S_2$ is connected (see Theorem 5, § 2), and hence $S_1 \cup S_2 \subset S_1$ and $S_1 \cup S_2 \subset S_2$, that is $S_1 = S_2$.

EXAMPLE. Let I_n denote the segment (situated in the plane) consisting of points $\langle x, y \rangle$ such that $x = 1/n$,

$0 \leqslant y \leqslant 1$ for $n = 1, 2, \ldots$ Let I_0 denote the segment $x = 0$, $0 \leqslant y \leqslant 1$. Let $A = I_0 \cup I_1 \cup I_2 \cup \ldots$ The components of the space A are segments I_m $(m \geqslant 0)$. Let us note that the component I_0 is not an open set in the space under consideration.

THEOREM 4. *If A is a connected subset of a connected space X and C is a component of the set $X-A$, then the set $X-C$ is connected.*

Proof. Let $X-C = M \cup N$, where the sets M and N are separated. We shall show that $M = \emptyset$ or $N = \emptyset$.

By assumption, we have $C \subset X-A$ and hence

$$A \subset X-C = M \cup N. \tag{16}$$

We can assume (see Theorem 4, § 2) that $A \subset M$, whence $A \cap N = \emptyset$. Since

$$A \cap (C \cup N) = (A \cap C) \cup (A \cap N) = \emptyset,$$

then $C \cup N \subset X-A$, whence

$$C \subset C \cup N \subset X-A. \tag{17}$$

Since C is a component of the set $X-A$, and the set $C \cup N$ is connected (by Theorem 8, § 2), formula (17) yields $C = C \cup N$ (cf. (15)). It follows that $N \subset C$. Since, by (16), we have $N \subset X-C$, hence $N = \emptyset$.

Exercises

1. Prove that if the spaces X and Y are connected, then the cartesian product $X \times Y$ is a connected space also.

Hint: Note that for every point $y \in Y$ the set $X \times \{y\}$ is connected and then use Theorem 5, § 2.

Generalize this theorem to the cartesian product of a countable number of spaces.

2. Prove that every connected space which contains more than one point has at least the power of the continuum.

3. Show that the Euclidean space $\mathcal{E}^n$ $(n > 1)$ remains connected after removing a countable number of points from it.

Hint: Let N be a countable set of points of the space $\mathcal{E}^n$ and let $p, q \in \mathcal{E}^n - N$. Further, let L be a straight line which does not pass through the points p and q. Notice that on the line L there always exists a point x such that the segments px and xq are disjoint from the set N.

4. Let the sets A and B be either both closed or both open. Show that if the sets $A \cup B$ and $A \cap B$ are connected, then the sets A and B are also connected.

Hint: Make use of Theorem 8, § 2, setting $X = A \cup B$, $C = A \cap B$, $M = A - B$, $N = B - A$, and of Theorem 4, § 1.

5. Let

$$X = \bigcup_t G_t$$

be a given open covering of the connected space X.

Prove that every pair of points $\langle a, b\rangle$ of the space X can be joined by a chain consisting of sets G_t, i. e. that there exists a finite system of indices $t_1, \ldots, t_n$ such that

$$a \in G_{t_1}, \quad G_{t_1} \cap G_{t_2} \neq \emptyset, \quad \ldots, \quad G_{t_{n-1}} \cap G_{t_n} \neq \emptyset, \quad b \in G_{t_n}.$$

Hint: Let Z be the set of all points which can be joined by a chain with the point a. Prove that the set Z is open-closed.

6. We say that the space X is *connected between the sets A and B*, if the space cannot be decomposed into two disjoint closed sets one of which contains A and the other contains B. Prove that if there is given a system of sets $A_0, \ldots, A_n$ such that the space is connected between no pair A_i, A_j (for $i \neq j$), then there exists a system of disjoint closed sets $F_0, \ldots, F_n$ satisfying the conditions

$$X = F_0 \cup \ldots \cup F_n, \quad A_i \subset F_i \quad \text{for} \quad i = 0, \ldots, n.$$

7. Show that the relation

$$p \varrho q \equiv (\textit{the space } X \textit{ is connected between the points } p \textit{ and } q)$$

is an equivalence relation (cf. Exercise 9, Chapter V).

8. The equivalence sets determined by the above considered relation are called *quasi-components* of the space.

Show that

1. every quasi-component is the interseetion of all closed-open sets containing a given point;

2. every component of the space is contained in a quasi-component, but the converse is not true;

3. if X is connected between x_1 and x_2, and Y is connected between y_1 and y_2, then $X \times Y$ is connected between $\langle x_1, y_1\rangle$ and $\langle x_2, y_2\rangle$;

4. generalize the last statement to the case of a cartesian product of n factors.

9. Let A be a subset of a given metric space. Show the equivalence:

(A is connected between p and q) $\equiv$ *(each open G containing A is connected between p and q).*

Hint: Use the theorem stated in Exercise 15, Chapter XII.

10. Prove that the relation ϱ defined in Exercise 7 is closed (cf. Exercise 18, Chapter XI).

Show that the above theorem is not true for the relation "x and y belong to a connected subset of the space" (construct the space having the required property on the plane).

11. Show that a connected, metric and locally separable space is separable.

CHAPTER XVII

CONTINUA

§ 1. Continua

Definition and examples. A *continuum* is a compact connected space.

For example, a closed interval is a continuum. Other examples of continua are a circular disk together with its boundary and the closed n-dimensional cube.

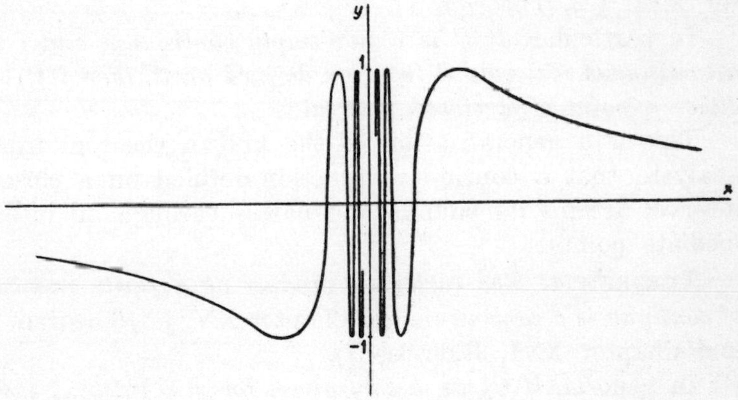

FIG. 9

The set S of points in the plane defined by the following equations:

$$(1) \qquad \begin{cases} y = \sin(1/x) & \text{for} \quad 0 < x \leqslant 1, \\ -1 \leqslant y \leqslant 1 & \text{for} \quad x = 0 \end{cases}$$

is a continuum (see Fig. 9).

The set consisting of a single point and the void set are obviously continua; closed intervals are the only other sets which are continua on the real line.

§ 2. Properties of continua

The following five theorems are immediate consequences of the corresponding theorems in Chapters XV and XVI (these are specified more closely in parentheses).

THEOREM 1. *The union of two continua which have a common point is a continuum* (cf. Chapter XVI, § 2, Theorem 5).

THEOREM 2. *If the space X is a continuum, C is a continuum contained in X, and $X-C$ is the union of two disjoint sets M and N, then the sets $C \cup M$ and $C \cup N$ are continua* (cf. Chapter XVI, § 2, Theorem 8).

THEOREM 3. *The continuous image of a continuum is a continuum* (cf. Chapter XV, § 4, Theorem 1 and Chapter XVI, § 2, Theorem 1).

In particular, *if C is a non-empty continuum and f is a continuous real valued function defined on C, then $f(C)$ is either a point or a closed interval.*

This is a generalization of the known theorem from analysis, that a continuous function defined on a closed interval attains its bounds and passes through all intermediate points.

THEOREM 4. *The cartesian product of a finite number of continua is a continuum* (cf. Chapter XV, § 5, Theorem 1 and Chapter XVI, Exercise 1).

In general, *if C_m is a continuum for $m=1,2,\ldots$, then $C_1 \times C_2 \times \ldots$ is a continuum.*

In particular, *the cube $\mathcal{J}^n$ and the Hilbert cube $\mathcal{H}$ are continua.*

THEOREM 5. *Every component of a compact space is a continuum* (cf. Chapter XVI, § 3, Theorems 1 and 2).

We shall now prove the following theorems.

*THEOREM 6. *If A and B are two distinct components of a compact space X, then X can be decomposed into two disjoint closed sets F and K which contain the sets A and B, respectively:*

$$X = F \cup K, \quad F \cap K = \emptyset, \quad A \subset F \quad \textit{and} \quad B \subset K.$$

In other words, *there exists an open-closed set F which satisfies the conditions $A \subset F$ and $F \cap B = \emptyset$* (we can, of course, take $K = X - F$).

We shall base the proof on the following lemma:

LEMMA. *The intersection C of all open-closed subsets of a compact space, which contain a given point p, is connected.*

Proof. Let us assume the contrary. Then let P and Q be two closed sets such that

(2) $$C = P \cup Q,$$

(3) $$P \cap Q = \emptyset,$$

(4) $$P \neq \emptyset \neq Q,$$

(5) $$p \in P.$$

By virtue of (3) and of the fact that the space is normal (cf. Chapter XII, § 7, Theorem 6), there exist two open sets G and H such that

(6) $$P \subset G, \quad Q \subset H \quad \text{and} \quad G \cap H = \emptyset.$$

Therefore, setting $G^c = X - G$ and $H^c = X - H$, we have

(7) $$P \cap G^c = \emptyset,$$

(8) $$Q \cap H^c = \emptyset,$$

(9) $$X = G^c \cup H^c,$$

where the sets G^c and H^c are closed.

Let

(10) $$D_1, D_2, \ldots, D_n, \ldots$$

be the sequence of all open-closed sets which contain the point p (cf. Chapter XV, § 3, Theorem 4). From the definition of the set C we have

(11) $$C = \bigcap_{n=1}^{\infty} D_n.$$

Let

(12) $$E_n = D_1 \cap D_2 \cap \ldots \cap D_n.$$

Then formulas (11) and (12) immediately yield

$$C = \bigcap_{n=1}^{\infty} E_n \tag{13}$$

and

$$E_1 \supset E_2 \supset \ldots \supset E_n \supset \ldots \tag{14}$$

Let us set $F_n = E_n \cap G^c \cap H^c$. Then, because of (13), we obtain

$$\bigcap_{n=1}^{\infty} F_n = (\bigcap_{n=1}^{\infty} E_n) \cap G^c \cap H^c = C \cap G^c \cap H^c = \emptyset\,, \tag{15}$$

for formulas (2) and (6) yield $C = (P \cup Q) \subset (G \cup H)$.

At the same time, the sets F_n form a decreasing sequence (cf. (14)) and are closed (cf. (12)). Hence, if they are nonvoid, then by the Cantor theorem (Chapter XV, § 3, Theorem 1) their intersection would not be empty, contrary to (15). Therefore, there exists an index n such that $F_n = \emptyset$, i. e. such that

$$E_n \cap G^c \cap H^c = \emptyset\,, \quad \text{i. e.} \quad E_n \cap H^c \subset G\,. \tag{16}$$

The set $E_n \cap G$ is open-closed. It is obviously an open set since it is the intersection of two open sets. It is also closed because, by (9) and (16), we have

$$E_n \cap G = E_n \cap G \cap (G^c \cup H^c) = E_n \cap H^c, \tag{17}$$

and the set $E_n \cap H^c$ is the intersection of two closed sets.

As the open-closed set $E_n \cap G$ contains the point p (cf. (5) and (6)), it is therefore one of the terms of the sequence (10): $E_n \cap G = D_k$. Hence, by (11) and (17), we have

$$C \subset D_k = E_n \cap G = E_n \cap H^c \subset H^c,$$

whence by (2):

$$Q \subset C \subset H^c, \quad \text{i. e.} \quad Q = Q \cap H^c = \emptyset$$

by (8). But this contradicts the inequality (4).

Proof of Theorem 6. Let $p \in A$ and let C (as in the lemma) be the intersection of all open-closed sets which contain the point p. Each of these open-closed sets obviously contains the set A, since A is connected (cf. Chapter XVI, § 2, Theorem 4); and therefore

$$A \subset C. \tag{18}$$

Since C is a connected set and A is a component of the space, inclusion (18) yields the equality

$$C = A \tag{19}$$

(cf. Chapter XVI, § 3, (15)).

If every open-closed set containing A also contained B, contrary to the hypothesis of Theorem 6, then we should have $B \subset C$, whence $B \subset A$ (cf. (19)). But this is impossible, because the components are disjoint (see Chapter XVI, § 3, Theorem 3). Therefore, there exists a closed set F such that $A \subset F$ and $B - F \neq \emptyset$. Since the set B is connected, the last inequality yields $F \cap B = \emptyset$.

COROLLARY. *For every compact space there exists a continuous mapping of this space into a subset of the Cantor set which maps two distinct components into two distinct points of the Cantor set.*

Proof. Let $D_1, D_2, \ldots$ be the sequence of all open-closed subsets of the given space. We shall define the function f as follows:

$$f(x) = t_1/3 + t_2/9 + \ldots + t_n/3^n + \ldots,$$

where $t_n = 2$ if $x \in D_n$, and $t_n = 0$ if $x \notin D_n$. (This is called the *characteristic function* of the sequence $D_1, D_2, \ldots$)

Hence the values of the function f are points of the Cantor set.

Since the set D_n is open-closed a function assuming the value 2 on it, and the value 0 on its complement is continuous. It easily follows from this that the function f is continuous.

Finally, if A and B are two distinct components, then by virtue of Theorem 6 there exists an n such that $A \subset D_n$, and $B \cap D_n = \emptyset$; and hence we have $t_n = 2$ for

$x \in A$ and $t_n = 0$ for $x \in B$. Therefore the values of the function f on the sets A and B are distinct.

Let us add that every component is mapped under this mapping into some point (and distinct components map onto distinct points); this follows from the fact that the continuous image of a connected set is connected, and the Cantor set does not contain nonvoid connected sets other than sets consisting of a single point.

*THEOREM 7. *The intersection of a decreasing sequence of continua is a continuum.*

Proof. Let C_n $(n = 1, 2, \ldots)$ be continua and let

$$C_1 \supset C_2 \supset \ldots \supset C_n \supset \ldots \tag{20}$$

and

$$C = \bigcap_{n=1}^{\infty} C_n . \tag{21}$$

Let us assume that C is not a continuum. Then there exist two closed sets P and Q which satisfy conditions (2)-(4). Let G and H be two open sets which satisfy conditions (6) and hence also conditions (7)-(9). Let us set

$$F_n = C_n \cap G^c \cap H^c . \tag{22}$$

Then, by (22) and (21), we have

$$\bigcap_{n=1}^{\infty} F_n = \left(\bigcap_{n=1}^{\infty} C_n\right) \cap G^c \cap H^c = C \cap G^c \cap H^c = \emptyset$$

because formulas (2) and (6) yield $C = (P \cup Q) \subset (G \cup H)$.

Since the sets F_n are closed and form a decreasing sequence (because of (20)), we therefore deduce from this (using the Cantor theorem) that not all these sets are non-empty, i. e. that $F_n = \emptyset$ for some n, i. e.

$$C_n \cap G^c \cap H^c = \emptyset . \tag{23}$$

At the same time, by (9), we have

$$C_n \subset G^c \cup H^c, \quad \text{i. e.} \quad C_n = (C_n \cap G^c) \cup (C_n \cap H^c) . \tag{24}$$

It follows from formulas (23) and (24) that C_n is the union of two closed disjoint closed sets $C_n \cap G^c$ and

$C_n \cap H^c$. Since C_n is a continuum, one of these two sets is void. Let, for instance, $C_n \cap G^c = \emptyset$, i. e. $C_n \subset G$, and therefore, because of (2) and (21), $Q \subset C \subset C_n \subset G$, i. e. $Q \subset G$, whence by (6) we have $Q \subset G \cap H = \emptyset$. In this manner we have arrived at the conclusion that $Q = \emptyset$, contrary to formula (4).

Exercises

1. Prove that for every two points a and b in the continuum C and for every $\varepsilon > 0$, there exists in C a finite sequence of points

$$a = p_0, p_1, \ldots, p_n = b$$

such that $|p_{i-1} - p_i| < \varepsilon$ for $i = 1, 2, \ldots, n$. Show that this property distinguishes the continua from all other compact spaces (Cantor's definition).

2. Show by means of an example that in Theorem 7 it is essential to make the compactness assumption: the intersection of a decreasing sequence of closed connected sets may be not connected.

CHAPTER XVIII

LOCALLY CONNECTED SPACES

§ 1. Locally connected spaces

Definition. We say that a space is *locally connected at the point* p if for every real number $\varepsilon > 0$ there exists a connected set E such that

$$p \in \operatorname{Int}(E) \quad \text{and} \quad \delta(E) < \varepsilon .$$

A space is said to be *locally connected* if it is locally connected at each of its points.

We can also say that spaces which are locally connected at the point p are spaces for which every neighborhood of the point p contains a connected neighborhood of this point.

EXAMPLES. 1. The set of all real numbers, the Euclidean n-space, and the n-dimensional cube are locally connected spaces.

2. The set S defined in Chapter XVII, § 1, (1), is not

FIG. 10

locally connected at the points of this set which are situated on the y-axis.

3. The so-called "whisk-broom" set, shown in Fig. 10, is not locally connected.

We obtain this set by joining the point $\langle 0, 1\rangle$ with segments to the point $\langle 0, 0\rangle$ and to the points $\langle 1/n, 0\rangle$ for $n = 1, 2, \ldots$

This set is not locally connected at the points on the segment on the y-axis, except at the point $\langle 0, 1\rangle$.

§ 2. Properties of locally connected spaces

THEOREM 1. *In a locally connected space every component is an open set.*

Proof. Let S be a component and let $p \in S$. Let E be a connected neighborhood of the point p, i. e. $p \in \mathrm{Int}(E)$ (such a neighborhood exists by virtue of the definition). Therefore $E \subset S$, whence we have $\mathrm{Int}(E) \subset \mathrm{Int}(S)$. It follows that $p \in \mathrm{Int}(S)$, i. e. every point of the component S is its interior point. Thus the component S is an open set.

THEOREM 2. *Every open subset G of a locally connected space X is a locally connected set.*

Proof. Let $p \in G$ and let $0 < \varepsilon < \varrho(p, X-G)$. Since the space is locally connected at the point p, there exists a connected neighborhood E of the point p such that $\delta(E) < \varepsilon$, whence $E \subset G$. At the same time E is a neighborhood of p with respect to the set G, i. e. $p \notin \overline{G-E}$ (because $p \notin \overline{X-E}$ by assumption). This means that the set G is locally connected at the point p.

THEOREM 3. *The components of open subsets of a locally connected space are open sets.*

This is an immediate consequence of Theorems 1 and 2.

Remark. Theorem 3 characterizes locally connected spaces, i. e. that every space in which the components of open sets are open sets is locally connected.

THEOREM 4. *An open subset of a locally connected separable space has a countable number of components.*

For, every family of disjoint open sets in a separable space is countable (see Chapter XIII, § 3, Theorem 3).

THEOREM 5. *A locally connected separable space has a base consisting of sets which are simultaneously open and connected.*

Proof. Let $G_1, G_2, \ldots, G_n, \ldots$ be a base of the space (consisting of open but not necessarily connected sets). Let $S_{n1}, S_{n2}, \ldots$ be a finite or infinite (cf. Theorem 4) sequence of components of the set G_n. The sets S_{nk}, $n = 1, 2, \ldots$ and $k = 1, 2, \ldots$, form a base consisting of open connected sets (by virtue of Theorem 3).

THEOREM 6. *If S is a component of an open set G then*

$$\mathrm{Fr}(S) \cap G = \emptyset .$$

Proof. $\mathrm{Fr}(S) = \bar{S} - S$ since S is an open set. But since $G - S$ is also an open set, being the union of open sets, we therefore have $\bar{S} \cap (G-S) = S \cap (G-S) = \emptyset$, which is what we wished to prove.

§ 3. Arcs. Arcwise connectedness

Definition 1. An *arc* is a set which is homeomorphic to the closed interval $0 \leqslant t \leqslant 1$.

We can easily verify that every arc is a locally connected continuum.

An arc with endpoints x and y is usually denoted by the symbol xy (or yx).

THEOREM 1. *If $ab \cap bc = \{b\}$, then the union $ab \cup bc$ is an arc ac.*

For, we can define a continuous one-to-one mapping of the closed interval $[0, \frac{1}{2}]$ onto the arc ab and a continuous one-to-one mapping of the closed interval $[\frac{1}{2}, 1]$ onto the arc bc in such a way that both of these mappings map the point $\frac{1}{2}$ onto the point b. In this manner we obtain a homeomorphic mapping of the closed interval $[0, 1]$ onto the set $ab \cup bc$.

THEOREM 2. *If $ab \cap bc \neq \emptyset$, then the union $ab \cup bc$ contains an arc which connects a with c.*

For, let d be the first point on the arc ab (ordered from a to b) which lies on the arc bc. Let ad denote the arc contained in ab, and let dc be the arc contained in bc. We therefore have $ad \cap dc = \{d\}$. By Theorem 1 the set $ad \cup dc$ is an arc ac.

Definition 2. A space is said to be *locally arcwise connected*, if for every point p and every $\varepsilon > 0$, there exists an $\eta > 0$ such that if $|x-p| < \eta$, then the point x can be connected with the point p by means of an arc of diameter $< \varepsilon$.

THEOREM 3. *A space which is locally arcwise connected at the point p is locally connected at p.*

For if we denote by E the set of points which can be connected with p by means of an arc of diameter $< \varepsilon$ we can easily prove that E is a connected neighborhood of the point p with diameter $\leqslant 2\varepsilon$.

THEOREM 4. *Every two points of a connected and locally arcwise connected space can be connected by an arc in the space.*

Proof. Let p be a given point of the space X. Let us denote by F the set of all points x which can be connected to p by an arc. We have to prove that $F = X$ or equivalently (since the space is connected), that the set F is closed and open.

In order to prove that $F = \overline{F}$ let us assume that

$$x = \lim_{n\to\infty} x_n, \quad \text{where} \quad x_n \in F.$$

Since the space is arcwise locally connected at the point x, the point x_n can be connected with x, for sufficiently large n, by means of an arc $x_n x$. But since $x_n \in F$ there exists an arc px_n. By Theorem 2 the union $px_n \cup x_n x$ of the arcs px_n and $x_n x$ contains an arc px. Therefore $x \in F$.

In order to prove that the set F is open, let us assume that $x \in F$. Since points situated sufficiently closely to the point x can be connected with x by means of an arc, then, by Theorem 2, they can be connected by an arc to p (because by assumption, x can be connected with p by means of an arc). Therefore $x \in \mathrm{Int}(F)$. From this it follows that the set F is open.

THEOREM 5. *If a compact space is locally arcwise connected, then for each* $\varepsilon > 0$, *there exists an* $\eta > 0$ *such that if* $|x-x'| < \eta$ *then the points* x *and* x' *can be connected by means of an arc* xx' *of diameter* $< \varepsilon$.

Thus uniformity holds for the choice of η corresponding to ε (independently of p). The proof is entirely analogous to the proof of Theorem 5 in Chapter XV, § 4.

§ 4. Locally connected continua

THEOREM 1 (Sierpiński). *A necessary and sufficient condition for the continuum* C *to be locally connected, is that for every* $\varepsilon > 0$, C *can be represented as the union of a finite number of continua each of which has diameter* $< \varepsilon$, *i. e.*

$$C = C_1 \cup C_2 \cup \ldots \cup C_n, \tag{1}$$

and

$$\delta(C_n) < \varepsilon. \tag{2}$$

Proof. *The condition is necessary.* Let C be a locally connected continuum, and let $\varepsilon > 0$. For every point $p \in C$ let us denote by R_p an open connected set such that $p \in R_p$ and $\delta(R_p) < \varepsilon$. Such a set exists by virtue of Theorem 5, § 2. The family of sets R_p is a covering of the space C. Therefore (cf. the Borel-Lebesgue theorem, Chapter XV, § 3, Theorem 3) there exists a finite number of open connected sets $R_{p_1}, R_{p_2}, \ldots, R_{p_n}$ which also covers C. Let

$$C_k = \bar{R}_{p_k} \quad (k = 1, 2, \ldots, n).$$

Conditions (1) and (2) are therefore satisfied. Furthermore, the set C_k is connected, being the closure of a connected set (see Chapter XVI, § 2, Theorem 7), and compact, being a closed subset of a compact set (see Chapter XV, § 2, Theorem 5). Hence C_k is a continuum.

We have thus proved that the condition is necessary.

We shall now prove that it is *sufficient.*

Let us therefore assume that the continua $C_1, C_2, \ldots, C_n$ satisfy conditions (1) and (2). Let $p \in C$. We shall choose a connected neighborhood E of the point p with diameter not greater than 2ε.

Let us denote by $C_{k_1}, C_{k_2}, \ldots, C_{k_r}$ continua which contain the point p and all the remaining ones by $C_{m_1}, C_{m_2}, \ldots, C_{m_s}$.

Let

$$E = C_{k_1} \cup C_{k_2} \cup \ldots \cup C_{k_r}.$$

We therefore have

$$C - E \subset C_{m_1} \cup C_{m_2} \cup \ldots \cup C_{m_s},$$

whence

$$\overline{C-E} \subset C_{m_1} \cup C_{m_2} \cup \ldots \cup C_{m_s}.$$

Thus $p \in C - \overline{C-E}$, i. e. $p \in \mathrm{Int}(E)$. The set E is therefore a neighborhood of the point p. It is a connected set, being the union of connected sets which contain p.

Finally, $\delta(E) \leqslant 2\varepsilon$. For, let $x, y \in E$. Let $x \in C_{k_i}$, $y \in C_{k_j}$. Since

$$|x-y| \leqslant |x-p| + |p-y|$$

and since by (2)

$$|x-p| \leqslant \delta(C_{k_i}) < \varepsilon \quad \text{and} \quad |p-y| \leqslant \delta(C_{k_j}) < \varepsilon,$$

we have $|x-y| < 2\varepsilon$. It follows that $\delta(E) \leqslant 2\varepsilon$.

THEOREM 2. *A continuous image of a locally connected continuum is a locally connected continuum.*

Proof. Let K be a locally connected continuum, f a continuous function and let $f(K) = C$.

By virtue of the Heine theorem on uniform continuity (Chapter XV, § 4, Theorem 5), for every $\varepsilon > 0$, there exists an $\eta > 0$ such that for an arbitrary pair $x_1, x_2 \in K$ the condition

$$(3) \qquad |x_1 - x_2| < \eta$$

implies

(4) $$|f(x_1)-f(x_2)| < \varepsilon .$$

By virtue of Theorem 1 there exist continua K_1, $K_2, \ldots, K_n$ such that

(5) $$K = K_1 \cup K_2 \cup \ldots \cup K_n ,$$

and

(6) $$\delta(K_i) < \eta .$$

It therefore follows from (5) (cf. Chapter IV, § 4, (14)) that

(7) $$C = f(K) = f(K_1) \cup f(K_2) \cup \ldots \cup f(K_n) .$$

By (6), for every pair of points x_1 and x_2 belonging to K_i formula (4) holds, and hence

(8) $$\delta[f(K_i)] \leqslant \varepsilon .$$

Since $f(K_i)$ is a continuum (see Chapter XVII, § 2, Theorem 3), we deduce from formulas (7) and (8) and Theorem 1 that C is a locally connected continuum.

Remark 1. A continuous image of a locally connected space which is not compact is not necessarily a locally connected space.

Let us consider the example of the space S in Chapter XVII, § 1, (1), and let us join the point $\langle 1, 0\rangle$ with the point $\langle 0, 1\rangle$ by means of an arc in such a manner that the arc does not cut the set S at any point. The set thus obtained is, as can easily be seen, a continuous image of the half-ray $0 \leqslant x < +\infty$, but is not locally connected.

Remark 2. From Theorem 2 it follows in particular that a continuous image of a closed segment or of a rectangle (together with boundary) is a locally connected continuum. Therefore the curves possessing continuous parametric representations on an interval of the form

$$x = x(t) , \quad y = y(t) , \quad z = z(t) , \quad \text{where} \quad a \leqslant t \leqslant b ,$$

are locally connected continua, as well as surfaces of the form

$$x = x(u, v), \quad y = y(u, v), \quad z = z(u, v),$$

where $a \leqslant u \leqslant b$, $c \leqslant v \leqslant d$.

Thus, the geometric configurations which are studied most frequently in analysis are locally connected.

Remark 3. The theorem asserting that a continuous image of a closed interval is a locally connected continuum has a converse, i. e. the following theorem (due to Mazurkiewicz) is valid:

Every locally connected continuum is a continuous image of the closed interval $0 \leqslant t \leqslant 1$.

We shall not give a detailed proof of this theorem here, but shall limit ourselves to proving it under the assumption of local arcwise connectedness; this limitation is after all only apparent, for it is possible to prove that every locally connected continuum is also locally arcwise connected (Mazurkiewicz-Moore theorem).

THEOREM 3. *Every locally arcwise connected continuum* C $(\neq \emptyset)$ *is a continuous image of an interval.*

Proof. On the basis of Theorem 3, Chapter XV, § 8, there exists a continuous function f defined on some closed subset H of the Cantor set and such that $f(H) = C$. Let α and β denote the initial and terminal points of the set H. We shall extend the function f to the entire segment $\alpha\beta$. The set $\alpha\beta - H$, being open in $\alpha\beta$, is the union of a sequence of open intervals $(a_1 b_1), (a_2 b_2), \ldots$

Obviously,

$$\lim_{n\to\infty}(b_n - a_n) = 0,$$

whence

$$\lim_{n\to\infty}|f(b_n) - f(a_n)| = 0, \tag{9}$$

because of the uniform continuity of the function f.

According to Theorem 5, § 4, there exists a sequence of numbers η_k, such that each two points p and q of the continuum C satisfying the inequality $|p-q| < \eta_k$ can be joined by an arc with diameter $<1/k$. Therefore by virtue of (9) there exists a sequence of arcs L_n with end-points $f(a_n)$ and $f(b_n)$ satisfying the equality

$$\lim_{n\to\infty} \delta(L_n) = 0 . \tag{10}$$

Let f_n denote a homeomorphism mapping the (closed) segment $a_n b_n$ onto the arc L_n, such that $f_n(a_n) = f(a_n)$ and $f_n(b_n) = f(b_n)$. Finally, let

$$g(t) = \begin{cases} f(t) & \text{for} \quad t \in H , \\ f_n(t) & \text{for} \quad a_n \leqslant t \leqslant b_n , \ n = 1, 2, \ldots \end{cases}$$

Hence the function g maps the segment $\alpha\beta$ onto the continuum C. It is a continuous function, which fact follows easily from formula (10).

Remark 4. It follows from Theorem 3 in particular that *a square together with its boundary is a continuous image of a segment*; the same is true of the n-dimensional cube $\mathcal{J}^n$, and even of the Hilbert cube $\mathcal{H}$.

This discovery made by Peano (in 1890) was considered to be very paradoxical. For it means that the square $\mathcal{J}^2$ has a continuous parametric representation over a closed interval, contrary to the opinion that this property applies only to curves. It follows from this that the hypothesis of differentiability usually made in analysis for parametric representations is essential from this point of view.

The following is a direct proof of the Peano theorem (given by Sierpiński).

We divide the square into 9 equal squares and draw in each of them the diagonal as shown in Fig. 11. We divide the segment $[0, 1]$ into 9 equal segments and we transform (linearly) each of them into the corresponding diagonal in the order given in Fig. 11. We denote by f_1 the function thus defined, mapping the segment $[0, 1]$ continuously into the polygonal line consisting of

9 diagonals. We call the squares considered squares of first approximation.

Next, we divide each of the 9 squares into 9 equal squares; they are the second approximation squares. We

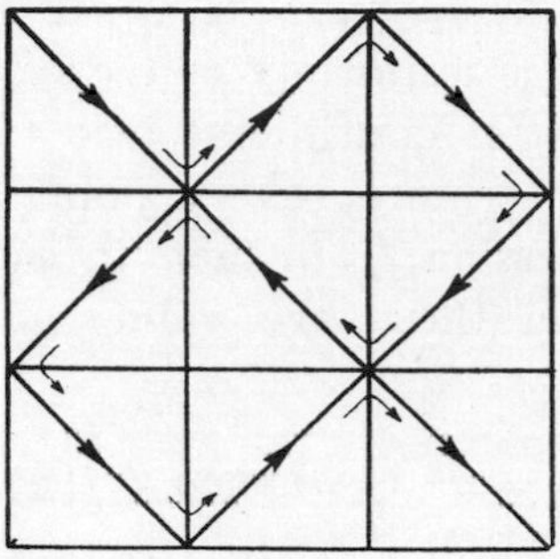

FIG. 11

draw a diagonal D in each of them; here in second approximation squares lying on a diagonal of a first approximation square we draw the diagonal lying on the diagonal D. Thus the first square of the first approximation appears as in Fig. 11 after the corresponding

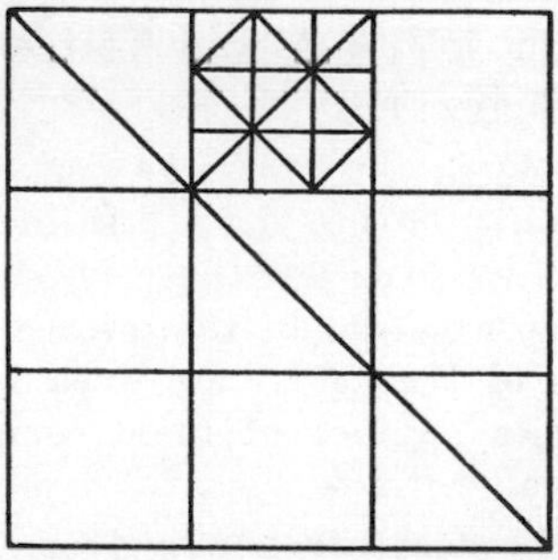

FIG. 12

reduction; the second square of the first approximation is given in Fig. 12.

We divide each of the intervals $(n-1)/9, n/9$, where $n = 1, 2, \ldots, 9$, onto 9 equal parts and we map each of these parts onto the diagonal of the corresponding square of the second subdivision. This defines the function f_2 which maps the interval $[0, 1]$ continuously onto the polygonal arc made up of 9^2 intervals.

Continuing thus, we define an infinite sequence of continuous functions $f_1, f_2, \ldots, f_n, \ldots$ It is easy to prove that this sequence is uniformly convergent; and therefore its limit function f is continuous (see Chapter XII, § 5, Theorem 1). Furthermore, every point of the square is a value of the function f; in fact, in each square of the n-th approximation there are values of the function f_n and consequently

$$\overline{\bigcup_n f_n(\mathcal{J})} = \mathcal{J}^2 \quad \text{whence} \quad f(\mathcal{J}) = \mathcal{J}^2.$$

Remark 5. Let us notice that the proof of Theorem 3 in the case where the continuum C is the n-dimensional cube can be somewhat simplified. Namely, in this case we can take the interval with endpoints $f(a_n)$ and $f(b_n)$ for the arc L_n; hence, we can define the function f_n as the linear transformation of the interval $a_n b_n$ into the interval $f(a_n)f(b_n)$.

This theorem can also be deduced directly from Theorem 3, Chapter XV, § 8, and Tietze theorem (Chapter XII, § 8, Corollary 1).

Exercises

1. Let E be an open subset of the interval $a < x < b$. Prove that the components of the set E are open intervals. Moreover, if there are an infinite number of these components then their diameters tend to zero.

2. Prove that local connectedness at a given point is a topological invariant; i. e. that if the space X is locally connected at the point p and f is a homeomorphism, then the space $f(X)$ is locally connected at the point $f(p)$.

3. Prove that a necessary and sufficient condition for a space to be locally connected at the point p, is that for every number $\varepsilon > 0$ there exists a number $\eta > 0$ such that the condition $|x-p| < \eta$ implies the existence of a connected set C satisfying the conditions $x, p \in C$ and $\delta(C) < \varepsilon$.

4. Let $p \in A \cap B$. If the sets A and B are locally connected at the point p, then the set $A \cup B$ is also locally connected at this point.

5. If the spaces X and Y are locally connected at the points a and b respectively, then the cartesian product $X \times Y$ is locally connected at the point $\langle a, b\rangle$.

6. Let E be an arbitrary subset of a locally connected space. If C is a connected subset of E and is open in E (i. e. it is of the form $C = E \cap G$, where G is an open set), then there exists an open connected set H such that $C = E \cap H$.

Hint: Use Theorem 3, § 2.

7. If a locally connected space can be represented as the union of two closed sets A and B with locally connected intersection, then the sets A and B are locally connected.

Hint: Use Exercises 4 and 6, above, and Exercise 4 of Chapter XVI.

8. Let X be a locally connected space. If F is a closed locally connected set and C is a component of the set $X - F$, then the sets $X - C$ and $C \cup F$ are locally connected.

Hint: Use Exercise 7.

9. Let E be an arbitrary subset of a locally connected space and let $E = S_1 \cup S_2 \cup \ldots$ be the decomposition of E into components. Then

$$\operatorname{Int}(E) = \overline{\bigcup_n \operatorname{Int}(S_n)}\,.$$

10. Let E_t be an arbitrary subset of a locally connected space. Prove that

$$\operatorname{Fr}\left(\bigcup_t E_t\right) \subset \overline{\bigcup_t \operatorname{Fr}(E_t)}\,.$$

Hint: Use Theorem 3 of Chapter XVI, § 2.

11. Let E be an arbitrary subset of a locally connected space and let S be a component of E. Prove that $\operatorname{Fr}(S) \subset \operatorname{Fr}(E)$.

12. Let E be an arbitrary subset of a locally connected space. If the set $\operatorname{Fr}(E)$ is locally connected, then $\bar{E}$ is locally connected.

Hint: Use Exercise 7.

13. Let X be a locally connected continuum. Prove that each of its subcontinua C is the intersection of a decreasing sequence of locally connected continua:

$$C = \bigcap_{n=1}^{\infty} C_n\,, \qquad C_1 \supset C_2 \supset \ldots$$

Hint: Use Theorem 1, § 4.

CHAPTER XIX

THE CONCEPT OF DIMENSION

§ 1. 0-dimensional sets

A space X is said to be 0-*dimensional at the point* p if there exist arbitrarily small open-closed sets which contain the point p. We write then $\dim_p X = 0$.

A non-empty space X which is 0-dimensional at each point is said to be 0-*dimensional*; we write this in the form of the equality: $\dim X = 0$.

Examples of 0-dimensional spaces are: the space of natural numbers, the space of rational numbers, the space of irrational numbers, the Cantor set and any finite set. The set consisting of the intervals

$$(1/3, 1/2), (1/5, 1/4), \ldots, (1/(2n+1), 1/2n), \ldots$$

and of the point 0, is 0-dimensional at the point 0 and only at that point.

An interval, as well as any connected space (which does not reduce to a single point), is not 0-dimensional; for it does not contain non-empty open-closed sets which are distinct from the entire space.

§ 2. Properties of 0-dimensional sets

We introduce here without proof the most important properties of 0-dimensional sets (see the references to the proofs in the exercises). We could already have observed some of these properties in the Cantor set.

THEOREM 1. *Every 0-dimensional separable space has a base consisting of open-closed sets.*

THEOREM 2. *Every 0-dimensional separable space is topologically contained in the Cantor set (i. e. it is homeomorphic to some subset of the Cantor set).*

THEOREM 3. *Every* 0*-dimensional compact space can be decomposed into disjoint closed sets of diameter* $<\varepsilon$ *(ε arbitrary positive):*

$$X = F_1 \cup F_2 \cup \ldots \cup F_m, \quad F_i \cap F_j = \emptyset \text{ for } i \neq j, \quad \delta(F_i) < \varepsilon.$$

THEOREM 4 (Sharpened normality property). *For every pair of disjoint closed sets A and B, there exists an open-closed set G such that $A \subset G$ and $G \cap B = \emptyset$.*

THEOREM 5. *The union of a finite or infinite sequence of* 0*-dimensional closed sets is a* 0*-dimensional set.*

§ 3. *n*-dimensional spaces

We define the dimension inductively:

1. the dimension of the void set is -1;
2. the dimension of a set X at the point p is $\leqslant n$, i. e.

$$\dim_p X \leqslant n, \tag{1}$$

if there exist arbitrarily small open sets containing p and having boundaries which are at most $(n-1)$-dimensional;

3. a set X which has dimension $\leqslant n$ at every point is at most of dimension n:

$$\dim X \leqslant n. \tag{2}$$

Furthermore, we assume that $\dim_p X = \infty$ if formula (1) does not hold for any natural n, and that $\dim X = \infty$ if formula (2) does not hold for any n.

The definition of dimension 0, given in § 2, is in agreement with the definition given here, for an open-closed set is a set with a void, and hence a (-1)-dimensional boundary.

In the sense of the above definition a closed interval has dimension 1. For, each of its points p can be surrounded by an arbitrarily small interval and hence by a set whose boundary consists of two points (or perhaps one, if p is an endpoint of an interval), but a finite set is 0-dimensional. It follows that the dimension of an interval is $\leqslant 1$; at the same time—as we know—the dimension of an interval is $\neq 0$, and hence it is $= 1$.

In an exactly analogous way we prove that the dimension of the circumference of a circle is 1. Similarly, the dimension of an unbounded straight line, of an arc (i. e. a set homeomorphic with a closed interval) and of a simple closed curve (i. e. a set homeomorphic with the circumference of a circle) is 1.

The plane has dimension $\leqslant 2$. For every point in the plane is the center of an arbitrarily small circle; and as we have shown, the circumference of a circle has dimension 1.

Similarly the surface of a 3-dimensional sphere has dimension $\leqslant 2$.

The proof that the plane does not have dimension 1 (and hence that it has dimension exactly 2) is not so simple. We shall come back to this proof in Chapter XX, § 3.

When we speak of the space $\mathcal{E}^n$ as being "n-dimensional" Euclidean space, we have in mind its so-called geometric dimension. A theorem of fundamental importance for topological dimension theory is the theorem which asserts that $\dim \mathcal{E}^n = n$.

We have given the proof of this theorem for $n = 1$. We have proved that $\dim \mathcal{E}^2 \leqslant 2$; in an exactly analogous manner we prove (by induction) that

$$\dim \mathcal{E}^n \leqslant n. \tag{3}$$

On the other hand, the proof that $\dim \mathcal{E}^n > n-1$ presents difficulties—as we have stated—already for $n = 2$ (cf. Theorem 3, Chapter XX, § 3).

THEOREM. *Dimension is a topological invariant.*

For, condition 2. means that in every neighborhood of the point p there exist open sets which contain p and have boundaries of dimension at most $n-1$.

§ 4. Properties of n-dimensional spaces

We shall state here, without proof, several theorems of the dimension theory. They are generalizations from 0 to n of the theorems in § 2.

THEOREM 1. *Every separable n-dimensional space has a base consisting of open sets with boundary of dimension at most $n-1$.*

THEOREM 2. *Every separable n-dimensional space is topologically contained in the cube $\mathcal{J}^{2n+1}$.*

In particular, every 1-dimensional set (and hence every curve) is contained topologically in the cube $\mathcal{J}^3$ and every 2-dimensional set (in particular the surfaces considered in analysis) are contained in the cube $\mathcal{J}^5$.

These exponents cannot be made smaller, i. e. for every n there exists an n-dimensional set which is not contained topologically in the cube $\mathcal{J}^{2n}$. For example, a polygonal line consisting of the edges of a tetrahedron and the segment connecting two disjoint edges (see Fig. 13) is not contained topologically in the plane (this follows easily from the Jordan theorem given in Chapter XXII, § 8).

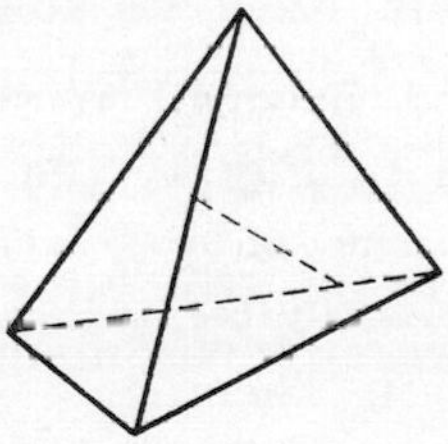

FIG. 13

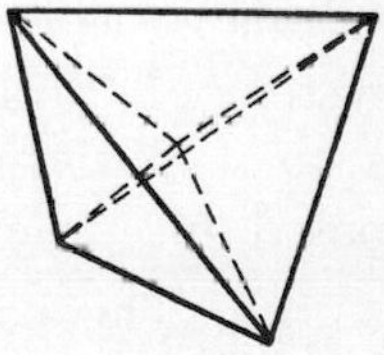

FIG. 14

The polygonal line shown in Fig. 14 has the same property. It consists of 6 edges of a tetrahedron and of 4 segments connecting the center of gravity of the tetrahedron with the vertices.

*Remark 1. Every polygonal line which cannot be embedded topologically in the plane contains topologically one of the two polygonal lines shown in Figs. 13 and 14.

*Remark 2. If $\dim X \leqslant n$, then the set of homeomorphisms is dense in the function space $(\mathcal{J}^{2n+1})^X$.

THEOREM 3. *Every n-dimensional compact space can be, for arbitrary $\varepsilon > 0$, decomposed into closed sets of diameter*

$<\varepsilon$ *in such a manner that no point belongs simultaneously to* $n+2$ *of these sets:*

(4) $$X = F_1 \cup F_2 \cup \ldots \cup F_m\,, \qquad \delta(F_i) < \varepsilon\,,$$

(5) $$F_{i_0} \cap F_{i_1} \cap \ldots \cap F_{i_{n+1}} = \emptyset \quad \textit{if} \quad i_0 < i_1 < \ldots < i_{n+1}\,.$$

For example, with the aid of a finite system of points a segment can be decomposed into arbitrarily small segments such that no point belongs to any three of them.

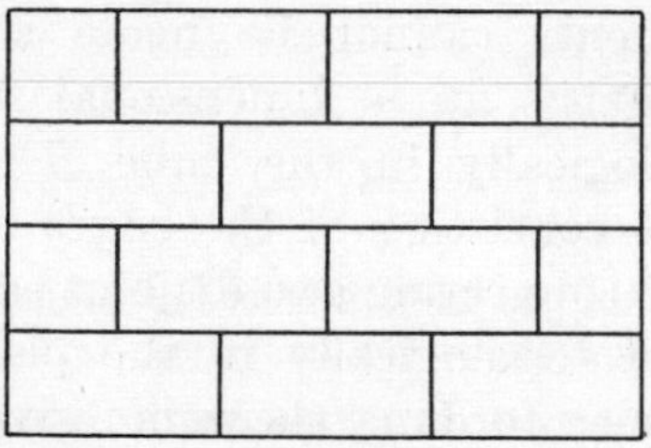

FIG. 15

A rectangle can be decomposed in small rectangles by a system of "bricks" as shown in Fig. 15 (no point belongs to 4 "bricks"). Similarly, the cube $\mathcal{J}^n$ can be decomposed in "bricks" satisfying formulas (4) and (5).

Remark. The condition given in Theorem 3 is necessary and sufficient in order that a compact space have dimension $\leqslant n$.

THEOREM 4 (Sharpened normality property). *For every pair of disjoint closed sets* A *and* B, *there exists an open set* G *such that*

$$A \subset G\,, \qquad \bar{G} \cap B = \emptyset\,, \qquad \dim \mathrm{Fr}(G) \leqslant n-1\,.$$

THEOREM 5. *The union of a (finite or infinite) sequence of* n*-dimensional closed sets is an* n*-dimensional set.*

THEOREM 6. *For every compact* n*-dimensional space* X, *there exists a closed subset* T *of the Cantor set and a continuous function* f *which maps the set* T *into* X *and which does not assume any value more than* $n+1$ *times.*

For example, a closed interval can be obtained from the Cantor set with the aid of a continuous function which does not assume any value more than twice (such a function is the step function defined in Chapter XV, § 8, Fig. 8).

Remark. The existence of a set T and of a function f having the properties stated in Theorem 6 forms a condition which is not only necessary but also sufficient in order that $\dim X \leqslant n$.

Exercises

1. Prove that every set of real numbers which contains no interval is 0-dimensional.

2. Prove that the set of points in the plane, one coordinate of which is rational and the other irrational, is 0-dimensional.

3. Prove that the set of points in Euclidean space $\mathscr{E}^n$ all of whose coordinates are irrational is 0-dimensional.

4. Hint to the proof of Theorem 1, § 2. Consider, for given n, all the open-closed sets with diameter $< 1/n$ and apply Lindelöf theorem (Chapter XIII, § 1, Theorem 3).

5. Hint to the proof of Theorem 2, § 2. Consider the characteristic function of a base consisting of open-closed sets.

CHAPTER XX

SIMPLEXES AND THEIR PROPERTIES

§ 1. Simplexes

Definition. Let $p_0, \ldots, p_n$ be a given system of $n+1$ points in Euclidean n-space. By the *simplex* $p_0 \ldots p_n$ we mean the set of all points p of the form

(1) $$p = \lambda_0 p_0 + \ldots + \lambda_n p_n ,$$

where

(2) $$\lambda_0 + \ldots + \lambda_n = 1 ,$$

(3) $$\lambda_i > 0 ,$$

and where the multiplication of the point by a scalar and the addition of points is to be understood as in the algebra of points (or vectors), i. e.

$$\lambda \cdot (x_1, \ldots, x_n) = (\lambda x_1, \ldots, \lambda x_n) ,$$

$$(x_1, \ldots, x_n) + (y_1, \ldots, y_n) = (x_1 + y_1, \ldots, x_n + y_n) .$$

In this connection we shall always assume that the points $p_0, \ldots, p_n$ are linearly independent, i. e. that they do not lie in the same $(n-1)$-dimensional hyperplane. This means, in the case $n = 2$, that the points p_0, p_1, p_2 do not lie on a line, or that $p_0 p_1 p_2$ is a triangle (without boundary); similarly, when $n = 3$, $p_0 p_1 p_2 p_3$ is the interior of a nondegenerate tetrahedron (i. e. the points p_0, p_1, p_2 and p_3 do not lie in one plane).

The coefficients $\lambda_0, \ldots, \lambda_n$ are the barycentric coordinates of the point p; they can be interpreted as masses which must be distributed at the points $p_0, \ldots, p_n$, respectively (retaining conditions (2) and (3)), in order that the point p be the center of mass. It is clear that each of the barycentric coordinates is a continuous function of the point p.

Each of the points $p_0, \ldots, p_n$ is said to be a *vertex* of the simplex $p_0 \ldots p_n$; each of the simplexes $p_{i_0} \ldots p_{i_k}$, where $i_0 < \ldots < i_k \leqslant n$, is said to be a *face* (or edge) of the simplex.

We include the vertices as well as the entire simplex S in the faces of the simplex $S = p_0 \ldots p_n$ (for k assumes the values from 0 to n).

Let us note that

$$\bar{S} = \bigcup p_{i_0} \ldots p_{i_k}, \tag{4}$$

for all possible systems of numbers $i_0, \ldots, i_k$, whereby k assumes all integral values from 0 to n.

Finally, let us note that:

1. *the simplexes* $p_{i_0} \ldots p_{i_k}$ *in* (4) *are disjoint,*

2. *the point* p *belongs to* $\bar{S}$ *when and only when it fulfils conditions* (1), (2) *and*

$$\lambda_i \geqslant 0 \, . \tag{5}$$

§ 2. Simplicial subdivision

Let

$$S = p_0 \ldots p_n \, .$$

By a *simplicial subdivision* of $\bar{S}$ is understood its subdivision into simplexes such that the intersection of

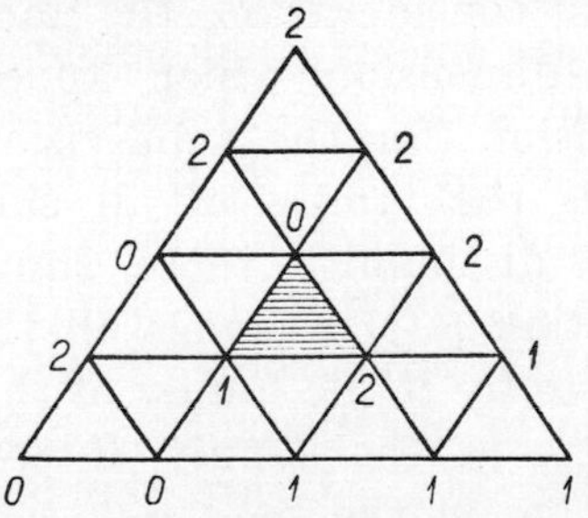

FIG. 16

the closures of each pair of simplexes is the closure of their common face (which might be the null set). Figure 16 shows a simplicial subdivision of a triangle.

If in Figure 16 the edges of the shaded triangle were

omitted, then the figure would no longer represent a simplicial subdivision.

It can be proved that:

1. *For every* $\varepsilon > 0$ *there exists a simplicial subdivision of* $\bar{S}$ *into simplexes with diameter* $< \varepsilon$.

2. SPERNER THEOREM. *Let* $\bar{S}$ *be subdivided simplicially and let the function* $m(s)$ *assign to each vertex of the simplexes of this subdivision the integer* $m(s)$ *which satisfies the following condition*:

(6) *if* $s \in p_{i_0} \dots p_{i_k}$, *then* $m(s)$ *is one of the integers* $i_0, \dots, i_k$.

Then there exists among the simplexes of the subdivision under consideration at least one simplex on whose vertices the function $m(s)$ *assumes all the values from* 0 *to* n.

(The shaded simplex in Fig. 16 is such a simplex.)

We shall carry out the proof by induction. We shall prove a stronger assertion, namely that the number r of simplexes on whose vertices the function $m(s)$ assumes all the values from 0 to n, is odd.

For $n = 0$ this is obvious; for then $S = \{p_0\}$ and $r = 1$.

Let us assume that the theorem (in the stronger formulation) is valid for $n-1$. We shall prove that it is valid for n.

We take into consideration the family of all simplexes of $(n-1)$-dimension which appear in the given simplicial subdivision (for the subdivision represented in the figure this is the family of all sides of triangles). Among them we distinguish those simplexes on whose vertices the function $m(s)$ assumes all the values from 0 to $n-1$. We denote by $\boldsymbol{R}$ the family of these distinguished simplexes. Finally, in the family $\boldsymbol{R}$ we consider those simplexes which lie on the face $p_0 \dots p_{n-1}$ (in the figure this is the segment [0, 1] lying at the base of the triangle); we denote by u the number of these simplexes. By our assumption, u is an odd number.

Let us write down the sequence

$$A_1, A_2, \dots, A_t, A_{t+1}, \dots, A_w$$

of all the simplexes appearing in the simplicial subdivision under consideration; let the simplexes $A_1, \ldots, A_t$ have the dimension n and let the remaining have dimension $<n$.

We denote by v_j for $j \leqslant t$ the number of faces of the simplex A_j belonging to $\boldsymbol{R}$. Denoting by W_j the set of values which the function $m(s)$ assumes on the vertices of the simplex A_j, we easily prove that

1. if $W_j = (0, 1, \ldots, n)$, then $v_j = 1$,
2. if $(0, 1, \ldots, n-1) \subset W_j \neq (0, 1, \ldots, n)$, then $v_j = 2$,
3. if $(0, 1, \ldots, n-1) \not\subset W_j$, then $v_j = 0$.

Therefore

$$r \equiv (v_1 + v_2 + \ldots + v_t) \bmod 2 .$$

On the other hand, if to each $j \leqslant t$ we assign the faces of the simplex A_j belonging to $\boldsymbol{R}$ (provided that such faces exist), then every simplex belonging to $\boldsymbol{R}$ will be assigned to one or two indices j depending on whether or not it lies on the face $p_0 \ldots p_{n-1}$. Hence, we have

$$v_1 + v_2 + \ldots + v_t \equiv u \bmod 2 , \quad \text{whence} \quad r \equiv u \bmod 2 ,$$

and therefore r is an odd number (because u is odd).

§ 3. Dimension of a simplex

LEMMA. *Let there be given in a compact space a finite system of closed sets $F_0, \ldots, F_n$ such that*

(7) $$F_0 \cap \ldots \cap F_n = \emptyset ;$$

then there exists an $\varepsilon > 0$ such that every set X, having points in common with each of the set $F_0, \ldots, F_n$, has a diameter $\geqslant \varepsilon$.

Proof. Let $f(x_0, \ldots, x_n)$, where $x_0 \in F_0, \ldots, x_n \in F_n$, denote the maximum of the numbers $|x_i - x_j|$, where the indices i and j assume all the values from 0 to n. It is easy to verify that the function f is continuous. Let ε denote the least upper bound of this function. Since the set $F_0 \times \ldots \times F_n$ is compact, the function f attains its greatest lower bound (see Chapter XV, § 4, Theorem 4). Hence, let $f(a_0, \ldots, a_n) = \varepsilon$. It follows from this that $\varepsilon > 0$

for otherwise we should have $a_0 = \dots = a_n$ contrary to equality (7).

At the same time, if $x_0 \in X \cap F_0, \dots, x_n \in X \cap F_n$, then

$$f(x_0, \dots, x_n) \geqslant \varepsilon \quad \text{whence} \quad \delta(X) \geqslant \varepsilon .$$

THEOREM 1. *If the system of closed sets $F_0, \dots, F_n$ satisfies the condition*

(8) $$p_{i_0} \dots p_{i_k} \subset F_{i_0} \cup \dots \cup F_{i_k}$$

for each face of the simplex $S = p_0 \dots p_n$, then

(9) $$F_0 \cap \dots \cap F_n \neq \emptyset .$$

Proof. Let us assume the contrary, i. e. that equality (7) holds, and then apply the lemma.

Let there be given a simplicial subdivision of $\bar{S}$ into simplexes of diameter $< \varepsilon$. Let s be a vertex of some simplexe of this subdivision. By virtue of formula (4) and because of the fact that the faces of the simplex S are disjoint (see § 1, 1), there exists only one face $p_{i_0} \dots p_{i_k}$ which contains s; and therefore, by (8), there exists an index i_j such that $s \in F_{i_j}$.

Let us set

(10) $$m(s) = i_j , \quad \text{i. e.} \quad s \in F_{m(s)} .$$

The function $m(s)$ thus defined satisfies condition (6). Hence there exists, by virtue of Sperner theorem, a simplex $s_0 \dots s_n$ such that for $i = 0, \dots, n$,

(11) $$m(s_i) = i , \text{ and hence } s_i \in F_i , \text{ i. e. } \overline{s_0 \dots s_n} \cap F_i = \emptyset,$$

contrary to the lemma, for $\delta(s_0 \dots s_n) < \varepsilon$.

THEOREM 2. *Let P_i be the union of all the faces of the simplex S having p_i for a vertex (in other words, P_i is the set of all the points of $\bar{S}$ for which $\lambda_i > 0$). Let the system of closed sets $F_0, \dots, F_n$ satisfy the conditions:*

(12) $$\bar{S} = F_0 \cup \dots \cup F_n ,$$

(13) $$F_i \subset P_i .$$

Then condition (8) is satisfied and hence (by virtue of Theorem 1) condition (9) also.

Proof. Let $p \in p_{i_0} \dots p_{i_k}$. Therefore, for every j distinct from each of the numbers $i_0, \dots, i_k$ we have $\lambda_j = 0$, i. e. $p \notin P_j$, whence $p \notin F_j$ by virtue of (13). Applying (12), we deduce from this that

$$p \in F_0 \cup \dots \cup F_{j-1} \cup F_{j+1} \cup \dots \cup F_n . \tag{14}$$

Since formula (14) holds for each j satisfying the inequalities

$$j \neq i_0, \quad \dots, \quad j \neq i_k ,$$

it follows that $p \in F_{i_0} \cup \dots \cup F_{i_k}$.

Thus, inclusion (8) is proved.

THEOREM 3. $\dim \overline{S} = n$.

Sketch of the proof. By virtue of formula (3), Chapter XIX, § 3, we have $\dim \mathcal{E}^n \leqslant n$. Therefore

$$\dim \overline{S} \leqslant n . \tag{15}$$

Thus, we have to prove that

$$\dim \overline{S} > n-1 . \tag{16}$$

Let

$$T_i = \overline{S} - P_i \tag{17}$$

(where P_i has the same meaning as in Theorem 2); thus, T_i is the set of those points p for which $\lambda_i = 0$ (in other words, this is the closure of the faces lying opposite the vertex p_i). By virtue of condition (2) we have

$$T_0 \cap \dots \cap T_n = \emptyset , \tag{18}$$

and since the sets T_i are closed we can apply the lemma to them.

Let us assume, contrary to inequality (16), that $\dim \overline{S} \leqslant n-1$. By virtue of Theorem 3 in Chapter XIX, § 4 (stated without proof), we can then decompose $\overline{S}$ into a finite number of closed sets

$$\overline{S} = H_1 \cup H_2 \cup \dots \cup H_m \tag{19}$$

such that

1. no point belongs simultaneously to $n+1$ of the sets H_j,

2. $\delta(H_j) < \varepsilon$ where ε is the number appearing in the lemma; this means that each of the sets H_j is disjoint with at least one of the sets T_i, or—by virtue of (17)—is contained in at least one of the sets P_i.

Let us divide the sets H_j into classes putting into the zero class those which are contained in P_0, into the 1-st class those which do not belong to the zero-th class and are contained in P_1, and so on, so that finally, to the n-th class belong those which do not belong to any of the preceding classes and are contained in P_n.

Since

$$\bar{S} = P_0 \cup \ldots \cup P_n \,, \tag{20}$$

each of the sets H_j has been put into one and only one class.

Let us denote by F_i the sum of sets belonging to the i-th class. Then conditions (13) and (12) are satisfied (by virtue of (19) and (20)). By virtue of Theorem 2 inequality (9) is therefore satisfied. Let $p \in F_0 \cap \ldots \cap F_n$; this means that the point p belongs for each $i = 0, \ldots, n$ to some one of the sets of the i-th class. But then this point belongs to $n+1$ of the sets H_j, contrary to condition 1.

This contradiction proves that the inequality (16) is satisfied.

Thus we obtained the fundamental formula of dimension theory: $\dim \bar{S} = n$, and hence $\dim \mathcal{E}^n = n$.

§ 4. The fixed point theorem

Let S be, as before, the simplex $p_0 \ldots p_n$.

BROUWER THEOREM. *For every continuous mapping f of the set $\bar{S}$ onto one of its subsets there exists a fixed point, i. e. a point p such that*

$$f(p) = p \,. \tag{21}$$

Proof. We shall use the following notation: for an arbitrary $p \in \bar{S}$ we write

$$f(p) = p^* = \lambda_0^* p_0 + \ldots + \lambda_n^* p_n \,, \tag{22}$$

where (analogously to (2) and (5)):

(23) $$\lambda_0^* + \ldots + \lambda_n^* = 1\,,$$

(24) $$\lambda_i^* \geqslant 0\,.$$

We have to prove that there exists a point p such that

(25) $$\lambda_i^* = \lambda_i \quad \text{for every } i\,.$$

Let us denote by F_i the set of all points p for which

(26) $$\lambda_i^* \leqslant \lambda_i\,.$$

By virtue of the continuity of the barycentric coordinates and of the function f, the sets F_i are closed. We shall prove that condition (8) is satisfied.

Let $p \in p_{i_0} \ldots p_{i_k}$. This means that

(27) $$\lambda_{i_0} + \ldots + \lambda_{i_k} = 1\,.$$

But since by (23):

(28) $$\lambda_{i_0}^* + \ldots + \lambda_{i_k}^* \leqslant 1\,,$$

hence from (27) and (28) it follows that

$$\lambda_{i_0}^* + \ldots + \lambda_{i_k}^* \leqslant \lambda_{i_0} + \ldots + \lambda_{i_k}\,,$$

and therefore (cf. (24)) for some $j \leqslant k$ we have $\lambda_{i_j}^* \leqslant \lambda_{i_j}$. By (26) this means that $p \in F_{i_j}$. And therefore inclusion (8) is proved.

Owing to Theorem 1, § 3, inequality (9) is satisfied. Hence let $p \in F_0 \cdot \ldots \cdot F_n$. This means that

(29) $$\begin{aligned} &\lambda_0^* \leqslant \lambda_0\,,\\ &\ldots\ldots\\ &\lambda_n^* \leqslant \lambda_n\,. \end{aligned}$$

Adding these inequalities we obtain

$$\lambda_0^* + \ldots + \lambda_n^* \leqslant \lambda_0 + \ldots + \lambda_n\,,$$

which yields, by (23) and (2),

$$\lambda_0^* + \ldots + \lambda_n^* = \lambda_0 + \ldots + \lambda_n\,.$$

Therefore in the system of inequalities (29) there cannot appear any strict inequality of the form $\lambda_i^* < \lambda_i$. In other words, formula (25) holds.

Remarks. 1. The Brouwer theorem for $n = 1$ states that for every continuous mapping f of the closed interval into any one of its subsets there exists a fixed point. This is an immediate consequence of the Darboux property of the function $f(x)-x$.

2. The Brouwer theorem is obviously also applicable to the n-dimensional cube as well as to any set homeomorphic to $\bar{S}$. It is interesting to note that this theorem can be generalized also to the Hilbert cube $\mathcal{H}$ and some function spaces.

This generalization has numerous applications in the theory of differential equations in proving the existence theorems [1]. For, a theorem on the existence of a solution of a differential equation can be formulated as a theorem on the existence of a fixed point of some mapping of the space of continuous functions into itself (under suitable hypotheses which we shall not give here).

Let us illustrate this by an example (cf. Chapter XV, Exercise 7).

To solve the differential equation

$$dy/dx = f(x, y) \tag{30}$$

with initial values x_0, y_0, means to find a function g of the variable x such that

$$dg(x)/dx = f(x, g(x)) \quad \text{and} \quad g(x_0) = y_0 .$$

In other words, we must find a function g such that

$$g(x) = y_0 + \int_{x_0}^{x} f(t, g(t))\, dt . \tag{31}$$

Let us denote by h the mapping which assigns to each function φ the function h_φ of the variable x defined by the condition

$$h_\varphi(x) = y_0 + \int_{x_0}^{x} f(t, \varphi(t))\, dt .$$

---

[1]) J. Schauder, *Der Fixpunktsatz in Funktionalräumen*, Studia Mathematica 2 (1930).

The fixed point of this mapping is a function g such that

$$h_g = g \quad \text{i. e.} \quad h_g(x) = g(x) \text{ for every } x\,,$$

which means that the function g satisfies equality (31).

Thus the proof of the existence of a solution of equation (30) reduces to the proof of the existence of a fixed point for the mapping h (which maps a certain function space onto one of its subspaces).

COROLLARY. *The surface C of the set $K = E_z|z| \leqslant 1$ (in Euclidean space of an arbitrary number of dimensions) is not a retract of it; i. e. there does not exist a continuous function f which maps K into C in such a way that*

$$(32) \qquad f(x) = x \quad \textit{for} \quad x \in C\,.$$

Proof. Would there exist a function f with the properties named, then the function

$$(33) \qquad g(x) = -f(x)$$

would map K onto $g(K) \subset K$ without a fixed point, contrary to Brouwer's theorem (see Remark 2).

In fact, if $x \in K - C$ then $g(x) \neq x$, as $g(x) \in C$. But if $x \in C$ then $g(x) = -x$ by virtue of (33) and (32) and hence we also have $g(x) \neq x$.

This completes the proof of the corollary.

We shall now give another formulation of this corollary, using the concept of *homotopy*.

Definition. Let there be given two continuous mappings of the space X into the space Y, i. e. $f, g \in Y^X$. We say that these two functions are *homotopic* if there exists a continuous function h of two variables x and t, where $0 \leqslant t \leqslant 1$ such that

$$(34) \quad h(x, t) \in Y\,, \quad h(x, 0) = f(x) \text{ and } h(x, 1) = g(x)\,.$$

We can state this in more graphic language: there exists a continuous transition from the mapping f to the mapping g (we interpret the parameter t to be time).

16

Let us note that if Y is the space $\mathcal{E}$ of real numbers (or more generally, $Y = \mathcal{E}^n$), then the functions f and g are always homotopic.

For it suffices to set

$$h(x, t) = f(x) + t\big(g(x) - f(x)\big).$$

If, however, Y denotes the circumference of a circle or more generally the sphere $\mathcal{S}_n$ (i. e. the set of points $x_1^2 + \ldots + x_{n+1}^2 = 1$ of the space $\mathcal{E}^{n+1}$), then this is no longer true. Namely, *the identity and a constant are not homotopic.* This means that if

$$X = Y = \mathcal{S}_n, \quad f(x) = x, \quad g(x) = c, \quad c \in \mathcal{S}_n,$$

then there does not exist a continuous function h satisfying conditions (34).

For let us assume that such a function h exists and set

$$f^*(tx) = h(x, 1-t) \quad \text{for} \quad x \in \mathcal{S}_n \text{ and } 0 \leqslant t \leqslant 1.$$

Let $\mathcal{K}_{n+1}$ consist of points $|z| \leqslant 1$; hence $\mathcal{S}_n$ is its surface.

Since every point of $\mathcal{K}_{n+1}$ can be represented uniquely in the form $z = tx$ (with the exception of the point $z = 0$), therefore the function f^* is continuous, i. e. $f^* \in (\mathcal{S}_n)^{\mathcal{K}_{n+1}}$. And at the same time we have

$$f^*(x) = h(x, 0) = f(x) = x,$$

i. e. the function f^* is a retract of $\mathcal{K}_{n+1}$ to its surface. But this is impossible by the last corollary.

Exercises

1. Let S be an n-dimensional simplex lying in the space $\mathcal{E}^n$. Prove that the boundary of the simplex S is the union of all its faces of dimension $< n$.

2. The continuum C consists of the closure of the graph of the function $y = \sin(1/x)$ for $0 < |x| < (1/\pi)$ and of an arc joining the points $(-1/\pi, 0)$, $(1/\pi, 0)$ outside of the rest of the continuum C. Prove that under every continuous mapping of the set C onto its subset there exists a fixed point.

3. Let $S = p_0 \dots p_n$ be a given simplex and let X be a given space covered with open sets: $X = G_0 \cup \dots \cup G_n$.

Consider the mapping

$$\varkappa(x) = \lambda_0(x)\cdot p_0 + \dots + \lambda_n(x)\cdot p_n,$$

where

$$\lambda_i(x) = \varrho(x, X-G_i)/\{\varrho(x, X-G_0) + \dots + \varrho(x, X-G_n)\}$$

(this is the so-called *kappa mapping*).

Prove that

(a) $\varkappa(x) \in \bar{S}$ where $\lambda_i(x)$ is the i-th barycentric coordinate of the point $\varkappa(x)$ (i. e. conditions (2) and (5) are satisfied);

(b) $\varkappa^{-1}(P_i) = G_i$, where P_i has the same meaning as in Theorem 2, § 3;

(c) $\varkappa^{-1}(p_{i_0} \dots p_{i_k}) = G_{i_0} \cap \dots \cap G_{i_k} - \bigcup_i G_i$, where the union is over all indices i different from $i_0, \dots, i_k$;

(d) $\varkappa(X-G_i) \cap P_i = \emptyset$;

(e) if every intersection of $m+2$ of the sets $G_0, \dots, G_n$ is void, then $\dim \varkappa(X) \leqslant m$.

4. Let $S = p_0 \dots p_n$ be a given simplex and let f be a continuous mapping of $\bar{S}$ into itself. We assume that, if $p \in \mathrm{Fr}(S)$, then $f(p) \in \mathrm{Fr}(S)$ and that $f(p) \neq p$. Prove that $f(\bar{S}) = \bar{S}$.

Hint: Assuming that $f(\bar{S}) \neq \bar{S}$ we denote by r the point belonging to $S - f(S)$ and by $g(p)$ the projection of the point $f(p)$ from r into $\mathrm{Fr}(S)$. We then arrive at a contradiction of Brouwer theorem.

5. Let $S = p_0 \dots p_n$ and let the sets $G_0, \dots, G_n$, open in $\bar{S}$, satisfy the conditions $\bar{S} = G_0 \cup \dots \cup G_n$ and $G_i \subset P_i$ for $i = 0, \dots, n$. Then $G_0 \cap \dots \cap G_n \neq \emptyset$.

Hint: Make use of Theorem 2, § 3, and of Exercise 18, Chapter XII.

6. Let T_i denote the closure of the face lying opposite the vertex p_i (cf. (17)). Prove that if the closed sets $F_0, \dots, F_n$ satisfy the conditions $\bar{S} = F_0 \cup \dots \cup F_n$ and $T_i \subset F_i$, then $F_0 \cap \dots \cap F_n \neq \emptyset$.

Hint: Use Exercise 5.

7. Let $S = p_0 \dots p_n$ and let f be a continuous mapping of $\bar{S}$ into itself such that $f(T_i) \subset T_i$ for $i = 0, \dots, n$. Then $f(\bar{S}) = \bar{S}$.

Hint: Argue as in the solution of Exercise 4 and set $F_i = g^{-1}(T_i)$. Then apply Exercise 5.

CHAPTER XXI

COMPLEXES, CHAINS, AND HOMOLOGIES

§ 1. Abelian groups

We shall now give the concepts and theorems from the theory of groups which we shall use in this chapter.

Definition 1. An abstract set G is said to be an *abelian* or *commutative group* if an operation, called *addition*, is defined in this set such that to every pair a and b of elements in G there is assigned a certain element $a+b$ of the set G (called the *sum* of the elements a and b) in such a way that the following conditions, called the *axioms of the theory of groups*, are satisfied:

(i) $(a+b)+c = a+(b+c)$,

(ii) $a+b = b+a$,

(iii) there exists exactly one element (denoted by 0) of the set G which possesses the property that $a+0 = a$ for every $a \in G$,

(iv) for every element $a \in G$ there exists exactly one inverse element (which we denote by $(-a)$) possessing the property that $a+(-a) = 0$.

EXAMPLES. 1. The set of integers forms a group with respect to addition but, on the other hand, it does not form a group if we define the group operation to be multiplication because in this case axiom (iv) is not satisfied.

2. The set of complex numbers z such that $|z| = 1$ (these are numbers of the form e^{ix}) forms an abelian group with respect to the operation of multiplication of complex numbers.

3. The set of all continuous functions f, defined on a space X and which assume non-zero complex values,

forms an abelian group if we define the group operation as follows:

$$(f_3 = f_1 \cdot f_2) \equiv \bigwedge_x [f_3(x) = f_1(x) \cdot f_2(x)] .$$

Definition 2. If a subset G_0 of the group G itself forms a group with respect to the group operation defined in G, i. e. if the condition $a, b \in G_0$ implies that $(a+b) \in G_0$ and $(-a) \in G_0$, then we call G_0 a *subgroup* of the group G. We define the relation $a \sim b (\mathrm{mod}\, G_0)$ for elements of the group G as follows:

(v) $[a \sim b (\mathrm{mod}\, G_0)] \equiv [(a-b) \in G_0]$.

THEOREM. *Relation* (v) *is an equivalence relation, i. e. it is reflexive, symmetric and transitive.*

Proof. $a \sim a (\mathrm{mod}\, G_0)$, i. e. $a - a = 0 \in G_0$ (for G_0 is a subgroup of G).

$$[a \sim b (\mathrm{mod}\, G_0)] \equiv [a - b \in G_0]$$
$$\equiv [b - a \in G_0] \equiv [b \sim a (\mathrm{mod}\, G_0)] .$$

Let $(a \sim b)$ and $(b \sim c)$, i. e. $a - b \in G_0$ and $b - c \in G_0$; from this we obtain $(a-b)+(b-c) \in G_0$, and therefore $a \sim c (\mathrm{mod}\, G_0)$.

Relation (v) leads to a decomposition of the elements of the group G into disjoint sets of mutually conjugate elements, called *cosets* (cf. Exercise 9, Chapter V).

We denote by $G_0(a)$ the set of elements which are conjugate mod G_0 to a. Thus

$$[G_0(a) = G_0(b)] \equiv [a \sim b (\mathrm{mod}\, G_0)] .$$

We introduce the operation of addition of cosets in the following way:

(vi) $G_0(a) + G_0(b) \underset{\mathrm{def}}{=} G_0(a+b)$.

We can easily prove that addition defined by formula (vi) does not depend on the choice of the element chosen in the cosets and that with this operation the class of cosets forms an abelian group.

Definition 3. The group of cosets is called the *quotient group* and is denoted by G/G_0.

Definition 4. Let G and H be two abelian groups. A function f which maps the group G onto a subset of the group H is said to be a *homomorphism* of the group G into the group H if

$$f(a+b) = f(a)+f(b).$$

We call the homomorphism f an *isomorphism* if the function f is one-to-one; if moreover $f(G) = H$, then the groups G and H are said to be *isomorphic*.

Just as topology deals with the invariants of homeomorphisms, the theory of groups deals with the invariants of isomorphisms. From the point of view of group theory two isomorphic groups have the same properties.

Remark. The connection between the concepts of homomorphism and quotient group is established by the following theorem (which will not be used in this book):

Assume f is a homomorphism of the group G onto the group H. Let G_0 denote the set of those elements of the group G which map under f onto the zero element of the group H (this set is called the kernel of the homomorphism f), i. e.

$$(x \in G_0) \equiv [f(x) = 0].$$

Then

1. *the set G_0 is a subgroup of the group G,*
2. *the quotient group G/G_0 is isomorphic to the group H.*

§ 2. Oriented simplexes. Chains

Let $S = p_0 \dots p_n$ be an n-dimensional simplex ($n \geqslant 0$) (see Chapter XX, § 1). Every sequence consisting of $n+1$ of its vertices (without repetition) is called an *oriented simplex*; we identify any two oriented simplexes if one can be obtained from the other by an even permutation; we then say that these simplexes have the same orientation (of course, a 0-dimensional simplex has just one orientation); e. g.

$$(p_0, p_1, p_2) = (p_1, p_2, p_0) = (p_2, p_0, p_1),$$

$$(p_0, p_1, p_2) \neq (p_1, p_0, p_2).$$

Figure 17 illustrates this.

By a (closed) *complex* we understand a finite set of simplexes having the property that if any simplex belongs to it then all the faces of this simplex belong to it also.

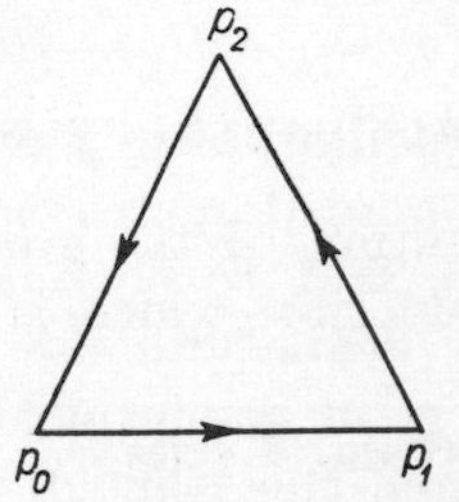

FIG. 17

Let K be a complex. The n-dimensional simplexes belonging to K, after they have been oriented, are considered as elements of an abelian group, denoted by $L^n(K)$; thus the elements of this group, called *n-dimensional chains*, are linear forms:

$$(1) \qquad L = k_1 S_1 + k_2 S_2 + \ldots + k_m S_m ,$$

where $S_1, S_2, \ldots, S_m$ are oriented n-dimensional simplexes, and $k_1, \ldots, k_m$ are integers.

We assume here that the multiplication of a simplex S of dimension $\geqslant 1$ by -1 denotes a change of its orientation, and we identify the chain $1 \cdot S$ with S, e. g.

$$-1(p_0, p_1) = (p_1, p_0) = 1(p_1, p_0),$$

$$-1(p_0, p_1, p_2) = (p_1, p_0, p_2), \qquad -1(p) = (p).$$

As usual we denote by 0 the zero of the group $L^n(K)$, and consider 0 to be an n-dimensional chain for every $n = 0, 1, 2, \ldots$

Remark. Obviously, an n-dimensional chain is defined when the coefficients $k_1, k_2, \ldots$ are given for all n-dimensional simplexes of the complex K (some of the k_i may vanish). Hence it is possible to define an n-dimensional chain as a function f which assigns to every oriented n-dimensional simplex S an integer $k = f(S)$; this function is odd (in the sense that a change in the orientation of the simplex S leads to a change in sign of the function); the addition of functions $h = f + g$ is defined by the rule

$$h(S) = f(S) + g(S) .$$

For such a definition of the group $\boldsymbol{L}^n(\boldsymbol{K})$, the zero of this group is the function which is identically zero.

§ 3. Boundary of a chain. Cycles

In order to define the *boundary* ∂L of the chain L we first define the boundary of an oriented simplex:

$$(2) \qquad \begin{cases} \textit{if } L = (p_0, \ldots, p_n), \textit{ then} \\ \partial L = \sum_{k=0}^{n} (-1)^k (p_0, \ldots, p_{k-1}, p_{k+1}, \ldots, p_n), \\ \partial(p_0) = 1 . \end{cases}$$

Furthermore, we assume that if L is of the form (1), then

$$(3) \qquad \partial L = \sum_{j=1}^{m} k_j \cdot \partial S_j .$$

For example,

$$\partial(p_0, p_1) = (p_1) - (p_0) , \qquad \partial[5(p_0)] = 5 ,$$

$$\partial(p_0, p_1, p_2) = (p_1, p_2) + (p_2, p_0) + (p_0, p_1) ,$$

$$\partial[(p_0, p_1, p_2) + (p_2, p_1, p_3)] = (p_0, p_1) + (p_1, p_3) + (p_3, p_2) + (p_2, p_0)$$

(see Fig. 18).

From the above definitions it follows immediately that the boundary of an n-dimensional chain for $n \geqslant 1$ is an $(n-1)$-dimensional chain, and that the operation ∂L is additive, i. e.

$$(4) \qquad \partial(L_1 + L_2) = \partial L_1 + \partial L_2 .$$

Thus, for $n \geqslant 1$, *the operation* ∂L *is a homomorphism which maps the group* $\mathbf{L}^n(\boldsymbol{K})$ *onto a subgroup of the group* $\mathbf{L}^{n-1}(\boldsymbol{K})$.

By a *cycle* we mean a chain L such that $\partial L = 0$.

It is easy to prove that

(5) $$\partial\partial L = 0\,,$$

i. e. that *the boundary of an arbitrary chain (of dimension* $n \geqslant 1$*) is a cycle*; the proof is carried out first for the

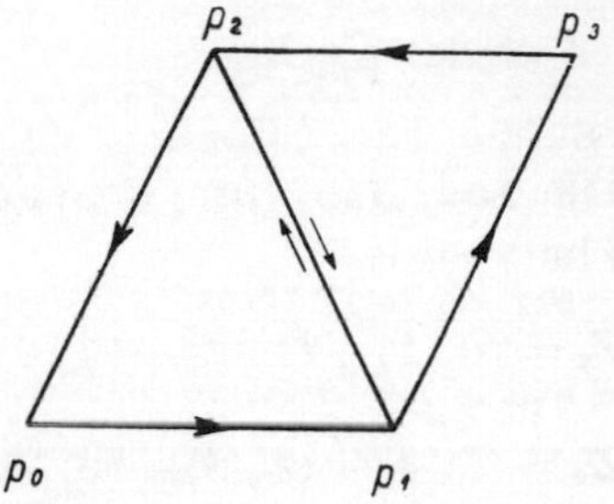

FIG. 18

case where L reduces to a simplex (formula (2)) and then formula (4) is applied.

(6) *The sum of two cycles is a cycle.*

For if $\partial L_1 = 0 = \partial L_2$, then $\partial(L_1+L_2) = \partial L_1 + \partial L_2 = 0$.

It follows that the n-dimensional cycles form a subgroup of the group of n-dimensional chains. We denote it by the symbol $\boldsymbol{Z}^n(\boldsymbol{K})$.

§ 4. Homology (or Betti) groups

We say that the cycle $Z \in \boldsymbol{Z}^n(\boldsymbol{K})$ is *homologous to zero* in the complex $\boldsymbol{K}$, which we write as

(7) $$Z \approx 0 \quad \text{in} \quad \boldsymbol{K}\,,$$

if Z is the boundary of some chain $L \in \boldsymbol{L}^{n+1}(\boldsymbol{K})$:

(8) $$Z = \partial(L)\,.$$

EXAMPLE. Let $\boldsymbol{K}$ be a complex consisting of all (0-, 1- and 2-dimensional) simplexes given in Fig. 19, except

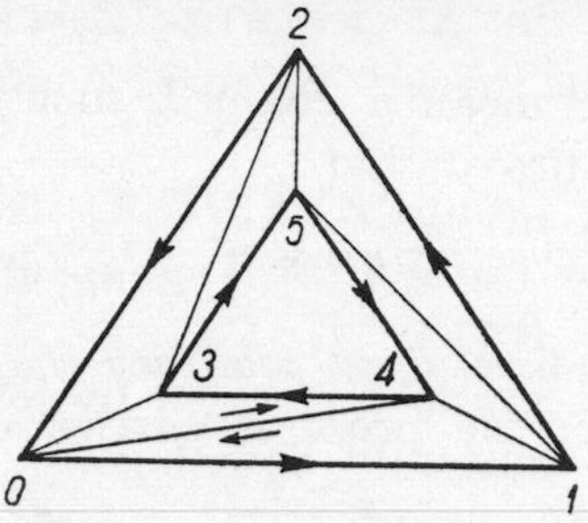

FIG. 19

the simplexes 012 and 345 (for simplicity we write k instead of p_k). The chains

$$Z_1 = (0,1) + (1,2) + (2,0)$$

and

$$Z_2 = (3,4) + (4,5) + (5,3)$$

are cycles which are not homologous to zero in $\boldsymbol{K}$. On the other hand we have

$$Z_1 - Z_2 \approx 0 \quad \text{in} \quad \boldsymbol{K}$$

because $Z_1 - Z_2 = \partial L$, where

$$L = (0,4,3) + (0,1,4) + (1,5,4) + \\ + (1,2,5) + (2,3,5) + (0,3,2).$$

The sum of two cycles homologous to zero in $\boldsymbol{K}$ *is a cycle homologous to zero in* $\boldsymbol{K}$, i. e.

(9) $\quad (Z_1 \approx 0 \text{ in } \boldsymbol{K}) \quad \text{and} \quad (Z_2 \approx 0 \text{ in } \boldsymbol{K}) \Rightarrow (Z_1 + Z_2 \approx 0 \text{ in } \boldsymbol{K}).$

For if $Z_1 = \partial(L_1)$ and $Z_2 = \partial(L_2)$, then

$$Z_1 + Z_2 = \partial(L_1) + \partial(L_2) = \partial(L_1 + L_2).$$

It follows from this that *the* n*-dimensional cycles which are homologous to zero in* $\boldsymbol{K}$ *form a group*, which is a subgroup of the group $\boldsymbol{Z}^n(\boldsymbol{K})$. We denote it by the symbol $\boldsymbol{H}^n(\boldsymbol{K})$.

If $Z_1 - Z_2 \approx 0$ in $\boldsymbol{K}$, we write $Z_1 \approx Z_2$ in K and we then say that the cycles Z_1 and Z_2 are *homologous to each other.*

The quotient group $\boldsymbol{Z}^n(\boldsymbol{K})/\boldsymbol{H}^n(\boldsymbol{K})$ is called the *n-th homology group* or the *n-th Betti group* of the complex $\boldsymbol{K}$. We denote it by $\boldsymbol{B}^n(\boldsymbol{K})$.

Thus, a Betti group is formed by joining into classes cycles which are mutually homologous.

We say that the cycles $C_1, C_2, \dots, C_m$ are *homologously independent* (or *linearly independent* modulo $\boldsymbol{H}^n(\boldsymbol{K})$) if the condition

$$k_1 C_1 + \dots + k_m C_m \approx 0 \quad \text{in} \quad \boldsymbol{K}$$

implies that

$$k_1 = \dots = k_m = 0 \, .$$

The maximal number of homologously independent n-dimensional cycles is called the n-th *Betti number* of the complex $\boldsymbol{K}$.

For example, in the complex given in Figure 19 the first Betti number is 1 because there exist 1-dimensional cycles which are not homologous to zero, but there do not exist two such homologously independent cycles.

For an arbitrary simplex, the complex consisting of all its faces has all Betti numbers equal to zero.

Let $S(\boldsymbol{K})$ denote the union of all simplexes belonging to the complex $\boldsymbol{K}$. It is therefore some polyhedron (a polygon, if $\boldsymbol{K}$ is a one- or two-dimensional complex). It is clear that this same polyhedron P can be represented in the form $P = S(\boldsymbol{K})$ for different $\boldsymbol{K}$; for example, a two-dimensional polyhedron can be triangulated in various ways. It can be proved that the Betti numbers do not depend on the method of simplicial subdivision: if $S(\boldsymbol{K}) = S(\boldsymbol{K}_1)$, then the n-th Betti numbers for $\boldsymbol{K}$ and for $\boldsymbol{K}_1$ are equal; hence they are a property of polyhedra. These numbers are *invariant under a homeomorphism.*

In particular, the zero-th Betti number is the number of components of the polyhedron under consideration minus 1. The first Betti number of a polygon in the plane is the number of regions in the complement minus 1. More generally: the n-th Betti number of a polyhedron in the space $\mathcal{E}^{n+1}$ is the number of components of its complement minus 1.

Exercises

1. The complex K consists of all the segments $S_1 = p_0p_1$, $S_2 = p_1p_2, \ldots, S_m = p_{m-1}p_m$ together with the vertices $p_0, p_1, \ldots, p_m$ of the polygonal arc L (see Fig. 20). Let the chain $Z = k_1S_1 + k_2S_2 + \ldots + k_mS_m$ be a cycle. Prove that $k_1 = k_2 = \ldots = k_m = 0$.

2. K consists of all the segments and vertices of the polygonal line L given in Fig. 21.

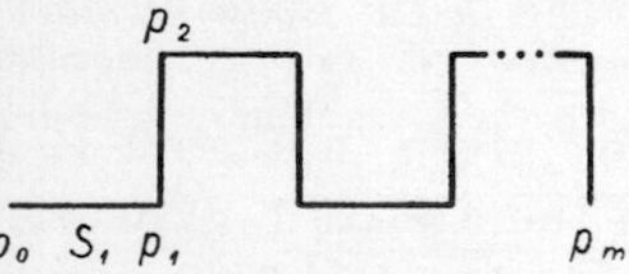

FIG. 20

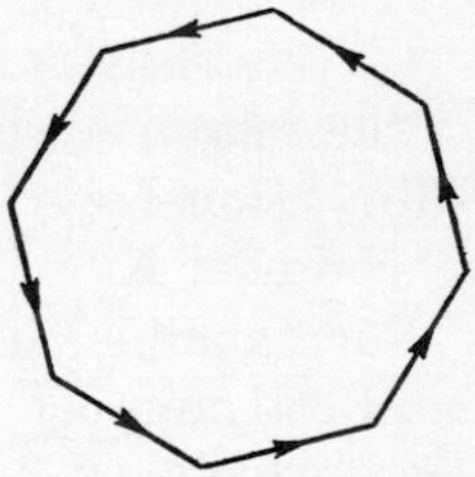

FIG. 21

We assign an orientation to the segments of L in the direction indicated on the figure. We denote the 1-dimensional simplexes thus obtained by $S_1, S_2, \ldots, S_8$. Prove:

(a) that every chain of the form

(i) $$k \cdot \sum_{i=1}^{8} S_i$$

is a cycle;

(b) that every 1-dimensional cycle of the complex K is of the form (i);

(c) that (a) and (b) imply that the first Betti group of the complex K is isomorphic to the group of integers.

3. K consists of the segments and vertices of two polygonal lines L_1, L_2 having one vertex in common (see Fig. 22). The segments of the complex $\boldsymbol{K}$ are oriented (as in Fig. 22); let us denote them by S_{1i} and S_{2i} depending on whether the segment belongs to L_1 or to L_2. Let us set

$$Z_1 = \sum_{i=1}^{4} S_{1i}, \quad Z_2 = \sum_{i=1}^{4} S_{2i}.$$

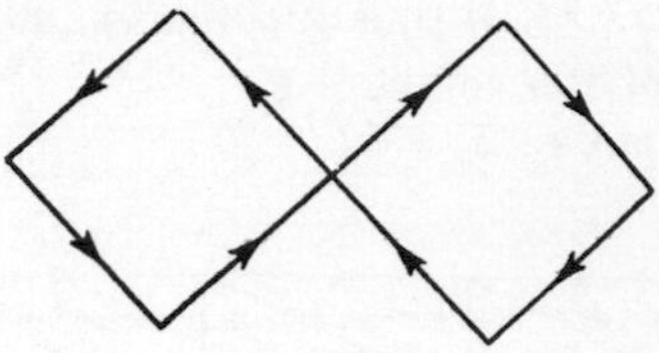

FIG. 22

Prove that

(a) every one-dimensional cycle Z of the complex $\boldsymbol{K}$ is of the form

(ii) $$Z = k_1 Z_1 + k_2 Z_2 ;$$

(b) every chain of the form (ii) is a cycle.

Deduce from (a) and (b) the nature of the Betti group of the complex $\boldsymbol{K}$.

4. Fig. 23, after identifying the sides t_7^1 and t_8^1, represents a triangulation of a surface called the *Möbius band.* The orientation t_i^2

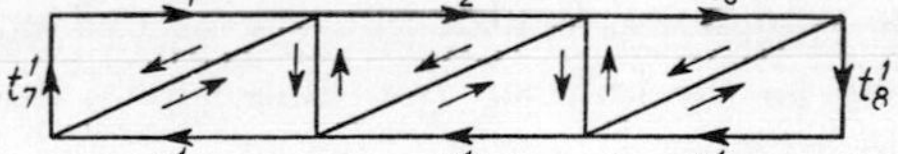

FIG. 23

of the triangles of this triangulation and also the orientation of the segments t_j^1 are denoted on the figure.

Set

$$L = \sum_{i=1}^{6} t_i^2 \quad \text{and} \quad Z = \sum_{i=1}^{6} t_i^1,$$

and prove that $\partial L = Z + 2t_7^1$.

5. We can obtain a triangulation of the *projective plane* in the following way: we consider the triangulation of the square given in Fig. 24 consisting of the 24 oriented triangles $t_1^2, t_2^2, \ldots, t_{24}^2$, the 12 segments $t_1^1, t_2^1, \ldots, t_{12}^1$ and the vertices; next we identify t_1^1 with t_7^1, t_2^1 with t_8^1, t_3^1 with t_9^1, t_4^1 with t_{10}^1, t_5^1 with t_{11}^1, and t_6^1 with t_{12}^1.

Instead of 12 oriented segments we obtain 6 segments which we denote as before by $t_1^1, t_2^1, \ldots, t_6^1$. We have thus obtained a triangulation $\boldsymbol{K}$ of the projective plane. Set

$$L = \sum_{i=1}^{24} t_i^2, \qquad Z = \sum_{j=1}^{6} t_j^1$$

and prove that $\partial L = 2Z$ and that Z is not the boundary of any two-dimensional chain of the complex $\boldsymbol{K}$.

Hint: $\partial L_1 = Z$ implies $L_1 = kL$.

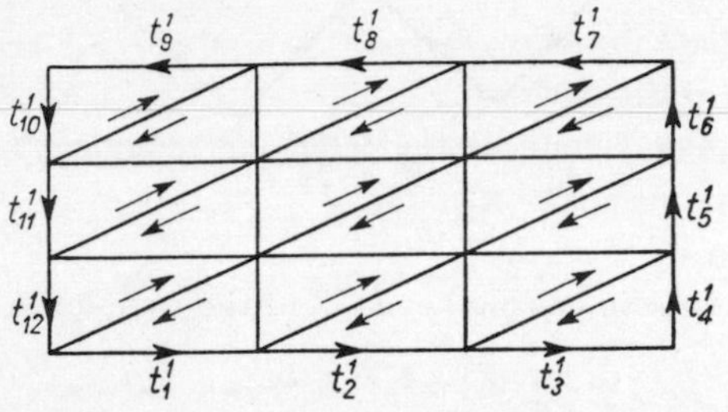

FIG. 24

6. Let $\boldsymbol{K}$ be a complex formed of all the faces of a tetrahedron S and let $\boldsymbol{L}$ be the complex formed of all the faces of dimension < 3 of the tetrahedron S. Show that all the Betti numbers of the complex $\boldsymbol{K}$, from the zero-th to the third, vanish. The zero-th and first numbers of the complex $\boldsymbol{L}$ vanish but the second equals 1.

7. Denote by m_r the number of r-dimensional simplexes of the complex $\boldsymbol{K}$. The number

$$\chi(\boldsymbol{K}) = \sum_{r=0}^{n} (-1)^r m_r$$

is called the *Euler characteristic of the complex* $\boldsymbol{K}$. The following formula (of Euler-Poincaré):

$$\chi(\boldsymbol{K}) = \sum_{r=0}^{n} (-1)^r \cdot b_r(\boldsymbol{K}) + 1,$$

where $b_r(\boldsymbol{K})$ denotes the r-th Betti number of the complex $\boldsymbol{K}$, holds. Compute $\chi(\boldsymbol{K})$ and the Betti numbers for the complexes considered in the preceding exercises.

8. Let the function f assign to each vertex of the complex $\boldsymbol{K}_1$ some vertex $f(p)$ of the complex $\boldsymbol{K}_2$ (we do not assume that to distinct vertices of the complex K_1 correspond distinct vertices of the complex K_2). If the condition

$$(p_0 p_1 \dots p_n) \in K_1$$

implies

$$[f(p_0) f(p_1) \dots f(p_n)] \in K_2,$$

then we say that f is a *simplicial mapping* of the complex K_1 into the complex K_2. For each simplex $S = p_0 p_1 \dots, p_n \in K_1$ we write

$$f(S) = f(p_0) f(p_1) \dots f(p_n)$$

in the case where the vertices $f(p_0), f(p_1), \dots, f(p_n)$ are distinct and we write $f(S) = 0$ otherwise.

The mapping f induces the following mapping $\bar{f}$ of the group $L^n(K_1)$ into the group $L^n(K_2)$: for

$$L = k_1 S_1 + k_2 S_2 + \dots + k_m S_m$$

we put

$$\bar{f}(L) = k_1 f(S_1) + k_2 f(S_2) + \dots + k_m f(S_m).$$

Prove the following properties of the function $\bar{f}$:

(a) $\bar{f}(L_1 + L_2) = \bar{f}(L_1) + \bar{f}(L_2)$

(i. e. $\bar{f}$ is a homomorphism of the group $L^n(K_1)$ into the group $L^n(K_2)$).

(b) $\partial \bar{f}(L) = \bar{f}(\partial L)$,

(c) if $Z \in Z^n(K_1)$, then $\bar{f}(Z) \in Z^n(K_2)$,

if $Z \approx 0$ in K_1, then $\bar{f}(Z) \approx 0$ in K_2,

if $Z_1 \approx Z_2$ in K_1, then $\bar{f}(Z_1) \approx \bar{f}(Z_2)$ in K_2.

Deduce from (a), (b) and (c) that the mapping $\bar{f}$ induces a homomorphism of the group $B^n(K_1)$ into the group $B^n(K_2)$.

CHAPTER XXII

CUTTINGS OF THE PLANE

§ 1. Auxiliary properties of polygonal arcs

As usual, we shall denote the plane of complex numbers by $\mathcal{E}^2$. By $\mathcal{S}_2$ we denote the plane $\mathcal{E}^2$ extended by the point at infinity (called the *Gauss plane*); topologically $\mathcal{S}_2$ does not differ from the surface of a three-dimensional sphere.

THEOREM 1. *Any two points of a connected open set R (i. e. of a region) situated on $\mathcal{S}_2$ can be joined by a polygonal arc.*

The proof is completely analogous to the proof of Theorem 4 of Chapter XVIII, § 4: by F we denote the set of all points of the region R which can be joined by a polygonal arc with the fixed point $p \in R$ and then we prove that this set is nonvoid and open and that the set $R-F$ is open; taking into consideration the connectedness of the set R we deduce from this that $F = R$.

THEOREM 2. *If L is a polygonal arc $\subset \mathcal{S}_2$, then the set $\mathcal{S}_2 - L$ is homeomorphic to the plane $\mathcal{E}^2$.*

The proof is by induction on the number n of links in the polygonal arc.

For $n = 1$ we have to prove that the Gauss plane minus a segment is homeomorphic with the Gauss plane minus a point.

To this end, we describe about the center of the segment L a sequence of concentric circles $K_1, K_2, \ldots$ with radii tending to 0. Let $E_1, E_2, \ldots$ be a sequence of ellipses (together with their interiors) whose intersection is the segment L; we may assume here that $E_1 = K_1$ (Fig. 25).

We define the required homeomorphism h as follows: on the exterior of the circle K_1 we set $h(z) = z$. Next we map the annulus $\overline{E_1-E_2}$ homeomorphically onto the annulus $\overline{K_1-K_2}$; in general, we map the annulus $\overline{E_m-E_{m+1}}$ onto $\overline{K_m-K_{m+1}}$.

The theorem is thus proved for $n=1$.

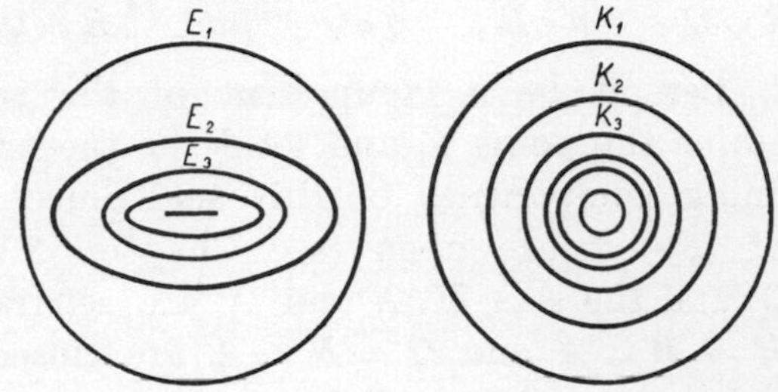

FIG. 25

For $n=2$ the polygonal arc L consists of two segments A_1 and A_2. We carry out a homeomorphic mapping of $\mathcal{S}_2$ onto $\mathcal{S}_2$, which leaves the segment A_1 invariant, but maps A_2 into a rectilinear extension of the segment A_1. The proof thus reduces to the case $n=1$.

A similar method allows, in the case where L consists of $n+1$ segments to "straighten out" the last segment (perhaps contracting it) in order to obtain a polygonal arc consisting of n sides.

Remarks. Theorems 1 and 2 are valid in the space $\mathcal{E}^n$ for arbitrary n. For $n=2$ Theorem 2 can be sharpened by replacing the polygonal arc L by an arbitrary arc; namely, the complement of an arc contained in $\mathcal{E}^2$ is homeomorphic to the complement of a point. On the other hand, for $n=3$ the theorem thus sharpened is not valid: there exists in $\mathcal{E}^3$ an arc, the so-called *Antoine's arc*, whose complement is not homeomorphic to the complement of a point.

§ 2. Cuttings

We say that the (closed or open) set A is a *cutting* of the space $\mathcal{S}_2$ (or: that it separates or cuts this space) if the set $\mathcal{S}_2-A$ is not connected.

A separates $\mathcal{S}_2$ *between the points* p *and* q if these points belong to distinct components of $\mathcal{S}_2 - A$.

THEOREM. *If the closed set* A *cuts* $\mathcal{S}_2$ *between* p *and* q *then there exist two closed sets* R *and* Q *such that*

$$\mathcal{S}_2 = R \cup Q, \quad p \in R, \quad q \in Q \quad \textit{and} \quad R \cap Q = A.$$

Proof. Let M be a component of the set $\mathcal{S}_2 - A$ which contains the point p, and let N be the union of all the remaining components of this set. Since the components of $\mathcal{S}_2 - A$ are open (see Chapter XVIII, § 2, Theorem 3) and the sets M, N and A are separated, then the sets $R = M \cup A$ and $Q = N \cup A$ are closed and, as can easily be seen, they satisfy the desired conditions.

§ 3. Complex functions which vanish nowhere. Existence of the logarithm

We shall denote by the letter $\mathcal{P}$ the plane minus the point 0, i. e.

$$\mathcal{P} = \mathcal{E}^2 - \{0\}.$$

We say that the function $f \in \mathcal{P}^A$ (i. e. continuous, defined on A, complex valued and everywhere different from 0) has a *single-valued continuous branch of the logarithm* if it is of the form

$$(1) \qquad f(z) = e^{u(z)}, \quad \text{where} \quad u \in (\mathcal{E}^2)^A$$

(the function u is this branch). We then write

$$f \sim 1.$$

More generally: if $f \in \mathcal{P}^A$ and $B \subset A$, then we write

$$f \sim 1 \quad \text{on} \quad B,$$

if there exists a function $u \in (\mathcal{E}^2)^B$ such that

$$(2) \qquad f(z) = e^{u(z)} \quad \text{for} \quad z \in B.$$

A fundamental theorem for the topology of the plane, which is our nearest goal, is the following theorem:

EILENBERG THEOREM. *Let* A *be a compact or open subset of the space* $\mathcal{P}$. *A necessary and sufficient condition* *that the set A does not separate $\mathcal{S}_2$ between the points 0 and ∞ is, that the identity has, on the set A, a single-valued continuous branch of the logarithm, i. e. that there exists a function $u \in (\mathcal{E}^2)^A$ such that*

$$z = e^{u(z)} \quad \textit{for} \quad z \in A\,.$$

§ 4. Auxiliary theorems

THEOREM 1. *Let R denote a ray lying in the plane and emanating from the point 0. Then $z \sim 1$ on the set $\mathcal{E}^2 - R$.*

Proof. Let φ be the angle between R and the positive direction of the x-axis; we assume that $0 \leqslant \varphi < 2\pi$.

Since every point z of the plane is of the form $z = |z|\,e^{i\alpha}$, we can assume that $\varphi - 2\pi < \alpha < \varphi$ for points z not belonging to R. The function

$$u(z) = \log z = \log|z| + i\alpha \tag{3}$$

is continuous on $\mathcal{E}^2 - R$ and satisfies the identity

$$z = e^{u(z)} \quad \text{for} \quad z \in \mathcal{E}^2 - R\,.$$

From this we obtain the following theorem.

THEOREM 2. *If $f \in (\mathcal{E}^2 - R)^A$ then $f \sim 1$.*

For, the function $u\big(f(z)\big)$ is continuous on the set A and

$$f(z) = e^{u(f(z))} \quad \text{for} \quad z \in A$$

(where u is the function defined by the formula (3)).

THEOREM 3. *Let $f \in \mathcal{P}^A$. To every point $z \in A$ there corresponds a certain neighborhood G such that*

$$f \sim 1 \quad \textit{on} \quad G\,. \tag{4}$$

Proof. Let R be a ray emanating from the point 0 and not containing the point $f(z)$ (such a ray exists because $f(z) \neq 0$). Owing to the continuity of f we have

$$R \cap f(G) = \emptyset\,, \quad \text{i. e.} \quad f(G) \subset \mathcal{E}^2 - R$$

for some neighborhood G of the point z.

This means that the function f considered on G satisfies the assumption of Theorem 2. Hence, we have formula (4).

THEOREM 4. *Let* $f \in \mathfrak{P}^A$, *let* $a \in A$ *and let* c *be one of the values of* $\log f(a)$. *If* $f \sim 1$, *we can choose the function* u *satisfying formula* (1) *in such a way that its atisfies the "initial" condition:*

$$u(a) = c. \tag{5}$$

Proof. Since $f \sim 1$, the function f is of the form

$$f(z) = e^{v(z)} \quad \text{where} \quad v \in (\mathcal{E}^2)^A.$$

Let us set

$$u(z) = v(z) - v(a) + c. \tag{6}$$

Hence, we have

$$e^{u(z)} = e^{v(z)} \cdot e^{-v(a)} \cdot e^c = f(z),$$

since

$$e^{-v(a)} = 1/f(a) \quad \text{and} \quad e^c = e^{\log f(a)} = f(a).$$

Hence the function u satisfies condition (1). Moreover, formula (6) immediately implies formula (5).

Remark. The initial condition (5) in general does not determine the function u uniquely. We have uniqueness, however, under the assumption that the set A is connected. This follows from the following theorem:

THEOREM 5. *If the set* A *is connected and*

$$f(z) = e^{u(z)} = e^{v(z)}, \tag{7}$$

then $v(z) = u(z) + \text{constant}$.

Proof. By virtue of (7), $e^{v(z)-u(z)} = 1$, and therefore for every z there exists an integer $k(z)$ such that $v(z) - u(z) = 2k(z)\pi i$. Hence, the function $k(z)$ is continuous. Since $k(z)$ is defined on a connected set and has integral values, it is therefore constant (for the continuous image of a connected set is connected (cf. Chapter XVI, § 2, Theorem 1)).

THEOREM 6. *If* F *is a closed subset of* $\mathcal{S}_2$ *and the function* $f \in \mathfrak{P}^F$ *satisfies the condition* $f \sim 1$, *then there exists a function* $g \in \mathfrak{P}^{\mathcal{S}_2}$ *which is an extension of the function* f *and which satisfies the condition* $g \sim 1$.

Proof. By assumption, formula (1) is satisfied, and because of Tietze extension theorem (Chapter XII, § 8, Corollary 1) the function u can be extended to the entire space $\mathcal{S}_2$. Let v be this extension. Hence, we have

$$v \in (\mathcal{E}^2)^{\mathcal{S}_2} \quad \text{and} \quad v(z) = u(z) \text{ for } z \in F.$$

The function $g(z) = e^{v(z)}$ is the desired function.

THEOREM 7. *Let A and B be two closed or two open sets with connected intersection. Let $f \in \mathcal{P}^{A \cup B}$. If $f \sim 1$ on A and on B, then $f \sim 1$ on $A \cup B$.*

Proof. By assumption there exist two functions $u \in (\mathcal{E}^2)^A$ and $v \in (\mathcal{E}^2)^B$ such that

$$f(z) = \begin{cases} e^{u(z)} & \text{for} \quad z \in A, \\ e^{v(z)} & \text{for} \quad z \in B. \end{cases}$$

Let $A \cap B \neq \emptyset$, and $a \in A \cap B$. We can assume that v has been so chosen that $v(a) = u(a)$ (cf. Theorem 4). Since the set $A \cap B$ is connected, it follows (by virtue of Theorem 5) that $v(z) = u(z)$ for every $z \in A \cap B$. Hence, if we assume that

$$w(z) = \begin{cases} u(z) & \text{for} \quad z \in A, \\ v(z) & \text{for} \quad z \in B, \end{cases} \tag{8}$$

then—as can easily be verified (see Exercise 4, Chapter XII)—the function w is continuous, i. e. $w \in (\mathcal{E}^2)^{A \cup B}$. As $f(z) = e^{w(z)}$ for $z \in A \cup B$ (cf. (8)), hence $f \sim 1$.

We arrive the same conclusion if $A \cap B = \emptyset$.

THEOREM 8. *Let $f \in \mathcal{P}^G$ and let $C_1, C_2, \ldots, C_n, \ldots$ be a sequence of connected sets such that*

$$G = C_1 \cup C_2 \cup \ldots \cup C_n \cup \ldots, \tag{9}$$

and

$$C_n \subset \text{Int}(C_{n+1}) \quad \textit{for} \quad n = 1, 2, \ldots \tag{10}$$

If $f \sim 1$ on C_n for every n, then $f \sim 1$ (on G).

Proof. Let $a \in C_1$. By assumption we have

$$f(z) = e^{u_n(z)} \quad \text{for} \quad z \in C_n \text{ and } u_n \in (\mathcal{E}^2)^{C_n}. \tag{11}$$

We can assume (see Theorem 4) that $u_n(a) = u_1(a)$. It follows, by virtue of the connectedness of the set C_1, that $u_n(z) = u_1(z)$ for $z \in C_1$, and since $u_{n+1}(a) = u_n(a)$, we have similarly

(12) $$u_{n+1}(z) = u_n(z) \quad \text{for} \quad z \in C_n.$$

Let

(13) $$u(z) = u_n(z) \quad \text{for} \quad z \in C_n.$$

Because of (12) and (9), formula (13) defines the function u uniquely for every $z \in G$. This is a continuous function. For, if $z_0 \in C_n$, then by virtue of (10) $z_0 \in \mathrm{Int}(C_{n+1})$; but since $u(z) = u_{n+1}(z)$ for $z \in C_n$, the continuity of the function u_{n+1} at the point z_0 implies the continuity of the function u at this point (cf. Chapter XII, Exercise 5).

Finally, formulas (11) and (12) yield

$$f(z) = e^{u(z)} \text{ for } z \in G, \quad \text{i. e.} \quad f \sim 1.$$

THEOREM 9. *Let G be an open set (in $\mathcal{S}_2$) and let $f \in \mathfrak{P}^G$. If*

(14) $$f \sim 1 \quad on \quad C$$

for every subcontinuum C of the set G, then $f \sim 1$ (on G).

Proof. Let us first assume that the set G is connected. There obviously exists a sequence of open circular disks $K_1, K_2, \ldots, K_n, \ldots$ such that

(15) $$\overline{K}_n \subset G \quad \text{for} \quad n = 1, 2, \ldots,$$

and

(16) $$G = K_1 \cup K_2 \cup \ldots \cup K_n \cup \ldots$$

We shall define inductively a sequence of continua $C_1, C_2, \ldots, C_n, \ldots,$ satisfying conditions (9) and (10). Namely, let $C_1 = \overline{K}_1$. For given n, let m_n be an index $\geqslant n$ such that

(17) $$C_n \subset K_1 \cup \ldots \cup K_{m_n}$$

(the existence of the index m_n follows from the Borel theorem, Chapter XV, § 3, Theorem 2).

Since G is an open connected set (by assumption) we can join K_1 by means of polygonal arcs with each of the discs $K_2, K_3, \ldots, K_{m_n}$ in the interior of G (Theorem 1, § 1). The union of these polygonal arcs and sets $\overline{K}_1, \ldots, \overline{K}_{m_n}$ is denoted by C_{n+1}.

Inclusion (17) immediately yields inclusion (10), and equality (16) yields equality (9) (because of inclusion (15) and of inequality $m_n \geqslant n$).

Hence our theorem is proved for the case where the open set G is connected.

In the case where the set G is not connected we consider its decomposition into components (cf. Chapter XVIII, § 2, Theorem 4):

$$G = G_1 \cup G_2 \cup \ldots \cup G_n \cup \ldots$$

Since the set G_n is connected and open (by virtue of Theorem 3 of Chapter XVIII, § 2), it follows from the part of the theorem already proved that

$$f \sim 1 \text{ on } G_n,$$

i. e. $f(z) = e^{v_n(z)}$ for $z \in G_n$, and $v_n \in (\mathcal{E}^2)^{G_n}$.

Let us set $v(z) = v_n(z)$ for $z \in G_n$. Since the sets G_n are open, it follows (cf. Chapter XII, Exercise 5) that the function v is continuous. Hence we have

$$f(z) = e^{v(z)}, \text{ where } v \in (\mathcal{E}^2)^G, \quad \text{i. e.} \quad f \sim 1.$$

§ 5. Corollaries to the auxiliary theorems

COROLLARY 1. *Let $\mathcal{J}$ be the closed interval $0 \leqslant t \leqslant 1$. Every function $f \in \mathcal{P}^F$, where $F = \overline{F} \subset \mathcal{J}$, satisfies the formula $f \sim 1$.*

Proof. By Theorem 3, § 4, we can assign to every point $t \in F$ an open set G_t which contains t and is such that $f \sim 1$ on $F \cap G_t$. By virtue of the Borel-Lebesgue theorem (Chapter XV, § 3, Remark 2.), there therefore exists a finite number of open sets which cover the set F and are such that $f \sim 1$ on each of them individually. In other words, there exists a system of points

$$0 = a_0 < a_1 < \ldots < a_n = 1,$$

such that $f \sim 1$ on the intersection $F \cap (a_{k-1} a_k)$ for $k = 1, 2, \ldots, n$.

The intersection $[F \cap (a_0 a_1)] \cap [F \cap (a_1 a_2)]$ being contained in $\{a_1\}$ is connected (perhaps void). Hence we have $f \sim 1$ on $F \cap (a_0 a_1 \cup a_1 a_2) = F \cap (a_0 a_2)$ by virtue of Theorem 7, § 4.

Similarly, $f \sim 1$ on $F \cap (a_0 a_2 \cup a_2 a_3) = F \cap (a_0 a_3)$.

By induction we prove that $f \sim 1$ on $F \cap (a_0 a_n) = F$.

COROLLARY 2. *Let K be a square (with interior) $\subset \mathcal{E}^2$. Every function $f \in \mathcal{P}^K$ satisfies the formula $f \sim 1$.*

Proof. Let us decompose the square K into a finite number of squares $A_1, A_2, \ldots, A_n$, enumerating them in such a way that the intersection

$$A_k \cap (A_1 \cup \ldots \cup A_{k-1}) \tag{18}$$

is connected for $k = 2, 3, \ldots, n$ (cf. Fig. 26). We assume that these squares are so small that $f \sim 1$ on each of them

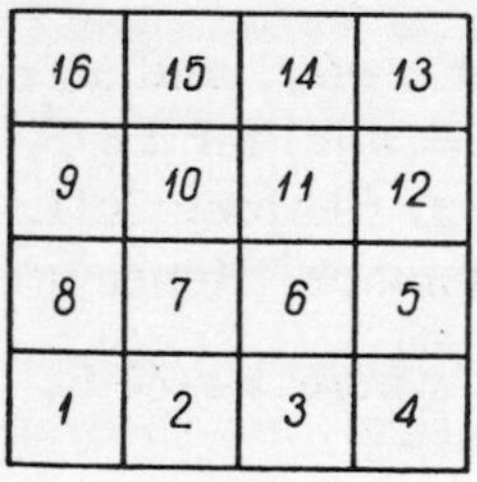

FIG. 26

individually (we reason as in the preceding proof making use of Theorem 3, § 4, and the Borel-Lebesgue theorem).

As $f \sim 1$ on A_1 and on A_2 and as the intersection $A_1 \cap A_2$ is connected, we have $f \sim 1$ on $A_1 \cup A_2$. Reasoning by induction and using the fact that the intersection (18) is connected, we deduce that $f \sim 1$ on $A_1 \cup \ldots \cup A_n$, i. e. on K.

COROLLARY 3. *Every function $f \in \mathcal{P}^{(\mathcal{E}^2)}$ satisfies the formula $f \sim 1$.*

Proof. Let K_n be a square with side n and with center 0. Since

$$\mathcal{E}^2 = K_1 \cup K_2 \cup \ldots \cup K_n \cup \ldots$$

and since $f \sim 1$ on K_n by virtue of the preceding theorem, we deduce from Theorem 8, § 4, that $f \sim 1$ on $\mathcal{E}^2$.

Remark. Theorems 1-3 hold not only for the sets $\mathcal{J}$, K and $\mathcal{E}^2$, but also for arbitrary sets which are homeomorphic to these sets; in particular, for arbitrary arcs, for a circular disk, for the complement (with respect to $\mathcal{S}_2$) of a polygonal arc.

Let us carry out the proof for the arc.

Let h be a homeomorphic mapping of the segment $\mathcal{J}$ onto the arc A. Let $f \in \mathcal{P}^A$. Substituting $z = h(x)$ for $x \in \mathcal{J}$, we therefore have

$$f(z) = fh(x) = e^{u(x)} = e^{uh^{-1}(z)} = e^{v(z)},$$

where $v(z) = uh^{-1}(z)$, $z \in A$.

COROLLARY 4. *Let C denote the circumference $|z| = r$. There does not exist a single-valued branch of the logarithm on C; that is,*

$$x \text{ not} \sim 1 \text{ on } C.$$

Proof. Let $z_0 = (r, 0)$, and $A = C - \{z_0\}$. For $z \in A$ we have

$$z = re^{i\alpha(z)}, \quad \text{where} \quad 0 < \alpha(z) < 2\pi. \tag{19}$$

Obviously the function α is continuous on A.

Let us assume that our theorem is false. Then

$$z = re^{i\beta(z)},$$

where β is a real valued function continuous on C.

As the set A is connected we have (see Theorem 5, § 4):

$$\alpha(z) = \beta(z) + \text{constant}. \tag{20}$$

It would then follow from this that the function α can be extended in a continuous manner onto C. But this is impossible. For, let

$$\lim_{n\to\infty} z_n = z_0.$$

If the points z_n lie above the x-axis, then

$$\lim_{n\to\infty} \alpha(z_n) = 0,$$

and if the points z_n lie below the x-axis, then

$$\lim_{n\to\infty} \alpha(z_n) = 2\pi .$$

§ 6. Theorems on the cuttings of the plane

Proof of Eilenberg theorem (see § 3). Let $A \subset \mathcal{P}$. We shall consider separately the case where A is a closed subset of $\mathcal{S}_2$ and the case where A is an open set.

1. $A = \bar{A} \subset \mathcal{P}$. Let us assume that A does not separate $\mathcal{S}_2$ between the points $p = 0$ and $q = \infty$. We have to prove that

$$(21) \qquad z \sim 1 \quad \text{on} \quad A .$$

Since the points p and q lie in one of the components of the set $\mathcal{S}_2 - A$, there exists a polygonal arc L (cf. Theorem 1, § 1) such that

$$(22) \qquad L = pq \subset \mathcal{S}_2 - A .$$

By Theorem 2, § 1, the set $\mathcal{S}_2 - L$ is homeomorphic to the plane $\mathcal{E}^2$, and hence by virtue of Corollary 3, § 5 (cf. Remark) we have $z \sim 1$ on $\mathcal{S}_2 - L$, whence formula (21) follows, for $A \subset \mathcal{S}_2 - L$ by (22).

Let us assume next that A separates $\mathcal{S}_2$ between the points $p = 0$ and $q = \infty$. Hence, there exist (see § 2) two closed sets R and Q such that

$$(23) \qquad \mathcal{S}_2 = R \cup Q , \quad p \in R , \quad q \in Q ,$$

$$(24) \qquad R \cap Q = A .$$

We shall show that the assumption (21) leads to a contradiction.

In fact, from (21) it follows that (cf. Theorem 6, § 4)

$$(25) \qquad z = e^{u(z)} \text{ on } A , \quad \text{where} \quad u \in (\mathcal{E}^2)^{\mathcal{S}_2}.$$

Let us set

$$(26) \qquad f(z) = \begin{cases} e^{u(z)} & \text{if} \quad z \in Q , \\ z & \text{if} \quad z \in R \text{ and } z \neq 0 . \end{cases}$$

By (24) and (25), the function f is defined and continuous for every $z \neq 0$ (cf. Chapter XII, Exercise 4), i. e.

$$(27) \qquad f \in \mathcal{P}^{\mathcal{S}_2-\{0\}}, \quad \text{whence} \quad f \sim 1$$

by virtue of Corollary 3, § 5 (cf. Remark).

Since the point 0 does not belong to Q, there exists a disk with center at the point 0 which is disjoint from Q and hence contained in R. Let C be the circumference of this disk. Hence we have (cf. (27)) $f \sim 1$ on C, i. e. by (26) $z \sim 1$ on C. But this contradicts Corollary 4, § 5.

2. The set A is open. Let us assume that the set A does not separate the plane $\mathcal{S}_2$ between the points $p = 0$ and $q = \infty$, i. e. that these points lie in the same component T of the set $\mathcal{S}_2 - A$. Hence, if $F = \overline{F} \subset A$, then the points p and q lie in one component of the set $\mathcal{S}_2 - F$ (namely in the one that contains the set T). As already proved, we therefore have $z \sim 1$ on F. From this, by virtue of Theorem 9, § 4, we obtain formula (21).

Let us assume next that the set A separates the plane $\mathcal{S}_2$ between the points $p = 0$ and $q = \infty$, i. e. that these points belong to distinct components of the set $\mathcal{S}_2 - A$. Therefore, there exist two closed sets M and N (see Chapter XVII, § 2, Theorem 6) such that

$$(28) \qquad \mathcal{S}_2 - A = M \cup N, \quad p \in M, \quad q \in N,$$

$$(29) \qquad M \cap N = \emptyset.$$

As the space $\mathcal{S}_2$ is normal (see Chapter XII, § 7, Theorem 6) and because of formula (29), there exist two open sets R and Q such that

$$(30) \qquad M \subset R, \quad N \subset Q,$$

$$(31) \qquad R \cap Q = \emptyset.$$

Let

$$(32) \qquad F = \mathcal{S}_2 - (R \cup Q).$$

The set F is therefore closed. Because of (30) and (28), we have

$$(33) \qquad F = \mathcal{S}_2 - (R \cup Q) \subset \mathcal{S}_2 - (M \cup N) = A,$$

$p \in R$ and $q \in Q$.

Therefore $\mathcal{S}_2 - F$ is the union of two open disjoint sets R and Q of which one contains p and the other contains q (cf. (32)). The set F therefore separates $\mathcal{S}_2$ between these points. By virtue of the part of the theorem already proved, we have z not~ 1 on F.

But since $F \subset A$ (because of (33)) we therefore have *a fortiori* that z not~ 1 on A.

§ 7. Janiszewski theorems

THEOREM 1. *Let A and B be two closed or two open subsets of $\mathcal{S}_2$. If neither of these sets separates $\mathcal{S}_2$ between the points p and q and if the intersection $A \cap B$ is connected, then the union $A \cup B$ also does not separate $\mathcal{S}_2$ between these points.*

Proof. By means of the homographic transformation

$$h(z) = (z-p)/(z-q) \tag{34}$$

we reduce the proof to the case where

$$p = 0, \quad q = \infty. \tag{35}$$

Hence let us assume that the equalities (35) hold.

Since neither A nor B separates the plane $\mathcal{S}_2$ between the points p and q, the relations

$$z \sim 1 \text{ on } A \quad \text{and} \quad z \sim 1 \text{ on } B$$

hold, by the Eilenberg theorem.

It follows from this, by virtue of Theorem 7, § 4, that $z \sim 1$ on $A \cup B$. And therefore, by the Eilenberg theorem, $A \cup B$ does not separate $\mathcal{S}_2$ between p and q.

THEOREM 2. *As before, let A and B be two open or two closed subsets of $\mathcal{S}_2$. If the sets A and B are connected but the intersection $A \cap B$ is not connected, then the union $A \cup B$ separates $\mathcal{S}_2$ between some pair of points.*

Proof. We use the usual notation

$$A^c = \mathcal{S}_2 - A, \quad B^c = \mathcal{S}_2 - B.$$

Let us assume—contrary to the assertion of our theorem—that the set $A \cup B$ does not separate $\mathcal{S}_2$,

i. e. that the set $\mathcal{S}_2-(A \cup B) = A^c \cap B^c$ is connected. We shall prove that then the assumptions of Theorem 1 are satisfied by the sets A^c and B^c where p, q is an arbitrary pair of points belonging to $A \cap B$.

In fact, both the sets A^c and B^c are open or both are closed, and their intersection $A^c \cap B^c$ is connected. It remains to prove that neither the set A^c nor the set B^c separates $\mathcal{S}_2$ between the points p and q, i. e. that these points belong to some component of the complement of the set A^c or to some component of the set A, and, similarly, to some component of the set B. But this follows immediately from the assumption that the sets A and B are connected and contain the points p and q.

Applying the first of the Janiszewski theorems to the sets A^c and B^c, we deduce that the union $A^c \cup B^c$ does not separate $\mathcal{S}_2$ between p and q, i. e. that p and q belong to the same component of the set $(A^c \cup B^c)^c = A \cap B$. But since the points p and q are arbitrary points belonging to $A \cap B$, it follows from this that the set $A \cap B$ is connected, contrary to assumption.

§ 8. Jordan theorem

For every simple closed curve $C \subset \mathcal{S}_2$ (i. e. for every set homeomorphic to the circumference of a circle), $\mathcal{S}_2-C$ decomposes $\mathcal{S}_2$ into two regions and C is their common boundary.

We precede the proof with the following lemma.

LEMMA. *No arc or closed subset of an arc separates $\mathcal{S}_2$.*

Proof. Let us assume, on the contrary, that some closed subset F of the arc L separates $\mathcal{S}_2$ between the points p and q. Applying the homographic transformation (34) we can assume that these points are $p = 0$ and $q = \infty$. By the Eilenberg theorem we have z not~ 1 on F. But this contradicts Theorem 1 of § 5 (see Remark, § 5).

Proof of the Jordan theorem. Since the curve C can be represented as the union of two arcs whose intersection is not connected (namely consisting of two points) we deduce from the second of the Janiszewski theorems that C separates $\mathcal{S}_2$.

Let

$$R_1, R_2, \ldots \tag{36}$$

denote the sequence of components of the set $\mathcal{S}_2 - C$. We have proved that this sequence contains at least two terms. It remains to prove that it does not contain more than two terms and that

$$\mathrm{Fr}(R_1) = C = \mathrm{Fr}(R_2)\,. \tag{37}$$

We shall begin with the proof of formula (37). By virtue of Theorem 6 of Chapter XVIII, § 2, we have

$$\mathrm{Fr}(R_1) \subset C\,. \tag{38}$$

If equality (37) did not hold, then the set $\mathrm{Fr}(R_1)$ would be a closed subset of some arc (contained in C) and therefore, by the lemma, it would not separate $\mathcal{S}_2$. But this is impossible because $\mathrm{Fr}(R_1)$ obviously separates $\mathcal{S}_2$ between every point of R_1 and every point of R_2.

Hence the first of the equalities (37) is proved and the second is obtained by symmetry.

It remains to prove that the sequence (36) consists of two terms.

Let us assume the contrary, i. e. that there exist at least three regions R_1, R_2, R_3. Let

$$p_j \in R_j \quad \text{for} \quad j = 1, 2, 3\,. \tag{39}$$

Let us assume that the region R_3 is bounded. Let Z be a straight line passing through the point p_3. This straight line therefore contains the segment $L = ap_3b$ lying in R_3 with the exception of the endpoints which belong to C:

$$L \subset R_3 \cup \{a\} \cup \{b\}\,. \tag{40}$$

Let aq_1b and aq_2b be two arcs of the curve C determined by the points a and b.

Hence we have

$$aq_1b \cup aq_2b = C\,, \tag{41}$$

and

(42) $$aq_1b \cap aq_2b = \{a, b\}.$$

Let

(43) $$A_1 = aq_1b \cup L, \quad A_2 = aq_2b \cup L.$$

It follows from formulas (42) and (43) that

(44) $$A_1 \cap A_2 = L.$$

Since $q_1, q_2 \in C$, we therefore deduce from (37) that the sets $R_1 \cup \{q_1\} \cup R_2$ and $R_1 \cup \{q_2\} \cup R_2$ are connected,

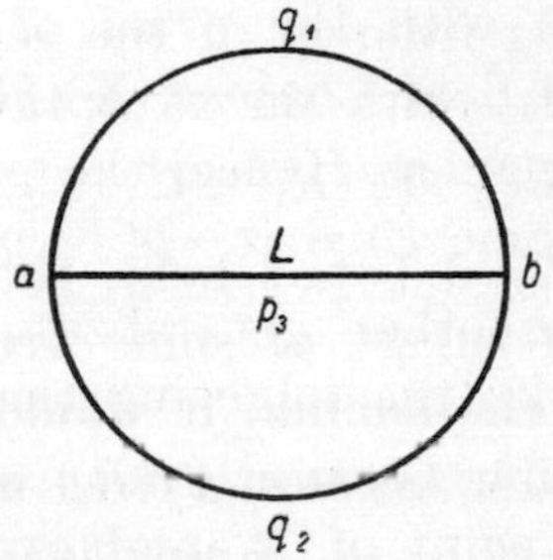

FIG. 27

and from (39), that they contain the points p_1 and p_2. As these sets are disjoint from A_2 and A_1 respectively (cf. (40) and (43)), the sets A_1 and A_2 do not separate $\mathcal{S}_2$ between p_1 and p_2. From formula (44) we deduce by virtue of the first Janiszewski theorem that $A_1 \cup A_2$ does not separate $\mathcal{S}_2$ between p_1 and p_2 either. But this is impossible because (cf. (41) and (43)) $A_1 \cup A_2 = C \cup L$, and C separates $\mathcal{S}_2$ between p_1 and p_2.

*Remark 1. We can sharpen the Jordan theorem by introducing the interesting concept of accessible point. Namely, we say that a point p lying on the boundary of the region R is *accessible* from this region if there exists an arc containing the point p and lying entirely—with the exception of the point p—in the region R.

An example of a point which is not accessible is the following. Let C be the closure of the curve $y = \sin(1/x)$, $0 < |x| \leqslant 1$, and let R be the complement of the continuum C; the point $\langle 0, 0\rangle$ is not accessible from the region R.

One can prove that *every point of a simple closed curve is accessible from both regions into which the curve separates the plane.*

In the general case of an arbitrary region R, the points which are accessible from R form a dense set on its boundary.

For let $p \in \mathrm{Fr}(R)$. For $\varepsilon > 0$ there exists a point $q \in R$ at a distance $< \varepsilon$ from p. On the segment qp let r be the first point (starting from q) of the set $\mathrm{Fr}(R)$. Therefore the segment qr lies—with the exception of the point r—entirely in the region R. Hence, the point r is accessible from R. At the same time $|r-p| \leqslant |q-p| < \varepsilon$.

*Remark 2. Another generalization of the Jordan theorem is given by the following theorem:

Let S be the circumference of a circle and let C be a simple closed curve contained in $\mathcal{S}_2$. Every homeomorphism h mapping S onto C can be extended to a homeomorphism h^* of the entire plane $\mathcal{S}_2$ onto itself; i. e. $h^*(\mathcal{S}_2) = \mathcal{S}_2$ and $h^*(p) = h(p)$ for $p \in S$.

On the basis of this theorem one can prove that every topological property of the circumference S with respect to the plane $\mathcal{S}_2$ (such as the number of components in $\mathcal{S}_2 - S$ and the accessibility of points on the circumference) also holds for any simple closed curve.

An analogous theorem concerns arcs lying in $\mathcal{S}_2$: *every homeomorphism defined on the segment $\mathcal{J}$ can be extended to a homeomorphism of $\mathcal{S}_2$ onto $\mathcal{S}_2$.*

However, this theorem is not valid for arcs (and also for simple closed curves) lying in $\mathcal{E}^3$. The Antoine arc referred to in the remark at the end of § 1 is a counter-example.

*Remark 3. Jordan theorem is a special case of the following theorem on the invariance of the number of components of the complement of a closed set lying on the sphere $\mathcal{S}_n$ (i. e. on the surface of the unit sphere of Euclidean space $\mathcal{E}^{n+1}$): *if* $F=\overline{F}\subset\mathcal{S}_n$ *and if the set* $\mathcal{S}_n-F$ *has* k *components, then for every homeomorphic transformation* h *of the set* F *onto a subset of the space* $\mathcal{S}_n$ *it follows that the set* $\mathcal{S}_n-h(F)$ *also has* k *components.*

The proof of this theorem can be carried out making use of the concept of homology extended to arbitrary compact sets [1]).

As for polyhedra, we then prove that the Betti numbers are topological invariants and that the $(n-1)$-st Betti number of the closed set F lying in $\mathcal{S}_n$ equals the number of components of the set $\mathcal{S}_n-F$ minus 1.

For sets lying in $\mathcal{S}_2$ the proof of the above theorem can be carried out considering the function space $\mathcal{P}^F$ to be a group. Namely, the group operation is defined as follows.

Let f_1, f_2 and f_3 be three elements of the space $\mathcal{P}^F$. We assume that $f_3=f_1\cdot f_2$ when $f_3(z)=f_1(z)\cdot f_2(z)$ for every $z\in F$.

The functions f satisfying the condition $f\sim 1$ form a subgroup of the group $\mathcal{P}^F$, as can easily be verified. Let us denote it by G and let us consider the quotient group $B(F)=\mathcal{P}^F/G$.

The rank of this group, or the maximal number of linearly independent elements, equals the number of components of the set $\mathcal{S}_2-F$ less one, as can be proved.

Let us note finally that the proof of the invariance of the property of a closed subset F of $\mathcal{S}_n$ of separating $\mathcal{S}_n$ can be carried out without the use of homology. For, the connectedness of $\mathcal{S}_n-F$ and of $\mathcal{S}_{n-1}^F$ are equivalent [2]).

[1]) Another proof was given by K. Borsuk. This proof requires an apparatus which goes significantly beyond the scope of this book. See Fundamenta Mathematicae 37 (1950), p. 217-241, and my *Topologie*, vol. II, third edition, 1961.

[2]) Borsuk theorem, see Monatshefte für Mathematik und Physik 38 (1931), p. 218, and Mathematische Annalen 106 (1932), p. 239. Cf. also P. Aleksandrov, *Dimensionstheorie*, § 5, Mathematische Annalen 106 (1932), p. 218 or my *Topologie*, vol. II, p. 347.

Exercises

1. Prove that z^n is not ~ 1 for $n \neq 0$ on the circumference of a circle with center 0.

2. Prove that if $f \in \mathcal{P}^{\mathcal{S}_2}$ then $f \sim 1$.

Hint: Decompose $\mathcal{S}_2$ by the equator and apply Corollary 2, § 5.

3. Prove that the star-shaped curve consisting of n arcs having one end in common, and having no other points in common, does not decompose the plane.

4. Prove that a curve consisting of three arcs having common endpoints, and having no other points in common (Fig. 27), decomposes the plane in three regions.

5. A connected space is said to be *unicoherent* if $A \cap B$ is connected for every decomposition of the space into two closed connected sets A and B. Prove that the circular disk and the space $\mathcal{S}_2$ are unicoherent.

6. Prove that if C is a subcontinuum of the plane $\mathcal{S}_2$ (or more generally, of a connected unicoherent space), and R is a component of the complement of C, then $\mathrm{Fr}(R)$ is a continuum.

Hint: Use Theorem 4 of Chapter XVI, § 3.

7. Let the space X be a locally connected unicoherent continuum. If the closed set F separates this space between the points a and b, then it contains a subcontinuum which also separates the space between these points.

Hint: Consider the component R of the set $X-F$ which contains the point a and the component P of the set $X-\bar{R}$ which contains the point b, and apply Exercise 6, above, and Exercise 11 of Chapter XVIII.

8. Under the preceding assumptions on the space X, let A and B be two disjoint closed sets neither one of which separates X between p and q. Prove then that $A \cup B$ does not separate the space between p and q either.

9. Show by an example that without the unicoherence assumption the theorems of Exercises 6-8 are false.

10. Let $\mathcal{S}$ denote the circumference of the circle of radius 1 and with center 0. Let the function $f \in \mathcal{S}^{\mathcal{S}}$ satisfy the condition $f(-z) = -f(z)$ for every $z \in \mathcal{S}$. Then the condition $f \sim 1$ is not satisfied.

11. The Borsuk-Ulam theorem on antipodes. For every function $f \in (\mathcal{E}^2)^{\mathcal{S}_2}$ there exists a point z_0 such that $f(z_0) = f(-z_0)$.

Hint: For every point p belonging to the disk Q_2 with radius 1 and center 0, let us denote by $p+$ the point belonging to the "upper half" of $\mathcal{S}_2$, whose projection is p. Let $h(p) = f(p+) - f(-p+)$. Let us assume, contrary to the assertion of the theorem, that $h(p) \neq 0$ for every p. Show (making use of Corollary 2, § 5, and of the remark immediately following it) that this assumption leads to a contradiction to the above theorem.

12. A region R lying in the plane $\mathcal{S}_2$ is said to be *simply connected* if its complement, i. e. the set $\mathcal{S}_2 - R$, is connected.

Prove that if a simply connected region $R \subset \mathcal{S}_2$ contains a simple closed curve C then it also contains one of the two components of its complement. In particular, if R does not contain the point at infinity, then it contains a bounded component of the set $\mathcal{S}_2 - C$.

Hint: Note that the set $\mathcal{S}_2 - R$ is contained in one of the components of the set $\mathcal{S}_2 - C$.

Remark. The property of simply connected regions formulated in the above theorem is also a sufficient condition for simple connectedness, as can be proved.

13. Let R be a simply connected region contained in $\mathcal{S}_2$, and let L be an arc which, except for its endpoints, lies in R. Prove that the arc L separates the region R (i. e. that $R - L$ is not connected).

14. Prove the following more general theorem: let R be an arbitrary region contained in $\mathcal{S}_2$, and let L be an arc which, except for its endpoints, lies in R; a necessary and sufficient condition for this arc to separate the region R, is that both its endpoints belong to the same component of the set $\mathcal{S}_2 - R$.

Hint: In the proof of the necessity of the above condition make use of Theorem 6, Chapter XVII, § 2, and of the first Janiszewski theorem. Make use of the second Janiszewski theorem in the proof of its sufficiency.

15. If C is a continuum contained in $\mathcal{S}_2$, then each of the components of the set $\mathcal{S}_2 - C$ is a simply connected region.

Hint: Cf. Theorem 4, Chapter XVI, § 3.

half of S_2 whose projection [illegible] [illegible] does not, contrary to the assertion of the theorem, then [illegible] for every [illegible] [illegible] [illegible] [illegible] [illegible] [illegible] [illegible] [illegible] [illegible] [illegible] [illegible] [illegible] contrary to the above assertion.

12. A region R lying in the plane S_2 is said to be simply connected if its complement [illegible] the set $S_2 - R$ is connected.

Prove that if a simply connected region R in S_2 contains a simple closed curve J then it also contains one of the two components of its complement. In particular, if R does not contain the point [illegible] then it contains a bounded component of the set $S_2 - J$.

Hint. Note that the set $S_2 - R$ is [illegible] and [illegible] of the components of the set $S_2 - J$.

Remark. The property of simply connected regions formulated in the above theorem is also a sufficient condition for simple connectedness, as can be proved.

13. Let R be a simply connected region contained in S_2 and let J be a set which, except for its endpoints, lies in R. Prove that [illegible] J [illegible] the region R (i.e. that $R - J$ is not connected).

14. Prove the following more general theorem: let R be an arbitrary region contained in S_2 and let J be an arc which, except for its endpoints, lies in R; then if $R - J$ is connected, then [illegible] [illegible] Theorem [illegible], R [illegible] the [illegible] [illegible] to the same component of the set $S_2 - R$.

Hint. In the proof of the sufficiency of this [illegible] condition make use of Theorem 6, Chapter XVII, [illegible], use of the first [illegible] theorem. [illegible] of the second [illegible] theorem [illegible] [illegible] of the [illegible].

15. If C is a continuum contained in S_2 then each of the components of the set $S_2 - C$ is a simply connected region.

[illegible] Theorem 1, Chapter XVI, [illegible].

LIST OF IMPORTANT SYMBOLS

INDEX